MEN IN ACTION

Equipping Men to Lead in the Home, the Church and the Community

James M. Cecy, D.Min.
Michael L. Wilhelm, J.D.

JARON
MINISTRIES
INTERNATIONAL

ISBN 978-0-9969556-8-3 PAPERBACK
ISBN 978-0-9969556-9-0 eBOOK

Unless otherwise noted, Scriptures taken from the NEW AMERICAN STANDARD BIBLE (NASB), Copyright © 1960, 1962, 1963, 1968, 1971, 1972, 1973, 1975, 1977, 1995 by THE LOCKMAN FOUNDATION. A Corporation Not for Profit, LA HABRA, CA. All Rights Reserved. Used by permission. http://www.lockman.org.

Some passages noted as NIV are taken from THE HOLY BIBLE, NEW INTERNATIONAL VERSION® NIV® Copyright © 1973, 1978, 1984 by International Bible Society® Used by permission. All rights reserved worldwide.

Transliterations of all Greek and Hebrew words were taken from a variety of sources such as *The Exhaustive Concordance of the Bible* by James Strong, *An Expository Dictionary of New Testament Words* by W.E. Vine, *An Expository Dictionary of Old Testament Words* by F.F. Bruce, and the authors' preferred transliterations to allow for ease of pronunciation.

Portions of this book are adapted from a wide variety of James Cecy's and Michael Wilhelm's audio, video, and written materials.

For further information about media, materials, seminars and training courses, contact:
JARON Ministries International, Inc.
4710 N Maple Ave, Fresno, CA. 93726   (559) 227-7997

JARON is a registered non-profit organization (501c3) in the State of California.

JARON Ministries website: www.jaron.org
Campus Bible Church website: www.campusbiblechurch.com
Jim Cecy's websites: www.jaron.org and www.puritywar.com and www.campusbiblechurch.com
Jim Cecy's email: jim.cecy@campusbiblechurch.com
Mike Wilhelm's email: mwilhelm@wjhattorneys.com

Published by JARON Ministries International, Inc.

We expect this manual to be revised as new materials are added. Keep informed of revisions at www.jaron.org.

Printed in the United States of America.

Dedication

From the Grateful Heart of Jim Cecy

I dedicate this work to:
- My wife, Karon, who has taught me more about being a friend, a pastor, a husband, a father, and a grandfather than anyone on earth.
- Mike Wilhelm, my fellow teacher, fellow elder, and dear friend. We share the same heart to disciple Men of God to be Men in Action.
- The elders and ministry team at Campus Bible Church who have supported Men in Action as a vital part of our church culture.

From the Grateful Heart of Michael Wilhelm

I dedicate this work to:
- My wife, Marilyn, who not only grounds me, but is more tolerant of me than I deserve.
- Pastor Jim for allowing me the personal privilege of having a role in this great adventure.

From the Grateful Hearts of both Jim Cecy and Mike Wilhelm

We dedicate this work to:
- Jon Dueck, who attended many times, even with three generations of his family. As a skilled and professional educator, he willingly joined us in occasional teaching, and assisted in developing the discussion questions.
- Matthew Schulz, who took on the daunting task of formatting and editing this material, written by two very different authors (i.e., a pastor and a lawyer!). His gracious spirit and commitment to clarity has been a blessing.
- Debby Tinnin, Pastor Jim's faithful ministry associate at Campus Bible Church, who spent countless hours preparing for the MIA classes. Her servant's heart is more than commendable; it is inspiring.
- Pastor George Posthumus, who added the session on evangelism. His love for equipping people is contagious.
- The hundreds of Men in Action graduates committed to becoming Mighty Men of Valor. Only heaven will reveal the impact they will have on their families, the generations, their churches, their communities, and the world.
- The wives and accountability partners of our Men in Action graduates who got their much-deserved PHT ("Put Him Through") award. Without their prayerful support, many of these men would not have finished the course.

We dedicate the MIA program to our Lord, Jesus Christ, who burdened our hearts and equipped us to be more intentional about raising up godly men. If we are in any way effective, we have absolute certainty that it is because of Him, and for Him.

A History of Our
Men in Action Adventure

A WORD FROM JIM CECY

FROM ONE LEADER TO ANOTHER

I began my ministry as a local church pastor some 45 years ago, and since 1995 I have served as the Senior Pastor at Campus Bible Church in Fresno, California. Over 30 years ago I founded JARON Ministries International, a ministry dedicated to motivating and equipping Christian leaders around the world. I have always taken very seriously my call to not only "preach the Word" (2 Timothy 4:2), but to "equip the saints for the work of ministry" (Ephesians 4:11-12).

I spent many years focusing my attention on teaching my people, training my pastoral staff, raising up elders and equipping our ministry leaders—all good things, for sure. But something was missing. I realized I was doing more to train and equip younger men overseas than I was in my local church. I had abrogated my own personal responsibility to be more directly involved in equipping all the men in our church, regardless of how busy I was as a lead pastor.

Yes, we were growing as a local church and everything seemed to be going well, except when it came to recruiting more men to lead or even participate in ministry. We found ourselves "bribing men with meat and money" (i.e., food and scholarships) in order for them to attend events. We resorted to begging men to serve as ministry leaders, deacons or elders. Pretty soon, we were "hiring doorkeepers" to do what volunteers used to do. It was also so much easier to equip the older and younger women. All we needed to do was decorate the room and the women showed up. And they didn't demand steak!

Men in Action (MIA) was born out of frustration, but even more so after I gained a clearer sense of my calling as a local church shepherd. In the Book of Titus the Apostle Paul assigned Titus to go into unhealthy churches to be an example of a faith-builder, knowledge-builder, and change-maker, as he helped them appoint mature local church leaders (cf. Titus 1:1-9). I believed I was doing a fair job at this but only as I observed men who I thought had the maturity to serve. I was not truly living out the clear instructions in the equally important second chapter:

> *"But as for you, speak the things which are fitting for sound (i.e. healthy) doctrine. Older men are to be temperate, dignified, sensible, sound in faith, in love, in perseverance. Older women likewise are to be reverent in their behavior, not malicious gossips nor enslaved to much wine, teaching what is good, so that they may encourage the young women to love their husbands, to love their children, to be sensible, pure, workers at home, kind, being subject to their own husbands, so that the word of God will not be dishonored. Likewise urge the young men to*

be sensible; in all things show yourself to be an example of good deeds, with purity in doctrine, dignified, sound in speech which is beyond reproach, so that the opponent will be put to shame, having nothing bad to say about us"
(Titus 2:1-8, NASB, my addition).

In 2006 something changed. Under conviction of the Holy Spirit regarding my lack of attention to my Titus 2 priorities, I decided to reach into our precious flock and invite a group of men I considered to be potential leaders. I had not really arrived at my current position that all men of God are called to lead in some way. By special invitation only, we began our first class. What an experience we had for all of us "MIA pioneers." After the class, I invited the graduates to recommend another group of men they considered as potential leaders. What a surprise to find on their list men I had never considered. The second class was equally exciting.

Soon Mike Wilhelm, a fellow elder and attorney joined me in leading and teaching the course. To date, 22 classes have been held at our church with as many as 80 men in each class. We have also witnessed other churches in our county and around the world use these materials. Now, as they say, the rest is history—one that will remain in the collective memory of our local church, and for good reason.

Since that first MIA class, our church attendance, our giving and our ministries, locally and globally, have increased substantially. Why? Because our Men in Action graduates attend with their families, serve willingly when asked, and give generously, cheerfully and sacrificially of their time, talent and treasures. Many also lead their extended families to do the same. Although the men still insist on steak, I genuinely believe they will show up at a men's event or accept an invitation to minister, even if we serve hot dogs!

We now welcome you to join other men in the amazing adventure of building our homes, churches and communities on the backs of strong men. Men of God. Men in Action. Mighty Men of Valor. Servant-leaders.

Soli Deo Gloria—to God alone be the glory!

Dr. Jim Cecy
Senior Pastor-Teacher
Campus Bible Church, Fresno CA

A WORD FROM MICHAEL WILHELM

SUPPORTING IMPORTANT MINISTRY

I read an article in *Christianity Today* years ago that argued that one of the primary jobs of a senior pastor was to raise up godly Christian men who could lead in the home, community, workplace, and the church. While it struck a chord with me at the time, I was uncertain as to what this would look like in practice. That was before attending Campus Bible Church.

I had only been at the church a few months when Pastor Cecy cajoled and wheedled me into attending a men's leadership course he called Men in Action. He said he wanted every man in the church to attend the class at least once, and for those in leadership it was mandatory. My hesitance was that it took two-and-half hours in a weekly meeting, along with an equal amount of homework. For an attorney with an already over-burdened schedule, this caused me some pause before I ultimately gave in.

I felt I was already a leader based on many of my life experiences. However, the class was a revelation. It both deconstructed the worldview of leadership and then reconstructed it with a heavy dose of Biblical truth, anchored in very practical realism. What I saw was a senior pastor carrying out the mandate I had seen years ago in *Christianity Today.* The program followed a logical course, beginning with self-leadership and culminating in leadership in the church.

In a macro sense, MIA directly confronts the five-decade assault on the role of men in our culture and especially in the church. All of this has left men, especially young men, in a state of confusion and indecision on what their proper role is in family and church. The goal is to provide a clear basis for men to step into the role of a leader but with an emphasis on servant-leadership. There appears to be a void when it comes to finding men in the church not only willing to take leadership positions, but just as important, who are equipped to do so.

In a micro sense, and at a personal level, it allowed me to feel like "one of the guys", which, to be honest, is not always easy for me. It caused me to assess many things in my life and to like some and to eliminate others. It gave me something in common with other men in the church centered around relationships with them and a sense of shared purpose.

It took one time through the class (I have now been involved in many classes) to realize that God wanted me to find a way to support this important work that Pastor Cecy created. It has been my privilege to provide structure to the materials and to supplement them where necessary. My greatest joy has been the opportunity to assist in the leadership of each class. Watching men connect with each other and being part of those connections is extremely fulfilling. Finally, to see men adopt change in their lives that benefit themselves, their families, their church, and society, brings a contentment beyond measure.

Michael Wilhelm, Esq.
Elder, Campus Bible Church, Fresno CA

Testimonials

WHAT PASTORS ARE SAYING

"My dear friend, Pastor Jim Cecy encouraged me for several years to try this program. As a senior pastor we had so many things happening and in place that I didn't see how Men in Action could be fit in. Ultimately, however, I decided to give it a go. The response of men was phenomenal. Men came out of the woodwork to be part of it. Friendships were developed, and accountability leading to rapid spiritual growth followed. Each year I sought out two men to assist in the program, providing an opportunity to not only train and equip over 150 men through the materials but provided discipleship time with two men each year. I only wish I had started Men in Action earlier in my ministry. It became one of the most significant training times in the life of our church for these past thirty years."
      Pastor George Posthumus
      Riverpark Bible Church
      Fresno, CA

"Here in Men in Action, Dr. Cecy addresses one of the greatest problems in the church: the lack of godly men and leaders. There are many books about Christian leadership, but there are few that help Christian men become godly men and leaders, whether at home or in the church. This material is thoroughly Biblical, with sound exegesis backing up the principles, as well as eminently practical insights. This is why this book on the subject of Christian leadership is so unique. It is as if a godly father is instructing his grown son about the Biblical qualities, character, and practices of being a man of honor and leader that the church and families desperately need today. I highly recommend this resource to men who want rocket fuel to go to the next level in their spiritual development."
      Pastor Ben Dosti
      New Harvest Church
      Fresno, CA

"Because our ministry is in London, England, often programs that originate in the United States are difficult to implement. Our church alone has around fifteen different nationalities represented. I was pleased to discover that Men In Action crossed over quite easily because of its emphasis on relationships. It is an excellent tool that helped me as a pastor to mentor and disciple the men in our fellowship. What made MIA so great was the way that it drew our men together and gave them a platform to share the issues that mattered to them, with the Word of God at the center of it all. So many of the men who went through the program thanked me over and over again for getting them involved. Fantastic!"
      Pastor Freddie Roberson
      Christians in Action Church
      London, England

"Many men approach their spiritual growth like putting together a Christmas bicycle, 'I don't need the instructions. I can figure this out as I go.' Men in Action is an excellent manual for men

who realize they do need help. Thoroughly Biblical, clear, concise, and applicable to anyone's situation, Men in Action gives men the tools and relationships they need to grow spiritually."

Pastor Chips Ross
Westwood Baptist Church
Fresno, CA

"When Dr. Cecy told me about Men in Action, I was wondering if it would work in our East-German context. As I prepared the very first course in our German church plant, I learned a lot myself. For the men attending and for me, it has been a life-changing experience. The great strength of this course is that it is not just theory, but that it is interwoven with many practical assignments and the need to interact with others in the family and church. Be it the questionnaires for couples, for the children, accountability meetings and so on—the combination of it all makes Men in Action an experience that changes the core of men and has impacted their spouses and children in our church as well. Another unexpected, but surprisingly helpful side-effect has been that I did not just get to know the men in my church more deeply, but it revealed which men are really committed to their family and God and which ones just want to have a Christian mask. I can recommend this course to any pastor and church!"

Pastor Torsten Klotzsche
Berlin, Germany

WHAT THE WIVES OF OUR MIA ALUMNI ARE SAYING

When asked to write about what they saw to be the area of most improvement, wives responded with enthusiasm…

"I saw him grow as a leader of our household, trusting God to handle the unexpected, stressful situations with grace, and turning to the Lord in prayer for guidance."

"As a wife of a husband who did not have any example of a father in his life, it is truly a blessing for our family to have a resource like Men in Action…it has been a gift to my husband."

"He relinquished the position as 'general manager of the universe.' As a result, we enjoy exceedingly more peace and sweet fellowship."

"He has improved in fostering and nurturing relationships with other men."

"I saw him living in more freedom from past mistakes."

"He is much more romantic!"

"He is much more sensitive to my needs."

"He has greater dedication to serving the church."

"He has greater faith during tough times…keeping a God-centered perspective."

"He is more open about his life and asking for prayer in personal matters."

Contents

Introduction

CALLING MEN TO ACTION

Read the news. Hear the reports. Listen to what's being said by society. Men are under attack on many fronts, even in Christ's Church. However, the *greatest* threat to Biblical manhood is men themselves. Men who abuse their authority. Men who neglect their responsibility. Men who do not act like men, either because they can't (i.e., they are untrained), or because they won't (i.e., they refuse to accept God's calling in their lives). It is time to accept the undeniable and irresistible:

- God is calling men to be Men of God
- God is calling Men of God to be Men in Action
- God is calling Men in Action to be Mighty Men of Valor
- God is calling Mighty Men of Valor to be Servant-Leaders

In Acts 13:36, we read King David "served the purpose of God in his own generation." We know he did not do that alone. He had amazing men in his life, like Jonathan his friend who supported him, and Nathan the prophet who confronted him. There was also another group of men who were equally important. They were called the *gibborim*, or more specifically, the *gibborim khahyil*, meaning "the mighty men of valor" (cf. 1 Chronicles 7:5). These are an army of strong, capable, valiant warriors and champions who were men of character and substance. The Bible calls them the "men of Issachar." Truly, they are a *tour de force*—men to be reckoned with! Let's consider a few of their attributes as a challenge to our own lives as Men of God:

Attribute #1: Mighty Men of Valor are well-equipped to do battle.

> *"…mighty men of valor, men trained for war who could handle shield and spear, and whose faces were like the faces of lions, and they were as swift as gazelles on the mountains" (1 Chronicles 12:8, NASB).*

Men in Action is designed to equip Men of God to do battle…

- …with the inward flesh (Galatians 5:19) that tries to have us return to our "vomit" and the "mire" of our old lives (2 Peter 2:22).
- …with the prowling devil (1 Peter 5:8-9) who seeks to devour us every moment.
- …with the world's value system (1 John 2:15-17) that seduces us with the "lust of the flesh and the lust of the eyes and the boastful pride of life" (i.e., sex, money, and power).

We will learn to identify and use the spiritual gifts and natural talents our Creator has given us to serve Him, equip others, and build Christ's Church.

Real Men seek to be well-trained!

Attribute #2: Mighty Men of Valor can expect to have great impact.

> *"…he who was least was equal to a hundred and the greatest to a thousand"*
> *(1 Chronicles 12:14, NASB).*

Many men love to build things, from fences to backyard patios. However, we were designed by God to be more than "brick and mortar" men. We were called to be faith-builders, family-builders, and even generation-builders, even when we are old and gray (cf. Psalm 71:17-18). Like David's mighty men, we, as Men in Action, need to keep growing as Men of God and Mighty Men of Valor in order to have even greater impact each day of our lives.

Real Men see real results!

Attribute #3: Mighty Men of Valor admit they need help from God and each other.

> *"We are yours, O David….Peace, peace to you, and peace to him who helps you; indeed, your God helps you"* *(1 Chronicles 12:18, NASB).*

When it comes to navigating the road to Biblical manhood, many of us were given no direction. Our fathers were gone or non-communicative. Perhaps they insisted we, like them, should try to learn this on our own. After all, real men don't need help. O yes, we do. Many of us are lost and we humbly cry out, "I need help and I need it now!" And, even more than admitting our need for help, Men in Action welcome it, just like King David did:

> *"…David received them (i.e. his mighty men of valor)…"*
> *(1 Chronicles 12:18, NASB, my addition).*

Real Men willingly admit their weaknesses and their need for help!

Attribute #4: Mighty Men of Valor never stop improving as leaders.

> *"They helped David…for they were all mighty men of valor, and were <u>captains</u> in the army"* *(1 Chronicles 12:21, NASB, emphasis added).*

No matter where we are as men, we need to take another step, to "excel beyond excellence" in becoming captains of faith, hope, and love in our family, church, and community.

> *"Finally then, brethren, we request and exhort you in the Lord Jesus, that as you received from us instruction as to how you ought to walk and please God (just as you actually do walk), that you excel still more"* *(1 Thessalonians 4:1, NASB).*

Real Men sharpen their skills!

Attribute #5: Mighty Men of Valor need to be equipped as effective soldiers of the cross.

> "…day by day men came to David to help him, until there was a great army like the army of God" (1 Chronicles 12:22, NASB).

We will work together to become a Mighty Army of Men of God and Men of the Cross, submitting to the Lord Jesus Christ, Our Commander in Chief—no matter how difficult the task.

> "Suffer hardship with me, as a good soldier of Christ Jesus. No soldier in active service entangles himself in the affairs of everyday life, so that he may please the one who enlisted him as a soldier" (2 Timothy 2:3-4, NASB).

Real Men always stand guard!

Attribute #6: Mighty Men of Valor seek to understand the times in which they live and serve.

> "…men who understood the times, with knowledge of what Israel should do…all their kinsman were at their command" (1 Chronicles 12:32, NASB).

We are called to be Men of the Word. We are also called to be men who understand the times. This requires we stay updated on current events and consider a range of perspectives. The Men of Issachar "knew the times..." We may not understand the times in which *they* lived, but we have no excuse for being unaware of the challenges of being Men of God in *our* day and age. Mighty Men of Valor are men who listen to people from all walks of life.

> "But realize this, that in the last days difficult ["violent," Greek: chalepos] times will come. For men will be lovers of self, lovers of money, boastful, arrogant, revilers, disobedient to parents, ungrateful, unholy, unloving, irreconcilable, malicious gossips, without self-control, brutal, haters of good, treacherous, reckless, conceited, lovers of pleasure rather than lovers of God, holding to a form of godliness, although they have denied its power; Avoid such men as these" (2 Timothy 3:1-5, NASB, my addition).

Real Men are well-informed!

Attribute #7: Mighty Men of Valor strive for a wholly-devoted and well-prepared heart.

> "All these, being men of war who could draw up in battle formation, came…with a perfect ["wholly devoted, full, prepared, uncut," Hebrew: shalem] heart" (1 Chronicles 12:38, NASB, my addition).

The way to a man's heart is not his stomach. The way to a man's heart is his heart. Biblically speaking, the heart is the control center. The place from which we make decisions, good or bad (cf. Proverbs 23:7; Mark 7:21-23). Men in Action is not just designed to fill your mind with information about how to be an effective leader. We are also going after the heart, the place where we will decide whether to apply what we learn.

Real Men are committed to excellence!

Attribute #8: Mighty Men of Valor pursue a unity of purpose with other men of God.

> *"…all the rest…were of one mind" (1 Chronicles 12:38, NASB).*

> *"Behold, how good and how pleasant it is for brothers to dwell together in unity!" (Psalm 133:1, NASB).*

In 2 Samuel 16:6, we learn of the mighty men who protected David when people threw stones at him. It says these men "…were at his right and his left hand." Mighty Men of Valor stand in solidarity with other Men of God. In a world tearing men apart, we will stand together—"of one mind"—as we pursue a godly life-focus.

Real Men have each other's backs!

Attribute #9: Mighty Men of Valor witness lasting fruit in their lives and in the lives of the people around them.

> *"There was joy indeed in Israel" (1 Chronicles 12:40, NASB).*

In these challenging days, real Men of God need clear evidence of being under the control of God's Holy Spirit, manifesting the fruit of that obedient relationship—love, joy, peace, patience, kindness, goodness, faithfulness, gentleness, and self-control (cf. Galatians 5:22-23). During Men in Action we will do more than memorize and examine the Fruit of the Spirit. We will testify openly about their impact and be honest about what our lives look like when they are missing.

Real Men look for lasting impact!

Attribute #10: Men become Mighty Men of Valor by first becoming Men of God.

We are born men; we are *not* born Men of God. That only comes by trusting in Jesus Christ— the Crucified and Risen Lord—alone for our salvation.

> *"But as many as received Him, to them He gave the right to become children of God, even to those who believe in His name, who were born, not of blood nor of the will of the flesh nor of the will of man, but of God" (John 1:12-13, NASB).*

> *"He saved us, not on the basis of deeds which we have done in righteousness, but according to His mercy, by the washing of regeneration and renewing by the Holy Spirit, whom He poured out upon us richly through Jesus Christ our Savior,*

so that being justified by His grace we would be made heirs according to the hope of eternal life" (Titus 3:5-7, NASB).

Our desire is for every man who takes this course to know he has peace with God (cf. Romans 5:1) and a personal relationship with God, as his "Abba" Father (cf. Romans 8:15, Galatians 4:6).

Real Men follow Christ as Lord of their lives!

Attribute #11: Men of God become Mighty Men of Valor by becoming Men of the Word.

"…the people who know their God will display strength and take action" (Daniel 11:32b, NASB).

We become Men of God once we trust in Christ alone for our salvation. We then begin the discipleship journey for all born-again believers, growing healthy in fellowship, doctrine, worship, service, evangelism, discipleship, and prayer. To become Mighty Men of Valor we must grow in our confidence in the Word of God and our ability to use it to find wisdom, make decisions and lead others.

"For the word of God is living and active and sharper than any two-edged sword, and piercing as far as the division of soul and spirit, of both joints and marrow, and able to judge the thoughts and intentions of the heart" (Hebrews 4:12, NASB).

As we hold onto these doctrines, we develop a fuller heart of understanding that believes that to know Him is to love Him, to love Him is to obey Him, and to obey Him is to serve Him.

Real Men rely on the Word of God for guidance!

Attribute #12: Men in Action take to heart they are called by God to act like men.

Let's review a few passages specifically addressed to men:

"Be strong, therefore, and show yourself a man" (1 Kings 2:2, NASB).

"…I want you to understand that Christ is the head of every man, and the man is the head of a woman, and God is the head of Christ" (1 Corinthians 11:3, NASB).

"Be on the alert, stand firm in the faith, act like men (Greek: andrizomai), be strong" (1 Corinthians 16:13, NASB).

"Older men are to be temperate, dignified, sensible, sound in faith, in love, in perseverance" (Titus 2:2, NASB).

"Likewise urge the young men to be sensible; in all things show yourself to be an example of good deeds, with purity in doctrine, dignified, sound in speech which is beyond reproach, so that the opponent will be put to shame, having nothing bad to say about us" (Titus 2:6-8, NASB; cf. 1 Timothy 3:1-10, 12-13).

Real Men are real men!

Attribute #13: Men in Action take to heart their calling as Servant-Leaders.

The Japanese word *samurai* is a familiar word. Sadly, our first impression is of sword-wielding noblemen who cut people's heads off with one fell swoop. Actually, the word *samurai* originally meant "one who serves". We, too, as Men of God, Men in Action, and men who aspire to be Mighty Men of Valor, are called to be foot-washing, humble Servant-leaders, just like Jesus.

> *"If I then, the Lord and the Teacher, washed your feet, you also ought to wash one another's feet. For I gave you an example that you also should do as I did to you" (John 13:14-15, NASB).*

Real Men are slaves of God and servants of others!

Attribute #14: Men of God never stop growing as Men in Action and Men of Valor.

Perhaps you know the feeling of wearing a sturdy pair of boots. There is security in their stability and strength. The Apostle Paul spoke about the need to be firm-footed in our battle to be effective Men of God this side of heaven.

> *"Finally, be strong in the Lord and in the strength of His might. Put on the full armor of God, so that you will be able to stand firm against the schemes of the devil" (Ephesians 6:10-11, NASB).*

> *"Stand firm therefore, having girded your loins with truth, and having put on the breastplate of righteousness, and having shod your feet with the preparation of the gospel of peace…" (Ephesians 6:14-15, NASB).*

Christ's Mighty Men are to stand, fully suited with the armor of God. They are to be Men in Action, who stand firm on the peace of God, no matter the battle. They strive to become Mighty Men of Valor who never give up on their family, their jobs, and their ministries.

Real Men "keep on keeping on!"

THE MANLY CHALLENGE

We are calling men—our "brothers from another mother"—to be Men of God. To be Men in Action. To be Mighty Men of Valor. To be Soldiers of the Cross. To be Servant-Leaders. We are committed to building our homes, our churches, and our communities on the backs of strong men of God, who alongside strong women of God, fulfill their unique roles, linking together for the cause of Christ. John Wesley may have said it best: "Give me one hundred men who fear nothing but sin, and desire nothing but God and I will shake the world." Anybody interested in shaking the world? In the words of the classic hymn:

"Rise up, O, Men of God! Have done with lesser things;
Give heart and soul and mind and strength, to serve the King of Kings."

MEN IN ACTION P.U.S.H.

"Therefore I want the men in every place to pray, lifting up holy hands, without wrath and dissension" (1 Timothy 2:8, NASB).

It is well said that a successful man is one who does what unsuccessful men don't do. Unsuccessful men in the eyes of God are not men of prayer. We want Men of God, Men in Action and men who aspire to be Men of Valor to be Men who P.U.S.H.—Men who **P**ray **U**ntil **S**omething **H**appens!

WHEN SHOULD WE PRAY?

- When all else fails…
- Before anything else…
- When you do not know what else to do…
- When you think you know what to do…
- Before you start…
- When you are in process…
- When you think it will never end…
- When you are done…
- When things go wrong…
- When nothing goes right…
- When all seems lost…
- When all seems right…
- In the worst of times…
- In the best of times…
- When in the lowest valley…
- When at the highest summit…
- When facing the most complex problem…
- When facing the simplest daily event…
- Daily, for your friends and family…
- Daily, for your enemies…
- Daily, for His will to be done…

HOW SHOULD WE PRAY?

We have been given the unique privilege of private communication with God, our very approachable Heavenly Father (cf. Matthew 7:7-11; Romans 8:15, 26). He loves to hear from us (cf. Proverbs 15:8)! Throughout MIA we will be encouraged to follow this pattern based on how Jesus taught His disciples to pray (cf. Matthew 6:5-13). Consider the acronym—P.R.A.Y.E.R.:

1. **Praising:** "God, I praise you for _____" (i.e., reciting or singing about His attributes and praising Him for His works).

   > "Pray, then, in this way: "Our Father who art in heaven, Hallowed be Thy name..." (Matthew 6:9, NASB).

2. **Repenting:** "God, forgive me for _____" (i.e., agreeing with God concerning the ways we fall short of His glory).

   > "And forgive us our debts, as we also have forgiven our debtors. And do not lead us into temptation, but deliver us from evil" (Matthew 6:12-13, NASB).

3. **Asking:** "God, I bring before you the following needs..." (i.e., presenting to God our specific requests).

   > "Give us this day our daily bread" (Matthew 6:11; cf. Jeremiah 33:3; John 14:7-14; Matthew 7:7-11; James 4:2-3).

4. **Yielding:** "God, do I really need what I'm asking for?" (i.e., desiring His will more than our own).

   > "Thy kingdom come. Thy will be done, On earth as it is in heaven" (Matthew 6:10; cf. 1 John 5:14).

5. **Entreating:** "God, I bring before you the needs of others."

   > "Give us this day our daily bread, and forgive us our debts, as we also have forgiven our debtors. And do not lead us into temptation, but deliver us from evil" (Matthew 6:11-13, NASB).

6. **Rejoicing:** "God, thank you, in advance, for what you are going to do" (i.e., expressing confidence before He answers).

   > "For Thine is the kingdom, and the power, and the glory, forever. Amen" (Matthew 6:13, NASB; cf. Mark. 11:24).

WHAT SHOULD WE PRAY FOR OTHERS?

> "As for me, far be it from me that I should sin against the LORD by ceasing to pray for you; but I will instruct you in the good and right way" (1 Samuel 12:23, NASB).

The many "one another" verses in the New Testament call us to bear burdens, encourage, challenge, and show love for one another. The Greek word *allelon*, used 100 times in the New Testament, conveys the idea of mutuality and reciprocity.

In addition to praying for the physical, emotional, and spiritual well-being of others we should also use Scripture to guide our prayers:

1. Pray through books of the Bible, asking God to direct the hearts of others to the application of each command to obey, promise to keep, truth to know, actions to take, sins to forsake, examples to follow, and new thoughts about God.
2. Pray through some of the Psalms (e.g., Psalm 1, 5, 8, 19, 23, 37, 42, 51, 103, 139, etc.).
3. Pray through Jesus' Sermon on the Mount (Matthew 5-7).
4. Pray the Fruit of the Spirit in your life (Galatians 5:22-23).
5. Pray through some of the Apostle Paul's prayers for his fellow believers.

> *"For this reason also, since the day we heard of it, we have not ceased to pray for you and to ask that you may be filled with the knowledge of His will in all spiritual wisdom and understanding, so that you will walk in a manner worthy of the Lord, to please Him in all respects, bearing fruit in every good work and increasing in the knowledge of God; strengthened with all power, according to His glorious might, for the attaining of all steadfastness and patience; joyously giving thanks to the Father, who has qualified us to share in the inheritance of the saints in Light. For He rescued us from the domain of darkness, and transferred us to the kingdom of His beloved Son, in whom we have redemption, the forgiveness of sins" (Colossians 1:9-14, NASB).*

(For further study, read "Roadblocks to an Effective Prayer-Life," in Appendix C.)

> ## *"Much prayer, much power. Little prayer, little power."*
> ### *(R.A. Torrey)*
>
> ## *"The world has yet to see what God will do with a man fully consecrated to Him."*
> ### *(D.L. Moody)*

NOTES

SESSION 1
Committing to the Adventure

Be on the alert, stand firm in the faith, act like men, be strong. (I Corinthians 16:13)

SESSION 1
Committing to the Adventure

Class discussion
The content below will be discussed during class. If you miss class this week, you are required to read them on your own time, prior to next week's class.

At the beginning of class
- For this first class only, arrive 30 minutes early. Pick up your class materials and put on your nametag. Be seated.
- Write your name and phone number on the first page of your manual and on the envelope found inside.

Class schedule
- 30 minutes: Dinner/Sign-in
- 10 minutes: Welcome
- 5 minutes: Attendance
- 5 minutes: Opening prayer
- 15 minutes: "Getting to Know Our Group"
- 30 minutes: Introduction: Calling Men to Action
- 20 minutes: The Nuts and Bolts of MIA – Part 1
    - Confidentiality
    - Flow of Class, Sessions 2-12
    - Review of Class Materials, Envelope
    - Major Projects
        o My Life Focus
        o Case Study
    - Prayer Time – "Men in Action P.U.S.H."
    - Attendance
    - Preparing Your Testimony
    - Accountability Partners (Appendix C)
    - Small Group Discussion
- 10 minutes: Men in Action Remember Names
- 10 minutes: Break
- 25 minutes: The Nuts and Bolts of MIA – Part 2
    - Bible Study
    - Church Attendance
    - Solo Initiative
    - Service Projects
    - Attending a Men's Event
    - Outreach to the Missing Chair
    - Review of Forms and Envelope

- o Personal Information and Class Payment
- o Statement of Class Commitment
- o Solo Initiative Commitment
- o Accountability Partner Questions
  - Review next week's assignments
  - Invitation for additional men to join MIA
- 5 minutes: Measuring My Progress
- 5 minutes: Men in Action Are Wholly Dedicated
- 5 minutes: I Am a Soldier
- 5 minutes: Class Dedication

Calling a missing chair
"…You will be missed because your seat will be empty" (1 Samuel 20:18).

Missing chair:	
Phone number:	Email:
Contacted:	Status:

Teaching goal
That men would understand the purpose of Men in Action and would see how this course has immediate and long-term benefits for their life as a man of God.

Frequently Asked Questions

QUESTION	ANSWER
What is the purpose of MIA?	To "excel still more..." and to take another step of growth in our leadership in the home, the workplace, the community, and the church.
Is this simply another men's Bible study?	While the Bible is the source for what is being taught, it is not a Bible study. This is a program aimed at personal growth as a man of God; it is about change.
What is the age range?	The class is beneficial to men of all age ranges and life stages. Typically, the youngest age is 18 (though sometimes younger men may join, but only when attending with their father).
How strict is the schedule?	We start on time and we get you out on time.
How much work outside of class is required?	The weekly average is 1-2 hours, but it varies week to week.
In addition to homework what else is required?	You are expected to do the following: • Pray regularly for your classmates • Read your Bible regularly • Give your testimony • Meet with your accountability partner at least weekly • Attend church weekly (give your time, talent and treasure) • Attend one men's event • Call those who are absent from class (The Missing Chair) • Participate in at least one service project (to be assigned) • Grow in Christ
How much memorization is required?	You will memorize: • Names of your fellow MIAs • The Fruit of the Spirit • The names of the books of the Bible
Are there written assignments to turn in?	You will complete two projects during the class. The first is called My Life Focus. You will work on this throughout the course. The second project is a case study. This will be completed near the end of the class and submitted.
What is the attendance policy?	To graduate, you cannot miss more than three sessions. If you are going to miss a session, please let us know ahead of time. You are also expected to read the notes and do the homework for any weeks you may miss.

If I show up will I be expected to say something?	Everyone does a short testimony, and everyone is encouraged to participate in all the discussions.
Will I feel out of place if I do not know much about the Bible?	We are all in different stages of our knowledge of the Bible. No one should stay away based on their current Bible knowledge.
What if I am not comfortable sharing with a bunch of men?	Everything you discuss is CONFIDENTIAL, and you will not be forced to share anything that makes you uncomfortable.
What do I need to bring to class each week?	<ul><li>A willing and teachable heart</li><li>Bible</li><li>Pen or pencil</li><li>Your workbook</li><li>Completed homework</li></ul>
What do I need outside of class?	Access to a copy machine so you can make copies of assignments/forms you will turn in.
Where do I find an accountability partner?	It is your choice. Any Christian man is a candidate (Many of the folks in the class pair up before or during the first class).
How do we stay in touch between classes?	Please make sure we have your email address and plan on receiving regular communication. Also provide your cell phone number.

Preparing for the Adventure

Hopefully you and your fellow Men in Action are excited about the important journey we are about to begin. You are making a 13-week commitment. There are 12 weeks of teaching and homework, culminating with a graduation event on the 13th week.

Men in Action is a program designed to challenge you in your personal growth as a man of God. At the same time, everything we say and do is rooted in the Bible and its truth, setting the direction for our lives. The goal of MIA is to see you focus on becoming the man God desires you to be.

We are committed to starting and ending class on time. Real men respect each other's time commitments, so make sure to arrive on time each week.

We ask you make this program a priority for the duration of the class. Each week builds on the previous weeks, laying foundations for future content, so attendance is important.

If for any reason you are unable to attend the first night, contact the class leader and he will go through the materials with you, or arrange for one of the more experienced members of the class to help you get oriented.

Below are some actions you can take as you begin to prepare:

1. **Start praying for yourself and your classmates.** This class is expected to result in major changes in the lives of the men who complete it. This means Satan does not want to see you involved. You will struggle at times with your own flesh and the discipline necessary to finish the class. Pray for your strength and diligence, as well as for your fellow men.

2. **Consider the commitment required.** You will be asked to sign a Class Commitment after the first session and turn it in at the beginning of the second session. This commitment requires your signature and your wife's (If you are married). Your wife's support and prayer is key to your success in this program. She will be invited to the graduation ceremony and to submit a brief written testimony.

3. **Begin thinking about your Solo Initiative.** Each man picks an activity he will engage in consistently during the class. We all have areas in our lives that could use improvement. It might include regular daily exercise, turning off the TV, filtering the internet, regular Bible reading, regular date nights with your wife, or more time with your children. Pick one thing you will do on a regular basis for the duration of the class and commit to it. Pick something that if it becomes a habit, will make you a better man. Each week your accountability partner will be encouraged to ask about your progress.

4. **Think about who might serve as your accountability partner.** Each man in the class is *required* to have an accountability partner for the duration of the class. This

is someone you will select. The most important motivational tool in keeping you on task will likely be your accountability partner. This can be someone in the class or another person you know. The two requirements are that your partner be a man and a Christian. He will also be invited to the graduation at the end of class. If you do not have someone selected prior to the second session, we will try to match you up with someone in the class.

5. **Let us know right away concerning any changes in your personal information.** We need your phone number, address, etc. Most important is we have the correct email address for you. Email will be the primary means of communication.

Be sure to write your name and phone number clearly on everything you turn in. You will be provided a large envelope you will use to submit copies of your assignments.

A note to those who choose to do this course with just a few men: We encourage you to do this course with at least one or two other men. Adjust the schedule and assignments accordingly but be very intentional about pushing each other to completion.

P.U.S.H. = <u>P</u>ray <u>U</u>ntil <u>S</u>omething <u>H</u>appens!

Getting to Know Our Group

[In-class activity]

1. Who among us are new to Men in Action?

2. Who are our "MIA alumni" (Share how many times you have taken the class)?

3. Who is the youngest member of our class?

4. Who is the oldest member of our class?

5. Who are our newlyweds? Most recent wedding?

6. Who has been married the longest? Years?

7. How many *total* years of marriage are represented in our group?

8. Who is our newest Christian?

9. Who has been a born-again Christian the longest?

10. How many total years of Christian experience are represented in our class?

(Add your own questions that will help your group get to know each other better.)

What do our combined answers say about the skill and wisdom we might learn from each other?

Preparing Your Testimony

Each man will give his testimony during one of the weekly sessions. The goal is to provide insight to other men in an area where you are struggling. Over the years this has been one of the most encouraging aspects of MIA. Sharing our testimony helps men to come alongside and support each other.

Your testimony should only be three minutes long (Please adhere to this standard). You will select one area from the Fruit of the Spirit (Love, Joy, Peace, Patience, Kindness, Goodness, Faithfulness, Gentleness and Self-Control) you find especially challenging and need to grow in.

Please review the definitions of the Fruit of the Spirit (Session 2) before selecting the one you will present in your testimony. During your testimony you will:

1. Give your name.
2. State the area from the "Fruit of the Spirit" you have selected.
3. Explain why this is a particular challenge for you (Use real life examples as much as possible).
4. State your struggles and why growth in this area is beneficial.
5. Provide some relevant verse(s) from the Bible on the subject.
6. Apply the verses to your struggles and share your plan to deal with the issue.
7. End your time by praying for the situation you have addressed and for your fellow Men in Action.

REMEMBER: WHAT IS SHARED IS STRICTLY CONFIDENTIAL

Real men respect each other's time.

Men in Action Remember Names

One of our MIA alumni was blessed with the name Les Moore. He loves to point out the words of a tombstone on Boot Hill:

Here Lies Lester Moore
Four Slugs from a 44
No Les, No More

How easy to remember a name like that. However, most names are not so easy or memorable. All of us can attest to seeing someone whose name we should remember, but don't. That's especially painful when we have been around them for a long time. What do we do? Run? Fake it? Face the embarrassment and admit it? Ignore it?

WHAT IS IN A NAME?

There is something very personal in a name. By using a person's name in conversation, you bridge a gap and create an intimacy that would not otherwise exist. By remembering a person's name and using it, you communicate they are important to you. Part of our goal with Men in Action is to build real relationships among men. A key to this process is breaking down the walls of isolation we often build around ourselves. Step one is learning and using each other's names.

BUT I AM REALLY BAD WITH NAMES

This is a common excuse and is true for most of us. All this means is you need a strategy for learning and retaining names. Commit to the process below and you will be surprised how quickly you will feel at home with your fellow MIAs. While we will continue to wear name tags throughout the class, by the third or fourth week you should be comfortable with the names of most of the men.

THE VALUE OF A NAME TAG

In a group setting, a clearly written name tag is an invaluable tool for helping folks remember names. Worn on the right side, it enables people to read the name carefully, shake a hand and look at a person's eyes, while repeating the name and forming some word pictures. Combined, these strategies will help you memorize someone's name the first time you meet. Trust us, it works!

DEVELOPING A STRATEGY TO LEARN AND REMEMBER NAMES

1. **Listen carefully and clarify the name**
   a. Focus on getting a person's name when they first introduce themselves, and then try to use it as quickly as possible in conversation with them. Make sure you get it right the first time or you will remember the wrong name. If you have any questions about their name or correct pronunciation, get it clarified up front.

b. Look them in the eye (this is very important!) and say: "It's Michael Howard, right? (wait for an answer). "It's nice to meet you, Michael, or do you prefer Mike?"

c. It is quite acceptable to ask the person to repeat their name the first couple of times you meet them. Try saying: "I really do want to learn your name. Please give me another chance."

d. Ask questions about the person (while repeating their name in your mind). You will associate their name with the information they give you.

e. End the conversation with, "It's been good to talk with you, Mike."

2. Repeat and review the name

a. After the conversation is over whisper their name to yourself, then repeat their name in your mind multiple times (Some teach that if you repeat the name 40 times it will be yours for life). Try it!

b. Note: You also have a list of all the men in your class. Use this as your quick study guide. Look at it right after class to identity who goes with each name. Review the list each week before class.

c. It is helpful if you write a key word next to each name that helps you remember the person. It could be a simple reminder like their job, who they are related to, or a physical characteristic like height, hair color, etc.

3. Associate the name

a. If there is something about the name or person that creates an association for you, all the better. Create an image using whatever associations their name triggers.

   i. Example: Associate the sounds of the name "Michael Howard" and come up with "microphone" and "coward". You could then envision him fearfully singing into a microphone.

b. Look closely at the person and observe their features as you form your image. The next time you see them, the picture will come back, and along with it, their name.

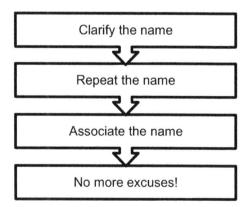

Personal Information and Class Payment

[Write legibly. Once completed, make a copy and turn this in]

Your teacher will inform you about the cost of the class. This covers the materials you receive and the graduation at the end of the class. Please fill out this form and place it in the envelope in your manual and turn it in.

No man should hesitate to take the class simply because he does not have enough money. Many men have taken the class with a full or partial scholarship. The important thing is to be an active participant of the class.

Your information

Name (first and last): _____

Employer: _____

Email: _____

Phone: _____

Spouse's name: _____

Church's name: _____

Pastor's name: _____

Payment information

Enclosed is a tuition payment of: ____Cash   ____Check   ____Paid online

I would like to request a scholarship: ____ Full   ____Partial (I can pay: _____)

I can help provide scholarships and have included an additional gift in the amount of: _____

Statement of Class Commitment

[Once completed, make a copy and turn this in]

What you get out of Men in Action is driven by what you personally invest in time and effort. To be successful you will need to dedicate a few hours each week outside of class for study, reflection and other requirements. Commit yourself to explore your responsibilities as a man and leader and you may walk out of our time together with a whole new vision of where you are headed with your life. Remember, this is a spiritual journey.

My Commitment

I, _____, will make this class a high priority in my life by:
[PRINT YOUR NAME]

1. Attending class faithfully and on time (to the best of my ability).
2. Participating wholeheartedly in class discussions and dialogues.
3. Completing all outside assignments.
4. If I miss a class I will read through the lesson on my own.
5. Being open and honest with my classmates.
6. Praying regularly for my fellow class members and their families.
7. Attending my local church services at least once a week.
8. Giving of my time, talent, and treasure in my local church.
9. Looking for regular application of the lessons I am learning.
10. Meeting at least weekly with my accountability partner.
11. Keeping all I hear from my fellow MIA's in strictest confidence.

_____   _____
Your signature   Date

My Wife's Commitment

I, _____, support my husband's decision to attend Men in Action and will make every effort to encourage and pray for him with respect to each of the above commitments.

_____   _____
Spouse signature   Date
[If you are married, this is required]

Solo Initiative Commitment

[Write legibly. Once completed, make a copy and turn this in]

Your Solo Initiative is something you commit to work on diligently while participating in Men in Action. By imposing this discipline on yourself the activity will move from practice to habit. Pick an area of weakness in your life that if addressed will make a real difference for you. It can be in the area of health (mental or physical), relationship(s) you need to work on, correcting sloppy personal habits, or anything else that will provide you with real benefit.

Sometimes commitments can be very personal and not something you want to share. Other times they are things you are willing to share with everyone. The only people that need to know about your commitment are you, the class teacher, and your accountability partner, since he must hold you accountable.

My Solo Initiative Commitment (print legibly)

I, _____, commit to make the following a regular practice in my life during my time in this class:

_____
_____
_____
_____
_____

I will make this commitment the subject of regular prayer, and will share my progress with my accountability partner, who is free to ask me hard questions about my commitment.

I hope at the end of this class to experience the following changes in my life as a result of the diligent pursuit of my solo initiative:

_____
_____
_____

_____   _____
Signature   Date

Accountability Partner Commitment

[Once completed, make a copy and turn this in]

You have been asked to serve as an accountability partner for a man who has committed to a men's leadership course called Men in Action. It is not necessary for you to be in the class to serve in the role of accountability partner. Your job is to pray for and hold this man accountable for all his commitments related to the course. Your role is extremely important, and in many ways is the key ingredient to the benefit derived by the person enrolled in the course.

If you or your partner have more questions about the importance of accountability, please see Appendix C for additional information ("The Value of Accountability").

Each man in Men in Action has committed to do the following for the duration of the class:

1. Attend class faithfully and on time (to the best of his ability).
2. Participate wholeheartedly in class discussions.
3. Complete all outside assignments (about an hour or so a week).
4. Be open and honest with his classmates.
5. Pray regularly for his fellow class members and their families.
6. Attend church services at least once a week.
7. Meet at least weekly with his accountability partner.
8. Look for regular application of the lessons he is learning.

In addition to the above commitments, he has committed to the following personal Solo Initiative (Write your Solo Initiative below):

_____

_____

_____

_____

Accountability Partner's Commitment

I, _____, commit to pray for my accountability
　　[Print Accountability Partner's name]
partner for the duration of the class, and to meet with him at least weekly to review his progress in all the above commitments. In love, I will ask hard questions and hold him accountable (see next page for a list of questions).

_____   _____
Accountability Partner's signature   Date

Accountability Partner Questions

Being an accountability partner is a relationship of extreme confidence and trust. We have to be vulnerable and open for the program to work, and our accountability partner must be completely trustworthy. Lack of accountability among men in our churches is one of our major weaknesses. This weakness is one of the areas Satan exploits in his efforts to render the local church impotent.

Give these questions to your accountability partner and authorize him to ask them to you each week along with praying for your needs.

1. How are you doing on your Solo Initiative?
2. Have you been faithful in the Word and prayer? Are you growing in your intimacy with God?
3. Have you been sensitive to the needs of your spouse and your family?
4. Is there anyone you are aware of whom you need to ask forgiveness?
5. Have you been struggling with impure thoughts?
6. Have you been looking at questionable material (i.e., movies, TV, books, magazines, internet, etc.), which would bring shame to the Lord?
7. Have you been alone with a woman in any kind of situation where your feelings became inappropriate, or where others could have suspected something which would be suspicious?
8. Are you experiencing any physical problems? Eating right? Getting adequate rest and sufficient exercise?
9. Are you facing challenges in your home life that are negatively affecting your physical, emotional, or spiritual well-being?
10. Are you facing challenges in your workplace that are negatively affecting your physical, emotional, or spiritual well-being?
11. Are you facing challenges in your ministry that are negatively affecting your physical, emotional, or spiritual well-being?
12. Have you lied or compromised your answers to any of the above questions?
13. As to any failures or issues noted above, what is your plan to deal with it this coming week?
14. What is your application from last week's MIA session and how are you applying it in your life?

(For further study, read "The Value of Accountability," in Appendix C.)

Measuring My Progress

By God's grace we will learn to be leaders who strive to become more effective in the home, workplace, community, and the church. Rate your understanding of the leadership concepts listed below. You will rate yourself again near the end of the program.

Scale			
0	No understanding/application	3	Reasonable understanding/application
1	Minimal understanding/application	4	Substantial understanding/application
2	Some understanding/application		

KEY CONCEPTS FOR TRUE LEADERSHIP

	Key Concept	Week 1	Week 12
1.	Consistent regular daily prayer defines the leader.		
2.	Without accountability, spiritual consistency is an illusion.		
3.	Leaders know how to work with and support other men.		
4.	Leaders strive to not allow others to fall behind or be lost.		
5.	A life without goals and focus is a life without purpose.		
6.	Remembering and using other's names builds positive relationships.		
7.	The Bible's standards for leaders is very different from the world's.		
8.	I am a Solider of the Cross, with a mission from God.		
9.	Openness around other men is important in building deep relationships.		
10.	Regular Bible reading is necessary to know the heart and mind of God.		
11.	Without application, Bible reading is a pointless exercise.		
12.	There are a multitude of roles in which a man shows leadership.		
13.	Submitting to the Holy Spirit is the only way to mature as a Christian.		
14.	My witness and growth is manifested through The Fruit of the Spirit.		
15.	There is vital connection between servanthood, sacrifice, and leadership.		
16.	The ability to prioritize and put "first things first" is a mark of good leaders.		
17.	Diligence (hanging in until the job is done), is a prerequisite to leadership.		
18.	Purity of heart and mind is something we all need to strive for.		
19.	I am the same person with family, friends, co-workers, Christians, etc.		
20.	I understand and use my spiritual gifts with family, work, church, community.		
21.	God has a master plan for His church.		
22.	The Bible defines non-optional requirements for church leadership.		
23.	The leader deals with the problems that confront him.		
	Total score:		

Men in Action are Wholly Dedicated

There is something about our hands that convey strong messages. A clenched fist displays anger and the desire to use force. An open-handed salute is more than a sign of respect; it signals to a superior there is no weapon or threat. A pat on the back communicates affirmation of a person. Applause is simply an affirming pat on the back from a distance. Open hands can also be a sign of peace (1 Timothy 2:8). We endeavor daily to lift up "holy hands" to the Lord (cf. 1 Timothy 2:8) as a symbol of His peace prevailing over our "anger, wrath, malice, slander, and abusive speech" (cf. Colossians 3:8). We also "lay hands on" and pray for those who are heading out on a new challenge in which they need our support and encouragement.

In addition to a symbol of the healing power of God, the Bible speaks of "laying hands" on someone as a means of endorsing and identifying with a person being sent to use their God-given gifts and talents in a ministry (cf. 1 Timothy 4:14; 5:22; 2 Timothy 1:6; etc.).

1. **We <u>lift</u> our hands to the Lord with a desire for His peace to prevail in our lives.**
    "Therefore I want the men in every place to pray, lifting up holy hands, without wrath and dissension" (1 Timothy 2:8, NASB).

2. **We <u>open</u> our hands to our fellow Men in Action to reveal we have no anger or malice toward them.**
    "…there is no evil or rebellion in my hands, and I have not sinned against you, though you are lying in wait for my life to take it…my hand shall not be against you" (1 Samuel 24:11, 13, NASB).

3. **We <u>pat</u> our fellow Men in Action on the back in recognition we believe in what God is doing in our midst.**
    "For I am confident of this very thing, that He who began a good work in you will perfect it until the day of Christ Jesus" (Philippians 1:6, NASB).

4. **We <u>applaud</u> our fellow Men in Action when they make the right choices.**
    "Be strong, therefore, and show yourself a man" (1 Kings 2:2, NASB).

    "Be on the alert, stand firm in the faith, act like men, be strong" (1 Corinthians 16:13, NASB).

5. **We <u>lay hands</u> on our fellow Men in Action in recognition they are commissioned for a holy purpose.**
    "Do not neglect the spiritual gift within you, which was bestowed on you through prophetic utterance with the laying on of hands..." (1 Timothy 4:14, NASB).

    "For David, after he had served the purpose of God in his own generation, fell asleep, and was laid among his fathers…" (Acts 13:36, NASB).

6. We <u>join with</u> our fellow Men in Action as soldiers of the Cross, saluting our divine commander-in-chief.

> *"You therefore, my son, be strong in the grace that is in Christ Jesus. The things which you have heard from me in the presence of many witnesses, entrust these to faithful men who will be able to teach others also. Suffer hardship with me, as a good soldier of Christ Jesus. No soldier in active service entangles himself in the affairs of everyday life, so that he may please the one who enlisted him as a soldier" (2 Timothy 2:1-4, NASB).*

I am a Soldier

Read the following, placing an emphasis on the word "I." Personalize every sentence and pause to consider its meaning. Remember, "I can do all things through Him who strengthens me" (Philippians 4:13). So, put on the full armor of God (Ephesians 6:11) and get in the fight.

I am a soldier in the Army of God. The Lord Jesus Christ is my commanding officer. The Holy Bible is my code of conduct. Faith, prayer and the Word are my weapons of warfare. I have been taught the Word of God, trained by experience, tried by adversity and tested by fire. I am a volunteer in this army, and I am enlisted for eternity. I will retire in this army at times end, or die in this army; but I will not sell out, be talked out or pushed out.

I am faithful, reliable, capable, and dependable. If my God needs me, I am there. If He needs me in Sunday school, to teach children, work with youth, help adults or just sit and learn, He can use me, because I am there. I am a soldier. I do not need to be pampered, petted, primed up, picked up or pepped up. I am a soldier. I am not a wimp. I am in place, saluting my King, obeying his orders, praising His name and building His kingdom. No one has to send me flowers, gifts, food, cards, candy, or give me handouts. I do not need to be cuddled, cradled, cared for or catered to.

I am committed. I cannot have my feelings hurt bad enough to turn me around. I cannot be discouraged enough to turn me aside. I cannot lose enough to cause me to quit. When Jesus called me into his army, I had nothing. If I end up with nothing, I will still break even. I will win. My God will supply all my needs. I am more than a conqueror. I will always triumph.

I can do all things through Christ. Demons cannot defeat me. People cannot disillusion me. Weather cannot weary me. Sickness cannot stop me. Battles cannot beat me. Money cannot buy me. Governments cannot silence me and hell cannot handle me. I am a soldier. Even death cannot destroy me, for when my commander calls me from this battlefield, He will promote me to live with Him. I am a soldier, and I am marching, claiming victory! I will not give up. I am a soldier! I will not turn around. I am a soldier marching heaven bound! Here I stand. Will you stand with me? - Author unknown

NOTES

SESSION 2
A Man's Spiritual Journey and the Fruit of the Spirit

> *"Grow deep roots to harvest rich fruit!*
> *When your roots run deep, you cannot help but*
> *bear the fruit of the spirit."*
> *(Michael Beckwith)*

SESSION 2
A Man's Spiritual Journey
and The Fruit of the Spirit

Class discussion
The content below will be discussed during class. If you miss class this week, you are required to read them on your own time, prior to next week's class.

Application from the last session
Each week you will pick one thing you learned from the last session you can apply in your life as either an action item or a truth you should embrace. Application from last session:

_____

_____

Before class
____ Completed "Class Tuition/Scholarship Request"
____ Completed "Statement of Class Commitment"
____ Completed "Solo Initiative Commitment"
____ Obtained an Accountability Partner (many men ask another MIA to be their partner)
____ Completed "Accountability Partner Commitment"
____ Continued your Solo Initiative
____ Attended church (Sermon topic: _____)
____ Reviewed the names of your fellow MIAs
____ Memorize the Fruit of the Spirit (Galatians 5:22-23)
____ Read the Bible at least four times this week (See "Bible Reading" below; "Daily Bible Reading Chart," in Appendix C)
____ Met with my Accountability Partner (See "Accountability Checklist" on next page)

Bible reading

Date	Book/Chapters	At least one thought from what you read

Accountability checklist

___ Asked accountability questions	___ Discussed Solo Initiative
___ Discussed what you are learning in class	___ Prayed

My prayer request:

Accountability partner's prayer request:

Time/Place of next meeting:

At the beginning of class

- Put on your name tag (On your right side)
- Pick up your envelope if you turned in forms last week (Re-file forms in your manual)
- Turn in any pending commitment forms (Use envelope in manual)
- Turn in your class tuition/scholarship request (Use envelope in manual)
- Join a prayer group (3-4 men), praying with different men each week (See "Weekly Prayer Requests" on next page)

Class schedule*

- 20 minutes: Small group prayer
    - Focus on requests personal to you. What are your needs and the needs of those closest to you?
    - Everything shared is confidential.
- 10 minutes: Attendance and announcements (e.g., missing chair, service projects)
- 20 minutes: Share testimonies (see "Testimonies" one the next page)
- 5 minutes: Recite the Fruit of the Spirit
- 20 minutes: Teach and discuss "The Role of the Holy Spirit in Our Christian Walk"
- 15 minutes: Small Group Discussion
- 10 minutes: Break
- 35 minutes: Teach and discuss "The Fruit of the Spirit"
- 10 minutes: Dedication of new MIA men
- 5 minutes: Review next week's assignments

If you missed Session One you should arrive for class 30 minutes early to get a quick orientation on the first session.

Weekly prayer requests

Name	Request
Yours	

Calling a missing chair

"…You will be missed because your seat will be empty" (1 Samuel 20:18).

Missing chair:	
Phone number:	Email:
Contacted:	Status:

Testimonies

Name	Application

Teaching goal

That men would understand the key to becoming who God wants them to be, and to see life as a spiritual journey, yielded and submitted to the Holy Spirit.

The Role of the Holy Spirit in a Man's Life

Everyone who wants to lead must first commit to follow. We follow Christ by following the leading of the indwelling Holy Spirit (Galatians 5:16, 18, 25). Understanding the ministry of the Holy Spirit in our lives is vital to being an effective leader and witness. We all have a witness, since that is simply how the world sees us. Do we have a witness that *serves* or *detracts* from the reputation of Christianity in this world? Christ knows the difference between a real and phony witness. As Christ said to the Church in Laodicea:

> *"I know your deeds, that you are neither cold nor hot. I wish you were either one or the other! So, because you are lukewarm—neither hot nor cold—I am about to spit you out of my mouth" (Revelation 3:15-16, NIV).*

There are many ways to examine one's witness from a Biblical perspective. For our purposes, we will look at the Fruit of the Spirit. It gives us a list of standards to measure our witness against. Each of the qualities presented in the list of the Fruit of the Spirit (Galatian 5:22-23) are somewhat easy to understand, but proper application takes a lifetime of effort.

The Fruit of the Spirit are not something we generate through our own efforts. Under our own power all we can do is generate the fruit of man, which by any definition is, at its best, a shadow of the real fruit. The fruit is "of the Spirit" and involves submitting and yielding to the work of the Holy Spirit in our lives. Thus, the starting point must be an understanding of the Spirit and His work. He is the source of the fruit, and so before we look for the fruit we must acknowledge and understand the source.

If we are eternal spiritual beings currently living in circumstances that have eternal spiritual consequences, then we had better align our lives with the source of spiritual resources. For man there is only one source offered, the Holy Spirit. Since that truth touches every aspect of our existence, the Holy Spirit must be an integral part of our lives. We cannot serve Christ independently of the Holy Spirit. The fruit flows from the Spirit through us. The question is, are we channels for the Spirit's work, or are we a dam, blocking Him from pouring out His attributes through us?

Even if our efforts are well intentioned, there is nothing we do in our Christian life that pleases God when we walk in the flesh. Our quest is to be more like Christ and less like man. We cannot rely on our own instincts, but we can always trust the leading of the Spirit in our lives. It takes daily communication (Prayer) to allow the Spirit to control our lives.

How would you describe the work of the Holy Spirit in your life?

_____

_____

When you pray to God, where do you imagine your prayers go?

_____

_____

How present is the Holy Spirit in your daily walk?

_____

_____

There are certain truths that we accept:

1. There is a physical and temporal world that is currently passing away.
2. There is a spiritual and eternal world that is not passing away.

In the spiritual world, God exists and is the final word. God created the physical and spiritual worlds. He is ultimately in control of both, though for a season, man has been given a certain amount of freedom to operate in the physical world. In no event does man control the rules by which either world operates.

Just like He created the physical world, God also created man. We are created physically and spiritually at a point in time. Our physical being is temporal and passing away. Our spiritual being is permanent. It is our eternal condition. In reality, everyone is a spiritual being. The issue is not spiritual _existence_, but spiritual _destination_ (i.e., heaven or hell).

Why do you think people focus so much on the physical over the spiritual world?

_____

_____

What is your level of awareness of the spiritual realm on a day-to-day basis? Where do you mentally spend your time? How aware are you that you are a spiritual being who is either growing or deteriorating spiritually?

_____

_____

We place great focus on our physical existence, worrying about it and using a phenomenal amount of energy. However, God gives us the privilege of investing in our eternity now, in order to focus on our spiritual growth and development. Yet so often we say, "No, thank you."

Read Galatians 5:16-25 and 1 Corinthians 3:1-3. What is the distinction the Apostle Paul draws between fleshly and spiritual pursuits?

_____

_____

Do you believe "carnal Christians" exist, and if so, how would you describe them?

_____

_____

The Christians in Corinth were carnal Christians. While the letter is addressed to the saints and those sanctified, the Apostle Paul goes on to deal with many sin issues in the church. So, while recognizing them as saved, he _also_ realized they had a multitude of sins to address. Modern Christianity bears a lot of similarity to the Church of Corinth. They were inclined to look to the _world_ and the flesh for answers, rather than the _Spirit_.

Faith is ultimately a spiritual exercise. Do we too often walk by sight?

_____

_____

It is not just that we are spiritual beings, but more to the point, as Christians we have the very Spirit of God residing in us. As you move through your daily life, how aware are you of this?

Describe your relationship to the Holy Spirit using a few key words. How do you relate to the Spirit, especially when it comes to your leadership?

_____

_____

Many of us might say we are _committed_ to the Holy Spirit's leadership in our lives. In modern Christian language the word _commitment_ has often replaced _submission_. Both words are powerful, but they're not the same. "Co-mmitment" conveys the idea of some degree of equality between the parties, with each giving something. "Sub-mission" is fundamentally different, in that we are placing ourselves under authority.

We must realize we are on a spiritual journey that has two very distinct paths we can take. We keep control, or we submit. Without submission the Holy Spirit cannot work in our lives.

Small Group Discussion

1. Get into groups of no more than five men.
2. Pick a leader to facilitate discussion and make sure everyone participates.
3. You have 15 minutes.
4. Topic: How do you personally interact with the Holy Spirit?
5. Discussion questions:
   a. Do you have a witness that serves or detracts from the reputation of Christianity in this world? Explain your answer.
   b. What is an area where you can serve others? Why is this an appropriate area for you to serve in?
   c. Think about your prayer life as an intimate conversation with the Holy Spirit. How can it be improved? What are some ways you can improve your prayer time and be more purposeful about your prayer life?

The Fruit of the Spirit

"But I say, walk by the Spirit, and you will not carry out the desire of the flesh. For the flesh sets its desire against the Spirit, and the Spirit against the flesh; for these are in opposition to one another, so that you may not do the things that you please. But if you are led by the Spirit, you are not under the Law. Now the deeds of the flesh are evident, which are: immorality, impurity, sensuality, idolatry, sorcery, enmities, strife, jealousy, outbursts of anger, disputes, dissensions, factions, envying, drunkenness, carousing, and things like these, of which I forewarn you, just as I have forewarned you, that those who practice such things will not inherit the kingdom of God. But the fruit of the Spirit is love, joy, peace, patience, kindness, goodness, faithfulness, gentleness, self-control; against such things there is no law. Now those who belong to Christ Jesus have crucified the flesh with its passions and desires. If we live by the Spirit, let us also walk by the Spirit" (Galatians 5:16-25, NASB).

THE BELIEVER'S TUG-OF-WAR

In the above verses, the Apostle Paul sets out two options by which we can chart the path of our lives. The natural man will be led by his fleshly desire, while the man who is spiritually attuned will allow the Holy Spirit to do His work in that man's life. This sets up a basic challenge in each man's life as he works to overcome the flesh, and to yield and submit to the Holy Spirit. This lesson explores what allowing the Holy Spirit to do His work looks like.

THE DEEDS OF THE FLESH

Before moving on to the work of the Spirit in our lives, let us look at the natural man. The natural man does not allow the indwelling Holy Spirit to produce His fruit. Instead, the natural man produces his own kind of fruit, which we call the "deeds of the flesh." The fruit of the natural man is rotten, full of rebellion and resists the Holy Spirit's leading and authority. That fruit comes in many forms. Galatians 5:19-21 lists a few:

Immorality – Impurity – Sensuality – Idolatry – Sorcery – Enmities – Strife – Jealousy – Outbursts of Anger – Disputes – Dissensions – Factions – Envying – Drunkenness – Carousing…"and things like these"

This can be a real tug-of-war between the two natures: Flesh vs. Spirit.

Which of the above deeds of the flesh are the greatest concern in your life?

1. At home? _____
2. At work or school? _____
3. In the community? _____
4. When alone? _____

WALKING BY THE SPIRIT—BEING LED BY THE SPIRIT

The Apostle Paul explains there is a stark distinction between the fruit of the natural man and the fruit of the maturing Christian. What fruit does *your* life display? What type of fruit are you producing? Are you in charge of your actions, or is the Holy Spirit? If we do not intentionally yield to the Spirit on a daily basis, our natural default is to the flesh.

THE FRUIT OF THE SPIRIT

Pomology is the scientific word for the study of fruit. Let's do a little "spiritual pomology" and study the Fruit of the Spirit. There are seven key principles for us to understand.

Principle #1: The Fruit of the Spirit is not automatic.

> *"You, however, are not in the realm of the flesh but are in the realm of the Spirit, if indeed the Spirit of God lives in you. And if anyone does not have the Spirit of Christ, they do not belong to Christ" (Romans 8:9, NIV).*

> *"So I say, walk by the Spirit, and you will not gratify the desires of the flesh. For the flesh desires what is contrary to the Spirit, and the Spirit what is contrary to the flesh. They are in conflict with each other, so that you are not to do whatever you want. But if you are led by the Spirit, you are not under the law" (Galatians 5:16-18, NIV).*

> *"Those who belong to Christ Jesus have crucified the flesh with its passions and desires. Since we live by the Spirit, let us keep in step with the Spirit" (Galatians 5:24-25, NIV).*

We must constantly tend to our spiritual lives if we want to yield the Fruit of the Spirit. The Fruit of the Spirit is the mark of a regenerated life well-watered, well-weeded, and well-cared for.

Principle #2: The Fruit of the Spirit is not limited.

While the list in Galatians lists nine specific attributes the Apostle Paul calls the Fruit of the Spirit, we know the work of the Holy Spirit is broader than just love, joy, peace, patience, kindness, goodness, faithfulness, gentleness and self-control. On the night he was betrayed, Jesus talked to His disciples about their need for the Holy Spirit:

> *"I will ask the Father, and He will give you another advocate to help you and be with you forever…" (John 14:16, NIV).*

> *"But the Advocate, the Holy Spirit, whom the Father will send in my name, will teach you all things and will remind you of everything I have said to you" (John 14:26, NIV).*

"When the Helper comes, whom I will send to you from the Father, that is the Spirit of truth who proceeds from the Father, He will testify about me…" (John 15:26, NIV).

"But very truly I tell you, it is for your good that I am going away. Unless I go away, the Advocate will not come to you; but if I go, I will send him to you. When he comes, he will prove the world to be in the wrong about sin and righteousness and judgment: about sin, because people do not believe in me; about righteousness, because I am going to the Father, where you can see me no longer; and about judgment, because the prince of this world now stands condemned" (John 16:7-11, NIV).

"But when he, the Spirit of truth, comes, he will guide you into all the truth. He will not speak on his own; he will speak only what he hears, and he will tell you what is yet to come" (John 16:13, NIV).

What are some things the Spirit does beyond producing the Fruit of the Spirit?

_____

_____

Principle #3: The Fruit of the Spirit is not produced in us immediately.

"…like newborn babies, crave pure spiritual milk, so that by it you may grow up in your salvation…" (1 Peter 2:2, NIV).

"We have much to say about this, but it is hard to make it clear to you because you no longer try to understand. In fact, though by this time you ought to be teachers, you need someone to teach you the elementary truths of God's word all over again. You need milk, not solid food! Anyone who lives on milk, being still an infant, is not acquainted with the teaching about righteousness. But solid food is for the mature, who by constant use have trained themselves to distinguish good from evil" (Hebrews 5:11-14, NIV).

Spiritual maturity is a lifelong process called sanctification. It is the Holy Spirit who is our Helper as we grow throughout our Christian lives.

Principle #4: The Fruit of the Spirit is all one harvest of the heart.

Note it is not "fruits" (plural) of the Spirit; it is a single fruit being produced. Instead of trying to separate the qualities, think of them as multiple attributes of one fruit being produced in our lives. If we take any actual fruit (apple, pear, banana) it is one fruit, but you can describe various attributes related to that fruit—size, texture, taste, color, etc.

Principle #5: The Fruit of the Spirit represents the life of Christ in us.

> *"But we all, with unveiled face beholding as in a mirror the glory of the Lord, are being transformed into the same image from glory to glory, just as from the Lord, the Spirit" (Greek: metamorphoó) (2 Corinthians 3:18, NASB).*

Jesus is our best example of each attribute:

1. Love (for the thief on the cross)
2. Joy (as He faced the pain of crucifixion on the cross)
3. Peace (while trusting in God's will, not His own)
4. Patience (while teaching His stubborn disciples)
5. Kindness (while healing the sick and the infirm)
6. Goodness (with zeal, as He cleared out the corrupt money changers)
7. Faithfulness (as He came to do His Father's work)
8. Gentleness (toward the woman caught in adultery)
9. Self-control (as He faced the devil's temptations in the wilderness)

Principle #6: The Fruit of the Spirit takes us beyond the law, to a life of grace.

Notice the last words at the end of the list of the Fruit of the Spirit "...against such things there is no law." Allowing the Spirit to work in our lives moves us beyond an effort to simply obey the rules, to a life of deep and meaningful service for Christ.

Principle #7: The Fruit of the Spirit attracts others to Christ.

> *"The fruit of the righteous is a tree of life, and he who is wise wins souls" (Proverbs 11:30, NASB).*

The key to our witness as men is tied directly to how these Christlike characteristics are displayed in every area of our lives. They cannot be attained by personal human effort. The Fruit of the Spirit are the results of a regenerated life that walks in daily submission to the work of the indwelling Holy Spirit in our lives. Therefore, the more submitted we are to His leading and authority, the more these characteristics shine at home, at work, and in the community.

THE NINE ATTRIBUTES OF THE FRUIT

1. **Love** (*agape*, pronunciation: ah-gah-pay)
   a. It is a selfless, sacrificial love which is displayed in its focus on caring for others. The Apostle Paul, discussing various attributes of the Christian in 1 Corinthians 13, says "the greatest of these is love." It is primary to our Christian walk. Without love we have no witness. It is Christ's message to us from the cross.
   b. It is the supernatural ability to value ourselves and others, with the worth God places on us and others.
   c. Scriptural support: Luke 6:32-35; John 3:16, 13:34-35, 15:14; 1 Corinthians 13:4-8; 1 John 4:7-13, 19; Romans 5:5-8; Ephesians 5:1-2.

2. **Joy** (*chara*, pronunciation: khar-ra')
    a. It is the ability to rejoice in all situations and is independent of circumstances. It is very different from happiness, which is tied to our circumstances. It is joy that comes from knowing God is working out all things to our benefit, and He never leaves us nor forsakes us. Thus, we are told to rejoice always.
    b. It is the supernatural ability to be sincerely grateful to God, regardless of circumstances.
    c. Scriptural support: Nehemiah 8:10; 2 Corinthians 6:10; 1 Peter 1:8; Hebrews 12:2; 1 Thessalonians 1:6, 5:16; Philippians 4:4; John 15:11; Romans 14:17.

    "Joy is the flag that flies over the castle of our hearts announcing that the King is in residence today" (Walter Knight).

3. **Peace** (*eirene*, pronunciation: i-ray'-nay)
    a. This flows from a firm reliance that God is ultimately in control, and holds us in His hands at all times. As we work to place our lives and will under God's control, our peace can do nothing but grow.
    b. A major work of the Holy Spirit in our life is to produce this peace. It is tied directly to our faith in who God is and His promises throughout Scripture. We not only receive God's peace, but we spread it to others.
    c. It is the supernatural ability to have a deep-seated confidence God is in control of the details of our lives.
    d. Scriptural support: Matthew 5:9, 26:39; John 14:27, 16:33; Romans 5:1, 14:17; Philippians 4:6-9; Ephesian 4:3.

4. **Patience** (*makrothumia*, pronunciation: mak-roth-oo-mee'-ah)
    a. It means slow to anger, long-suffering without complaint. Patience is a quality that clearly runs counter to man's natural tendencies. It focuses on our relationships with others. Our love is often expressed in the enduring patience we show others.
    b. Control of our anger is a key ingredient of our witness to the world. Patience allows the other attributes to come to the foreground when confronting challenging circumstances. If our reaction to people and circumstances is sinful anger then love, joy, peace, kindness, etc., are all pushed to the side.
    c. It is the supernatural ability to demonstrate a gentle tolerance with exasperating people and frustrating situations.
    d. Scriptural support: 1 Peter 3:20; 2 Peter 3:15; Romans 9:22; Joel 2:13; 1 Timothy 1:16; Colossians 3:11-13; Proverbs 19:11.

5. **Kindness** (*chrestotes*, pronunciation: khray-stot'-ace)
    a. This is similar to the concept of mercy. It is focused on others and blessing them. Compassion for others is another way to describe kindness.
    b. Another definition is "useful good deeds done for another at their point of need." It is not always soft and cuddly. Sometimes the truth can hurt, but the truth

delivered with compassion is a way of showing kindness. It is a lifestyle that endeavors to graciously deal with people. It is Christianity with its working clothes on.

    c. It is the supernatural ability to shrink from inflicting pain, and deal with people with grace and mercy.

    d. Scriptural support: Luke 6:35; John 8; Ephesians 4:32; Micah 6:8; Psalm 34:8; 1 Peter 2:3; Romans 2:4.

6. **Goodness** (*agathosune*, pronunciation: ag-ath-o-soo'-nay)

    a. This means doing that which is right, regardless of the consequences. It is closely related to the concept of righteousness (doing the right thing in all circumstances).

    b. This is a passion for what is true and right, a seeking after justice as seen by Holy God. It is rejecting the way of the world in favor of the way of the Master. When displaying this attribute, we are always pursuing the good in every situation, for both us and others. We flee evil wherever we find it.

    c. It is the supernatural ability to stand up for what is right in the eyes of God and, if necessary, expose and confront sin.

    d. Scriptural support: Romans 15:13-14; Matthew 21:12-13; Ephesians 5:7-13; 2 Thessalonians 1:11-12.

7. **Faithfulness** (*pistis*, pronunciation: pis'-tis)

    a. It means a steadfastness and trustworthiness. It starts with God's faithfulness. We can be truly faithful only when we have a complete reliance on the faithfulness of God. It is trusting God is not only in the details, but that, from a spiritual standpoint, He is working those details out in such a way that is always in our best interest.

    b. It is the supernatural ability to take God at His word and, as a result, become trustworthy and taken at our word.

    c. Scriptural support: Psalm 37:3; Hebrews 11; Deuteronomy 7:9; 1 John 1:9; John 17:17; Revelation 19:11; Ephesians 5:1; 1 Corinthians 4:2; 2 Samuel 15:21; 2 Timothy 2:22; Luke 16:10; Matthew 25:21.

8. **Gentleness** (*praiotes*, pronunciation: prai-ot'-ace)

    a. Biblical gentleness is the God-given ability to respond to a difficult person or a challenging situation with a strength under the control of the Holy Spirit. We are not trying to win arguments, but rather build relationships. We work to edify, not to incite anger.

    b. Gentleness meets people with compassion, especially those who we think might not deserve it. It has the sense of coming along side another and tenderly meeting them where they are. This is a key attribute whenever you have to confront someone.

    c. It is the supernatural ability to respond without over-reacting with a strength under divine control.

d. Scriptural support: 1 Corinthians. 4:21; 2 Corinthians 10:1; Matthew 11:29, 21:5; 26; 1 Timothy 6:11; 2 Timothy 2:25; Colossians 3:12; Ephesians 4:2; 1 Peter 3:4, 3:15; Galatians 6:1.

9. **Self-Control** (*egkrateia*, pronunciation: eng-krat'-i-ah)
   a. It means choosing to yield and submit to the guidance of the Holy Spirit on a daily basis.
   b. Without self-control the other attributes of the fruit will fall by the wayside. Out of this fruit comes a developing maturity that gives us the ability to weigh consequences before we act and to delay gratification.
   c. It is the supernatural ability to master our desires and subdue our cravings before things get out of control.
   d. Scriptural support: 1 Corinthians 6:12, 9:25; 2 Corinthians 10:5; 2 Timothy 3:1-4; 2 Peter 1:6; Proverbs 16:32.

Which of the Fruit of the Spirit are most evident in this season of your life?

1. At home? _____
2. At work or school? _____
3. In the community? _____
4. When alone? _____

CONCLUSION

These nine attributes all work together as a common whole. They build on each other and none of them individually possesses the entirety of the Fruit of the Spirit. The work of the Spirit far exceeds the boundaries of these nine qualities. Without them we have a poor witness for Christ.

Remember, the Fruit of the Spirit is not generated by self-will, but a will yielded, submitted, and attuned to the Holy Spirit.

(For further study on the Fruit of the Spirit: "Anger: The Worm in My Apple—Destroying the Rotten Fruit of Anger; Harvesting the Tasty Fruit of the Spirit." By Dr. James M. Cecy. Available at www.jaron.org and www.amazon.com).

SESSION 3
Leadership Basics:
What the Bible Teaches

*The Christian leader is the servant
of the servants of God.*

SESSION 3
Leadership Basics:
What the Bible Teaches

Class discussion

The content below will be discussed during class. If you miss class this week you are required to read them on your own time, prior to next week's class.

Application from the last session

Pick one thing you learned from the last session you can apply in your life as either an action item or a truth you should embrace.

_____

_____

Before class

____ Reviewed the names of your fellow MIAs

____ Started your Solo Initiative

____ Read the Bible four times this week (See "Daily Bible Reading Chart," in Appendix C)

____ Attended church (Sermon topic: _____)

____ Met with my Accountability Partner

____ Memorized the names of the 27 New Testament books of the Bible

____ Attended a men's event or completed a service project

____ Completed "Ten Qualities of an Effective Servant for Christ" assignment

Bible reading

Date	Book/Chapters	At least one thought from what you read

Accountability checklist

<table>
<tr><td>___ Asked accountability questions
___ Discussed what you are learning in class</td><td>___ Discussed Solo Initiative
___ Prayed</td></tr>
<tr><td colspan="2">My prayer request:

</td></tr>
<tr><td colspan="2">Accountability partner's prayer request:

</td></tr>
<tr><td colspan="2">Time/Place of next meeting:</td></tr>
</table>

At the beginning of class

- Put on your name tag (Right side)
- Pick up your envelope if you turned in forms last week (Re-file forms in your manual)
- Drop off envelope if you are turning in any new forms
- Join a prayer group (3-4 men), praying with different men each week

Class schedule

- 20 minutes: Small group prayer
- 10 minutes: Attendance and announcements (e.g., missing chair, service projects)
- 20 minutes: Share testimonies
- 10 minutes: Write the books of the New Testament from memory
- 20 minutes: Teach and discuss "New Testament Facets of Leadership"
- 15 minutes: Small Group Discussion
- 10 minutes: Break
- 25 minutes: Teach and discuss "The Ten Qualities of an Effective Servant Leader"
- 15 minutes: "Lifeboat Exercise" activity
- 5 minutes: Review next week's assignments

Weekly prayer requests

Name	Request
Yours	

Calling a missing chair

"…You will be missed because your seat will be empty" (1 Samuel 20:18).

Missing chair:	
Phone number:	Email:
Contacted:	Status:

Testimonies

Name	Application

Teaching goal

That men would understand while the world has multiple opinions on what makes a great leader, God has provided the only inspired truth on the subject. That men would be able to assess how much their lives align with God's principles.

The New Testament Books

[Complete this in class]

It is important to be able to find your way around the Bible. The New Testament consists of 27 books, all written in the 1st Century AD. See if you can name them in order based on their groupings.

Hints:
- All the "T" books are together in order.
- Fifteen of the books are people's names.
- There are four sets of 1st and 2nd books and one set of 1st, 2nd and 3rd books.

1. Gospels (4)

_____

2. History (1)

_____

3. Paul's letters (13)

_____

_____

_____

4. General letters (8)

_____

_____

_____

5. Prophecy (1)

_____

New Testament Facets of Leadership

The New Testament uses a number of Greek terms to describe different types of leadership. By considering the different types of leadership we can gain a better understanding of leadership characteristics the Bible calls men of Christ to exhibit in their lives.

It is important to note that New Testament writers, especially the Apostle Paul, addressed the qualities of leadership in a way that would have been foreign to the Greeks and Romans of their time. Greeks and Romans viewed humility as a weakness, while from a Christian standpoint it is the starting point for all true leadership.

	TERM	DEFINITION	SCRIPTURAL REFERENCE
1.	The Up-Front Leader *(Greek: prohistimi)*	One who stands before/presides over/rules/governs/gives direction/manages/takes risks.	1 Chronicles 12:32; Romans 12:8; 1 Timothy 5:17; 1 Thessalonians 5:12; 1 Timothy 3:4, 5 & 12
2.	The Intentional Leader *(Greek: hegeomai)*	One who is a careful, thoughtful and deliberate leader.	Luke 22:26; Hebrews 13:17
3.	The Maturing Elder *(Greek: presbuteros)*	One who is growing spiritually and emotionally as a man of character and wisdom.	Titus 1:5
4.	The Capable Overseer *(Greek: episcopos)*	One who overseers and is able to view the whole situation.	1 Timothy 3:1
5.	The Protecting Shepherd *(Greek: poimen)*	One who feeds, protects and warns the people he leads.	1 Peter 5:1-5
6.	The Willing Head *(Greek: kephale)*	One who accepts his God-given role as leader and source of wisdom and counsel.	1 Corinthians 11:3
7.	The Life-Skills Teacher *(Greek: didaskos)*	One who teaches by both precept and example; a man of content not just opinions.	1 Timothy 2:7
8.	The Managing Steward *(Greek: oikonomos)*	One who is able to manage his life and family; who knows the rules of life and is trustworthy and self-controlled.	Titus 1:7; 1 Corinthians 4:1-2
9.	The Hands-On Servant *(Greek: diakonos)*	One who leads through service and executing the commands of others (e.g., deacon).	Acts 20:24; Acts 26:16; Romans 15:31; 2 Corinthians 9:12-13
10.	The Obedient Slave *(Greek: doulos)*	One who leads as a bond slave of God and servant of men; protects and serves; humble.	Matt. 20:25-28; Acts 26:16; John 13:1ff
11.	The Dedicated Under-Rower *(Greek: huperetes)*	One who is under authority, chained to his responsibility, serving alongside others.	Luke 1:2; Acts 26:16

(For further study, read "Leadership Principles," in Appendix C.)

Small Group Discussion

1. Get into groups of no more than five men.
2. Pick a leader to facilitate discussion and make sure everyone participates.
3. You have 15 minutes.
4. Topic: Which of the facets of leadership are you most comfortable with? Which are the hardest for you?
5. Discussion questions:
    a. Look over the various terms for "Leader". Which ones best describes you? Why?
    b. Based on the leadership term that best describes you, how could you be serving and leading others?
    c. Share how you have been leading and if not, where you want to start.
    d. Which of the above facets of leadership are you most comfortable with, and which for you are the hardest roles to fill? Remember, there are many ways to show leadership.

Lead, follow or get out of the way.

Ten Qualities of an Effective Servant for Christ

List some of the skills and attributes *the world* expects of its leaders:

_____

_____

List some of the skills and attributes the world does *not* expect of its leaders:

_____

_____

JESUS CHRIST CAME TO PRESENT A COMPLETELY DIFFERENT VIEW OF EFFECTIVE LEADERSHIP.

> *"You know that those who are recognized as rulers of the Gentiles lord it over them; and their great men exercise authority over them. But it is not this way among you, but whoever wishes to become great among you shall be your servant; and whoever wishes to be first among you shall be slave of all. For even the Son of Man did not come to be served, but to serve, and to give His life a ransom for many" (Mark 10:42-45, NASB).*

> *"…the one who is least among all of you, this is the one who is great"*
> *(Luke 9:48, NASB).*

The Bible clearly presents true and effective leaders as servant-leaders. As is often said, "The Christian leader is the servant of the servants of God, a slave of God and servant of men."

THE STORY OF TIMOTHY, THE UNEXPECTED LEADER

Introduction to 2 Timothy: Paul's Last Will and Testament and Treatise on Leadership

The date is 67 A.D. The Apostle Paul is in prison in the city of Rome, writing to Timothy, his son in the faith, a few months before Paul will be martyred. This is Paul's last will and testament. It begins:

> *"Paul, an apostle of Christ Jesus by the will of God, according to the promise of life in Christ Jesus, to Timothy, my beloved son: Grace, mercy and peace from God the Father and Christ Jesus our Lord. I thank God, whom I serve with a clear conscience the way my forefathers did, as I constantly remember you in my prayers night and day, longing to see you, even as I recall your tears, so that I may be filled with joy. For I am mindful of the sincere faith within you, which first dwelt in your grandmother Lois and your mother Eunice, and I am sure that it is in you as well. For this reason I remind you to kindle afresh the gift of God which is in you through the laying on of my hands. For God has not given us a spirit of timidity, but of power and love and discipline" (2 Timothy 1:1-7, NASB).*

The Apostle Paul is looking to encourage Timothy, mentoring him in the leadership role in which Paul has placed him (i.e., serving in the Church of Ephesus). In this epistle the apostle explains principles for becoming an effective servant-leader, providing examples from his own life. All of us who are called to lead in our homes, churches and communities need to measure ourselves by these standards.

	The Effective Servant-Leader…	Scripture	Losing	Struggling	Winning
1.	Thanks God for fellow Christian workers.	2 Timothy 1:3a	1 2 3	4 5 6 7	8 9 10
2.	Serves God in the purity of a God-centered life.	2 Timothy 1:3b	1 2 3	4 5 6 7	8 9 10
3.	Communicates with God continually.	2 Timothy 1:3c	1 2 3	4 5 6 7	8 9 10
4.	Longs to fellowship with God's people.	2 Timothy 1:4a	1 2 3	4 5 6 7	8 9 10
5.	Acknowledges his need for other Christians.	2 Timothy 1:4b	1 2 3	4 5 6 7	8 9 10
6.	Expresses confidence in the faith of other believers.	2 Timothy 1:5	1 2 3	4 5 6 7	8 9 10
7.	Exhorts and encourages fellow Christians.	2 Timothy 1:6	1 2 3	4 5 6 7	8 9 10
8.	Relies on God for boldness in ministry.	2 Timothy 1:7a	1 2 3	4 5 6 7	8 9 10
9.	Relies on God for the ability to love those he ministers to.	2 Timothy 1:7b	1 2 3	4 5 6 7	8 9 10
10.	Relies on God for self-discipline.	2 Timothy 1:7c	1 2 3	4 5 6 7	8 9 10

HINDRANCES TO EFFECTIVE SERVICE FOR CHRIST

God's Commissions; Our Excuses

Read Exodus 3:7--4:14
    a. What was God's commission to Moses? _____
    b. What were Moses' excuses? _____

Read Judges 6:11-23
    a. What was God's commission to Gideon? _____
    b. What were Gideon's excuses? _____

Read Jeremiah 1:4-18

    a. What was God's commission to Jeremiah? _____

    b. What were Jeremiah's excuses? _____

Read Jonah 1:1-3 and Chapter 4

    a. What was God's commission to Jonah? _____

    b. What were Jonah's excuses? _____

Read Matthew 28:19-20

    a. What is Christ's commission to us? _____

    b. What are our excuses? _____

God's Answers to Our Excuses

    a. God's answer to Moses' excuses (Exodus 3:12): _____

    b. God's answer to Gideon's excuses (Judges 6:16):_____

    c. God's answer to Jeremiah's excuses (Jeremiah 1:8):_____

    d. God's answer to my excuses (Matthew 28:20):_____ALWAYS!

**Because of the indwelling Holy Spirit, God's _temporary_ provision for them
was replaced by God's _permanent_ provision for us!**

Lifeboat Exercise

Suppose you were in a lifeboat with your fellow Men in Action. Your ship has sunk and there is no assurance help is coming. You have no radio and storm clouds are forming.

Based on your personality, gifts, talents, and skills, what do you see as your primary and secondary role in the lifeboat? For each item below, mark primary "1" and secondary "2" (There are no right or wrong answers). After marking your answers, reflect on what it says about your leadership instincts.

Regarding leadership:
____ Immediately take the lead (if no official is on board)
____ Step into leadership only if none emerges, or if the initial leadership fails
____ Take charge only if asked by the group
____ Assist the leader by volunteering to carry out tasks as directed by him
____ Support the leader by encouraging the rest of the folks in the lifeboat to work with him
____ Try to stay out of the way until asked to do something
____ Point out the flaws and failures of the leader
____ Other: _____

Managing the situation:
____ Identify the skills and abilities of those on the lifeboat
____ Organize the men regardless of their skills
____ Inventory the resources on the lifeboat
____ Take care of any troublesome or disruptive men
____ Provide spiritual encouragement
____ Provide emotional support to those who are hurting or frightened
____ Row, paddle or steer
____ Discuss your favorite movie "Jaws"
____ Other: _____

Regarding survival:
____ Organize a system to begin search and rescue of other survivors
____ Immediately begin searching for other survivors
____ Figure out the maximum number that safely can be in the lifeboat
____ Preserve and allocate food and other items as needed for others
____ Fish for food and figure out how to make what you have work
____ Provide medical aid to those injured
____ Make necessary repairs to equipment or lifeboat
____ Start telling "Donner Party" jokes to try to cheer everyone up
____ Other: _____

**Leadership is taking responsibility for the
purposes that God has assigned to your life.**

NOTES

SESSION 4
Learning to Prioritize
as a Man of God

The gift of leading is found in people who have a clear, significant vision and are able to communicate it in such a way that they influence others to pursue that vision.

SESSION 4
Learning to Prioritize
as a Man of God

Class discussion
The content below will be discussed during class. If you miss class this week, you are required to read them on your own time, prior to next week's class.

Application from the last session
Pick one thing you learned from the last session you can apply in your life as either an action item or a truth you should embrace.

_____

_____

Before class
____ Reviewed the names of your fellow MIAs
____ Continued your Solo Initiative
____ Read the Bible four times this week (See "Daily Bible Reading Chart," in Appendix C)
____ Memorized the Fruit of the Spirit (Galatians 5:22-23)
____ Attended church (Sermon topic: _____)
____ Met with my Accountability Partner

Bible reading

Date	Book/Chapters	At least one thought from what you read

Accountability checklist

___ Asked accountability questions	___ Discussed Solo Initiative
___ Discussed what you are learning in class	___ Prayed
My prayer request:	
Accountability partner's prayer request:	
Time/Place of next meeting:	

Have you attended a men's event or done a service project yet?

At the beginning of class

- Put on your name tag (Right side)
- Pick up your envelope if you turned in forms last week (Re-file forms in your manual)
- Drop off envelope if you are turning in any new forms
- Join a prayer group (3-4 men), praying with different men each week

Class schedule

- 20 minutes: Small group prayer
- 10 minutes: Attendance & Announcements (e.g., missing chair, service projects)
- 20 minutes: Share testimonies
- 30 minutes: Teach and discuss "Setting Priorities, the Lifelong Challenge"
- 15 minutes: Small Group Discussion
- 10 minutes: Break
- 25 minutes: Continue "Setting Priorities, the Lifelong Challenge"
- 15 minutes: My Life Focus: Introduction and discussion
- 5 minutes: Review next week's assignments

Weekly prayer requests

Name	Request
Yours	

Calling a missing chair

"…You will be missed because your seat will be empty" (1 Samuel 20:18).

Missing chair:	
Phone number:	Email:
Contacted:	Status:

Testimonies

Name	Application

Teaching goal

That men would understand the importance of examining their own lives in light of God's standards so they can prioritize and be intentional in building the life God wants for them.

Setting Priorities: The Lifelong Challenge

What are your priorities? Take a minute and think about the most important aspects of your life. Hopefully, relationships with those closest to you were prominent in your thoughts. Ask yourself, how do you prioritize your relationship with God?

Now think about how you spend your resources, especially your most important resource—time. Does your allocation of time align with your greatest priorities? Objectively we know how much better our lives and the lives of those around us would be if we focused on building strong and healthy relationships with God, family, friends, neighbors, etc. Yet the reality is things often derail us from keeping our focus where it needs to be.

All of us can think of someone we would like to have a better relationship with. Think of the benefits of an improved relationship. For example, if you are married, common sense would tell you the stronger your marriage is the better, for you, your wife, and your children. If you have kids, how many of them would say, "I want a marriage just like my parents"?

If we brought in a group of experts on family dynamics and had them observe you for a few weeks, how would they answer these questions: How is this man's relationship with his wife different because they are Christians? What do his relationships with his kids, parents, siblings, co-workers, and neighbors look like? The truth is that the fewer positive aspects of your relationships they can identify, the less positive of a witness you have.

In this session we will look at the problem of priorities in detail and provide you with strategies to break out of whatever relational rut you are currently in. We will also introduce you to the first major project, developing My Life Focus.

In his book, *Future Shock,* Alvin Toffler wrote about how the world is speeding up and change is happening so fast it is almost impossible to stay up to date with anything. The book came out in the 1970's and things have only accelerated since. It is difficult to find ourselves in a world where, in order to stay current, we must constantly adapt.

Couple this with the consumer-centric, ego-driven world that bombards us and our families all day long. It is the unwinnable pursuit of more: more power, more money, more material possession, etc. Far too often we run our lives based on the mistaken belief that with a larger pile of these "things" we will find contentment.

> *"Like a rat in a maze, the path before me lies, and the pattern never alters until the rat dies"* (Paul Simon).

> *"Even if you win the rat race, you are still a rat"* (Lilly Tomlin).

> *"You were running a good race. Who cut in on you to keep you from obeying the truth"* (Galatians 5:7, NIV)?

"Therefore, since we are surrounded by such a great cloud of witnesses, let us throw off everything that hinders and the sin that so easily entangles. And let us run with perseverance the race marked out for us…" (Hebrews 12:1, NIV).

What does your specific rat race look like? Why are you so caught up in it?

_____

_____

At some level, most of us desire to become the person God wants us to be. But how does our desire translate into action when we do not even have the time to do the things that demand our immediate attention? The fact that the day only has 24 hours becomes a limitation that confounds many of us. We think the problem is a lack of time, but we must remember God gives every human the same 24 hours each day to serve Him and His purpose.

We would like to change, but we just can't get our act together. Consider the words of Jesus:

"Then Jesus said to the disciples: "Therefore I tell you, do not worry about your life, what you will eat; or about your body, what you will wear. Life is more than food, and the body more than clothes. Consider the ravens: They do not sow or reap, they have no storeroom or barn; yet God feeds them. And how much more valuable you are than birds! Who of you by worrying can add a single hour to your life? Since you cannot do this very little thing, why do you worry about the rest?" (Luke 12:22-26, NIV)

How does the world define the "good life"?

_____

_____

How is the world's definition different from God's definition?

_____

_____

If someone observed you for a month, which one of the worldly pursuits below might they say was confounding you? How do each of these factors play into your personal rat race?

Consumerism:

_____

_____

Influence of the media:

_____

_____

The ease of credit:

_____

_____

"No one can serve two masters. Either you will hate the one and love the other, or you will be devoted to the one and despise the other. You cannot serve both God and money" (Matthew 7:24, NIV).

Jesus did not say it is "difficult" or "not a good idea" to try to serve both God and money. He said it is *impossible*. "You *cannot* serve both God and money." When Jesus says something about the human condition, you can bet it is 100% true. Too many of us get hung up on possessions, sacrificing relationships in favor of "stuff." We become "stuff-aholics." While there is nothing more important than our relationships, we often prioritize our lives in a way that denies that truth.

The tragedy is that so many of us lead an unexamined life. We do not focus on what we really want to do and then plan how to get there. We are more *reactive* than *proactive.* We have no plan to accomplish important life goals, and far too often, we do not even have goals. The key is to determine what is important, and then to be intentional about getting there.

Do you know what a paradigm is? It is the lens through which we analyze everything that comes into our lives. It consists of your background and experiences. In and of themselves paradigms are neither negative nor positive. However, we often accept these personal prejudices without adequate consideration or reflection. One of the purposes of the My Life Focus is to evaluate your paradigms and determine where you need to adjust them.

When we accept Jesus Christ, we receive the gift of the Holy Spirit. How much do you allow the Holy Spirit to impact your paradigms? We make hundreds of decisions every day, all of which are guided by our paradigms. So, the more Christ-centered those paradigms are, the better your decision-making will be.

PROACTIVE VS. REACTIVE

We spend a lot of effort trying to avoid responsibility for all kinds of things. In the Garden of Eden, Adam tried to place responsibility for the actions he took with regard to the forbidden fruit first on Eve and ultimately on God…and so it began. A mature man, a real leader, understands we are responsible for the decisions we make, and he accepts that responsibility. James tells us when we do not think through things and make the right decision, we are in sin.

> *"If anyone, then, knows the good they ought to do and doesn't do it, it is sin for them" (James 4:17, NIV).*

Our daily lives are full of moments when we need to make decisions. Those decisions determine how we react to whatever is confronting us. Between every event (Catalyst) we face in life, a moment (Interval) exists before we react (Reaction).

Freedom to Choose

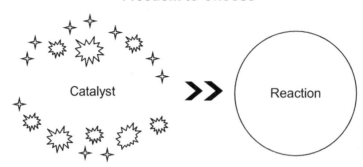

It is in this Interval we find our opportunity to wound or heal, crush or edify. How many of the daily decisions you make are reasoned, rational responses? How many of them are knee-jerk responses, based primarily (if not exclusively) on your emotions?

> *"Better a patient person than a warrior, one with self-control than one who takes a city" (Proverbs 16:32, NIV).*

> *"The plans of the diligent lead to profit as surely as haste leads to poverty" (Proverbs 21:5, NIV).*

We make decisions at two levels. The first level is when we react without any real, conscious contemplation prior to responding. We make decisions based on how we *feel* at the moment. Alternately, the second level of decision-making occurs when we consider our response *prior* to acting. This is a more thoughtful, proactive thought pattern. Our response is in alignment with what best serves our goals. It takes more effort to engage in proactive thinking, but if you are determined to move your life in a positive direction you must increase the amount of proactive thinking you engage in on a daily basis, especially when the decisions you are making are central to your goals.

> *"Whoever sows to please their flesh, from the flesh will reap destruction; whoever sows to please the Spirit, from the Spirit will reap eternal life" (Galatians 6:8, NIV).*

These decisions have a wide-ranging impact on those around you, especially those closest to you. So often though we give reactive responses. When we do this we are saying to those around us that while we are aware of their existence, and while we say they are important to us, it really does not positively impact the decisions we make.

Our daily interactions with people either build up or tear down relationships. Is your goal to edify those around you? If so, then you need to be intentional in those interactions. Use goal-related, proactive thinking as you engage those around you. Do you want a better relationship with your wife, kids, parents, friends, and co-workers? Then be more intentional. Between Catalyst and Reaction ask yourself "What would edify?", and then act accordingly.

WHAT ARE YOUR TRUE GOALS?

Since our natural inclination is to make ourselves happy rather than glorify the Lord, we need to learn to be deliberate in our decision-making processes. The natural man in his natural decision-making process will seek to please himself. To fight the natural man, you must practice being yielded and submitted to the Holy Spirit. Ask yourself, "What do I really want out of this life?" Is it about accumulating stuff, or is it about serving Christ and developing strong relationships with those around you?

Are you committed to the priority of building healthy, meaningful relationships, or are your goals more focused on "stuff" (ego and externals)? The two set of circles below show different ways you can structure your life. The first and most important circle is at the center. What is at the center of your life? Is God central to your thinking and planning (first circle), or is God just an aspect of your life (second circle), where your planning focuses on yourself?

The first concentric circle includes those things that represent your true purpose and are central to your goals in life. If God is in the center, then the middle circle (Goals) will be people-centric and focused on relationships. If Self is in the center (second concentric circle), then the things that fill the middle circle will often be those that bring you happiness and stroke your ego. The outer circle represents things that are resources that assist you in accomplishing your goals.

In and of themselves, none of the items in the middle and outer circle is a problem. In fact, all the items in the circles are legitimate areas of concern and deserve your attention. The question is one of prioritization. Into which circle are you placing the various items? Is your life about pursuing the development of the best relationships possible, or is it about accumulating as much stuff as possible?

Where do you place all the items in your life? Which represent true goals and which do you see as resources to actually accomplish those goals? Many people view relationships as a means to enhance their pursuit of self-satisfying goals. It is easy if we are not deliberate in our thinking to flip what items are in which circle.

How would the people closest to you evaluate you? Would they feel they are central to the important goals in your life? Are you *using* people, or are you *serving* people? Which set of concentric circles best exemplifies your life? What are goals and what are resources?

DO YOU HAVE GOALS?

Have you ever stopped and thought about where your life is headed? What are your goals for yourself and those around you? If someone asked you to describe where you are headed in life and what goals you have, would you be able to give a meaningful response?

Is where you are in life today the product of prior goals you set anchored in strategies you accomplished? Or are you living a life based on reacting to the circumstances that have come your way? God has given you one life, how are you spending it? While you cannot change the past, each day is a new opportunity to build towards the future you want and desire. How can you live your life as if the outcome does not matter?

Also remember, you do not live your life in isolation. The fact is, what you do in your life impacts people around you. Make a list of the people you interact with on a regular basis. What type of relationships are you building?

You may have a variety of roles in life where you are responsible for others. This is certainly true for husbands, fathers, employers, supervisors, and other roles where people look to you for direction and guidance. What are your goals for these relationships? If you are married what are your goals for your marriage? If you have children what are your goals for them? Are your goals vague or are they developed in a way they can be successfully pursued and accomplished?

Ask yourself how long you would want to follow a person in a leadership role if they were simply making it up as they go, with no real sense of purpose. What do you communicate to others about how you value your life and their life? Do people feel you care about them enough to take the time in being deliberate in your relationship with them?

We start with how we are building our relationship with God since this is the foundation upon which all other relationships are built. While God has a purpose for your life, do you? Do you even care what God's purpose is and how you can align your goals with His?

Small Group Discussion

1. Get into groups of no more than five men.
2. Pick a leader to facilitate discussion and make sure everyone participates.
3. You have 15 minutes.
4. Topic: Developing godly priorities.
5. Discussion questions:
    a. What are your plans for you and your family?
    b. What is your strategy for turning those plans into a reality?
    c. How can you prioritize those plans?
    d. What might be keeping you focused on material things?
    e. What consumes your emotional/mental energy?

What do you have control over? What happens when you spend your time dwelling on things you have no control over?

FOCUS FOR IMPACT

Life is full of things that compete for our attention. Some of these things are positive and some are negative. Our attention to them can result in them becoming the concerns of our day-to-day existence. While the Bible teaches that we should not worry, we seem to have trouble adopting this attitude. Whether big or small, concerns are real and always reside somewhere in our thinking. Even if we have learned to more fully trust God and set aside many of our fears, that doesn't mean we will not have concerns in this life. Christ had concerns, not fears.

What concerns you? What are the things that consume your waking hours and emotional energy? We all have a spectrum of things, both positive and negative, that consumes our attention. Have you considered the things that consume your attention from the perspective of what you have the ability to address and what matters are beyond your reach?

There are people who spend their waking hours focused on issues and events over which they have an infinitesimal ability to impact. Often this is done to the neglect of issues and events they can impact. Effective people understand the difference between focusing on things out of their control and living their life dedicated to impacting things they can influence.

For some people, focusing on things out of their control is an avoidance mechanism so they don't have to deal with things they are responsible for. Do you focus your life on things you can have a positive impact on, or do you drift along with no real sense of direction or purpose?

What happens when you live an unfocused life and don't address real issues? Your ability to influence your life and those around you will diminish. Conversely, when you focus on areas you can have a real impact, your ability to influence people and circumstances will increase. While it is good to be aware of things beyond our control, the effective person spends their time and energy focused on where they can have the greatest impact.

God has a purpose for our lives and He has equipped us with resources to address the things that enter our lives each day. How do you spend those resources? When you focus on today's issues and where your influence can make a difference, you will be successful and effective for His Kingdom purposes.

What things do you spend time on that are beyond your ability to impact?

_____

_____

What things within your ability to impact should get more of your time and attention?

_____

_____

TIME AS A PRECIOUS GIFT

Outside of the gift of our salvation, the gift of time may be the most precious gift God has granted us. It is also probably the most wasted gift we have available to us. How much thought do you give to how you spend your time? At the end of your life how much of the time you were given will you be able to say was well spent?

Successful people have well-defined goals, strategies, and tactics. They have thought through their goals and so are motivated by them. Time is a resource to use to accomplish goals. Look back at the concentric circle in the prior section. Success is in the eye of the beholder. A motivated, goal-oriented person can be successful in either one of the concentric circles.

Once you have sorted out what you want your life centered on and what goals really matter, you can focus on making time your ally in accomplishing your goals. You can look back on each day, week, month and year and know they were well-spent. To put time in context, here are the number of minutes in a:

Day	Week	Month	Year	Decade	80 Year Life
1,440	10,080	43,200	525,600	5,258,880	42,071,040

How are you using your time? Every day another 1,440 minutes is used and can never be reclaimed. One day, maybe when you are 80, you will reach the end and have no more minutes to use. At that point, if you could evaluate all the time between minutes used to accomplish real spiritual goals that have eternal value, and those that have no eternal value, what would you see? You have no ability to reclaim yesterday's minutes, but it is within your power to make today's minutes' matter.

We all have "To-Do" lists in our life. Some are highly organized and documented in checklists, while others are simply the result of whatever comes your way that you react to. While the person with the more formalized list is usually in better shape than the person who simply takes life as it comes, neither has necessarily put themselves on a path to accomplishing what is important in life.

It is not enough to simply organize your life around calendars and to-do lists. Life can be overwhelmingly busy. Often you face more "to-do's" than there is time available. Too many people are so busy with the "doing" they never take time to sort out the relevance of those items in relation to their life goals. They simply feel the pressure of all the things on the list.

While some things just have to get done, there are many things that consume time that don't serve any real purpose. Once you learn to prioritize the important over the merely pressing then you have a to-do list that has real power to it. One of the most powerful words in the world is "No." Work to ensure others are not setting your agenda for you.

Relationships are the most important thing in life. They are extremely important, but unless your teenager has been arrested, or your wife wants a divorce, they tend not to be immediately pressing. Far too often at the end of an exhausting day where do we retreat? Usually to the TV, internet, or some other mindless activity. Why? Because we are so burned out from the pressure. To live an intentional life, prioritize your time so you avoid moving from high pressure to mindless activities to decompress. You need to build your priorities around the things that are important. It is where strong relationships are developed and nurtured.

Take the time to organize your life by eliminating everything you can under the pressure category that is not important (It is a given some things still must be done). Then take the time you have saved and use it for those things that are your true priorities. Do not spend your time chasing the urgent at the sacrifice of the important. To do this requires some honest self-evaluation and the commitment to change.

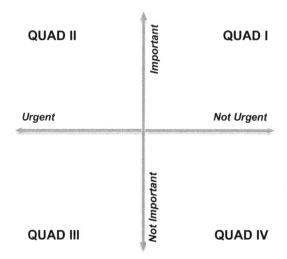

List activities in your life that are important but not urgent:

_____

_____

After spending a day chasing high pressure items, what type of activities attract you?

_____

_____

As you look at the things that consume your time, where does your life fall? Is this a lifelong pattern or temporary? Where do you choose to be? Given the reality of the indwelling presence of the Holy Spirit in your life, what do you believe He would want you to change?

_____

_____

At the end of the day, this is about you and the type of relationships you want with people around you. Good relationships are not the natural byproduct of the proximity of two individuals to each other. They are the result of real, intentional effort on the part of the parties involved. If you want better relationships with those around you, you had better get to work!

(For further study, read Alternative Sessions 1, 2 and 3, in Appendix A.)

Developing My Life Focus

INTRODUCTION

Hopefully, you are coming off a good discussion of things you can do to build better relationships with your family. We have been given the gift of life, in which we will live out a certain number of hours in each day (24), week (168), month (672-744), year (8,760) and lifetime (?????). Only God knows our beginning from our end. You cannot go back and recapture any of this time once it is past. Every hour is precious, and a lot is said about you as a person by how you spend this precious time.

As a man, you have received certain God-given responsibilities to lead. If you are leading, that means someone is supposed to be following. You have a responsibility to those expecting you to lead.

Do you have any idea as to the who, what, when, where, why and how of your leadership? Do you know what you are doing? Would you willingly follow a person who had no plan or even the knowledge of how to develop a plan? If not, why should anyone follow you?

What message do you send to others you are supposed to lead when you are simply reactive, making it up as you go? You operate at an emotional level in your decision-making and it often appears you have not considered those you are leading. If this is you, what message are you *really* sending them?

The purpose of My Life Focus is to challenge you to think through and develop a plan and a means of executing it; to take a life with no real direction and make it one of clear purpose for you and those around you.

There are some fundamental questions we need to ask if we are interested in using the time we have intentionally:

1. "Why am I here?"
2. "Who am I now?"
3. "Where am I going?"
4. "How do I get there?"
5. "Does my life have meaning and purpose?"
6. "Am I fulfilling my purpose?"
7. "Do I have God-sized dreams and specific objectives?"
8. "Do I have a clear strategy for pursuing those dreams and accomplishing those objectives?"

We exist "to glorify God and enjoy Him forever." As born-again believers, we are vested with the indwelling Holy Spirit, whose desire is for us to fulfill that very purpose. That kind of life takes daily focus and lifelong planning. Ultimately, we want said of us what was said of King David:

"For David, after he had served the purpose of God in his own generation, fell asleep, and was laid among his fathers..." (Acts 13:36, NASB).

As you develop your My Life Focus, bathe every step in prayer. As you seek to discover your own God-given purpose, your own Spirit-led goals and objectives, open your heart to the leading of the Holy Spirit. Allow God to reveal yourself to you.

Ask yourself what you would like your obituary to say if it was written by those closest to you. Once you figure that out, work backwards to the current day and figure out how to use your time in an intentional way, so you achieve the desired result. Would you want a husband like you? Would you want a son like you? Would you want a father like you? Would you want a neighbor like you? Would you want to be in a church made up of people with your record of service? Would you want you as an employee? Would you want you as a boss?

MY LIFE AS A BOOK

If you think of your life as a detailed autobiography still being written, how compelling is the story? If someone were to read what has been written so far, what would they conclude about you? Would they want to know you? Would they want to emulate any part of your life? Would they speak of you as one who is now living a fulfilled life? Would they want to read future chapters? When someone finishes your autobiography what will they say about the kind of person you were? What do you want them to say? What can you do today to work toward that end?

"THERE IS ALWAYS TOMORROW" – TIME AS OUR ENEMY

In the *Screwtape Letters,* C.S. Lewis writes about two demons talking to each other about how to best impact the life of a human. The mentor-demon tells his protégé the most effective strategy is simply to convince his mortal he has the luxury of time. As long as humans see themselves as having lots of time, they never seem to get around to doing anything that really matters. Time is both our friend and enemy. Life is the sum of the choices you make every day. As has been said, "Yesterday is a canceled check. Tomorrow is a promissory note. Today is the only cash you have—spend it wisely."

> *"See, I have set before you today life and prosperity, and death and adversity…" (Deuteronomy 30:15, NASB).*

> *"So teach us to number our days, that we may present to you a heart of wisdom" (Psalm 90:12, NASB).*

Someday your unlimited "tomorrows" will cease. What would be your biggest regret if today was it and there were no more tomorrows? Live today to correct as many of those regrets before you run out of "tomorrows". Today is precious, so treat it as such.

THE PROCESS OF CONVERGENCE

Hopefully, you are convinced to start developing a more substantive focus for your life. There is no time like the present to begin this journey. You are a bundle of assets, just waiting to be utilized. You have spiritual gifts, talents, education, experiences, dreams, and far more opportunities than you have ever imagined. You have both victories and failures in the past and God wants to use them to mature you. An honest evaluation of these areas of your life and seeing how they fit in God's plan is called the "Process of Convergence". With this knowledge comes a clearer focus and better planning. This concept is not new. Consider some key passages:

> *"The plans of the heart belong to man, but the answer of the tongue is from the Lord. All the ways of a man are clean in his own sight, but the Lord weighs the motives. Commit your works to the Lord and your plans will be established. The Lord has made everything for its own purpose, even the wicked for the day of evil" (Proverbs 16:1-4, NASB).*

> *"And my God will supply all your needs according to His riches in glory in Christ Jesus" (Philippians 4:19, NASB).*

> *"And God is able to bless you abundantly, so that in all things at all times, having all that you need, you will abound in every good work" (2 Corinthians 9:8, NIV).*

Once completed, your My Life Focus document will help you make informed, intentional daily decisions. It is a multi-step process of honest evaluation and assessment in several areas of your life. You are going to refuse to live the unexamined life and learn to live the proactive life. This truly is an amazing journey. Prepare well.

Each week you will wrestle with a different aspect of your life, identifying where you are and how you got there. Then you will look at where you would like to be and develop a plan to get there. The final step is to commit to a strategy to implement this plan.

After going through your exercise, you should be able to look at your Life Focus and see that your life and the lives of those around you will be significantly better under the plan. The most important step is commitment and dedication to implement your plan. Dedicating yourself to honesty and deep introspection is the first step. If you take it seriously you will have created a strategy for a life worth living for you and those under your care and leadership.

Turn to Appendix D: My Life Focus, to begin your work (To help make sure you get started on the right track we will review some of the content together).

SESSION 5
Becoming a Man of the Word

Leadership is seeing the consequences of our actions
further in the future than those around us can.

SESSION 5
Becoming a Man of the Word

Class discussion
The content below will be discussed during class. If you miss class this week, you are required to read them on your own time, prior to next week's class.

Application from the last session
Pick one thing you learned from the last session you can apply in your life as either an action item or a truth you should embrace.

_____

_____

Before class
____   Reviewed the names of your fellow MIAs
____   Continued your Solo Initiative
____   Memorize Old Testament Books of the Bible (You will be tested)
____   Read the Bible four times this week (See "Daily Bible Reading Chart," in Appendix C)
____   My Life Focus: Read introduction, completed goals and tasks 1-3 (Appendix D)
____   Attended church (Sermon topic: _____)
____   Met with my Accountability Partner

Bible reading

Date	Book/Chapters	At least one thought from what you read

Accountability checklist

___ Asked accountability questions ___ Discussed what you are learning in class	___ Discussed Solo Initiative ___ Prayed
My prayer request: 	
Accountability partner's prayer request: 	
Time/Place of next meeting:	

At the beginning of class
- Put on your name tag (Right side)
- Pick up your envelope if you turned in forms last week (Re-file forms in your manual)
- Drop off envelope if you are turning in any new forms
- Join a prayer group (3-4 men), praying with different men each week

Class schedule
- 20 minutes: Small group prayer
- 10 minutes: Attendance and announcements (e.g., missing chair, service projects)
- 20 minutes: Share testimonies
- 10 minutes: Write the books of the Old Testament from memory
- 20 minutes: Teach and discuss "God's Word: The Only Never-Failing Truth"
- 15 minutes: Small Group Discussion
- 10 minutes: Break
- 20 minutes: Teach and discuss "Mastering the Scriptures: Principles of Effective Bible Study"
- 20 minutes: Teach and discuss "A Simplified Guide for Effective Bible Study"
- 5 minutes: Review next week's assignments

Weekly prayer requests

Name	Request
Yours	

Calling a missing chair

"…You will be missed because your seat will be empty" (1 Samuel 20:18).

Missing Chair:	
Phone number:	Email:
Contacted:	Status:

Testimonies

Name	Application

Teaching goal

That men would understand the inspired Scriptures as approachable, authoritative, and the completely reliable source of faith and practice for every aspect of their lives.

The Old Testament Books

[Complete this in class]

It is important to be able to find your way around the Bible. The Old Testament is made up of 39 books, the last which was written at least 400 years before the birth of Christ. See if you can name them in order based on their groupings.

Hints:
- The first five books are also known as the "Torah" or the "Pentateuch." They were written by Moses.
- There are three sets of 1ˢᵗ and 2ⁿᵈ books in the "History" section.
- The "Major Prophet" books are named after well-known prophets, except for the "woe is me" Book of Lamentations.

The Law (5):

_____

_____

History (12):

_____

_____

Poetry/Wisdom Literature (5):

_____

_____

Major Prophets (5):

_____

_____

Minor Prophets (12):

_____

_____

God's Word: The Only Never-Failing Truth

INTRODUCTION

God is calling us to be Bible-believing men who stand without compromise on the truths of the Word of God as our only true source of faith and practice.

> "The secret things belong to the LORD our God, but the things revealed belong to us and to our sons forever, that we may observe all the words of this law" (Deuteronomy 29:29, NASB).

We exist as a body of believers to bring glory to God and have our lives shaped by the Word of God!

> "The law of the Lord is perfect, restoring the soul; The testimony of the Lord is sure, making wise the simple. The precepts of the Lord are right, rejoicing the heart; The commandment of the Lord is pure, enlightening the eyes. The fear of the Lord is clean, enduring forever; The judgments of the Lord are true; they are righteous altogether. They are more desirable than gold, yes, than much fine gold; Sweeter also than honey and the drippings of the honeycomb. Moreover, by them Your servant is warned; In keeping them there is great reward. Who can discern his errors? Acquit me of hidden faults. Also keep back Your servant from presumptuous sins; Let them not rule over me; Then I will be blameless, And I shall be acquitted of great transgression. Let the words of my mouth and the meditation of my heart Be acceptable in Your sight, O Lord, my rock and my Redeemer" (Psalm 19:7-14, NASB).

DAVID'S DETAILED DESCRIPTION OF THE WORD OF GOD

> The law of the Lord is perfect, restoring the soul; The testimony of the Lord is sure, making wise the simple. The precepts of the Lord are right, rejoicing the heart; The commandment of the Lord is pure, enlightening the eyes. The fear of the Lord is clean, enduring forever; The judgments of the Lord are true; they are righteous altogether" (Psalm 19:7-9, NASB).

David describes the Word of God as having certain purposes (facets), each of which is vitally important. Taken together, they form a complete whole so compelling they demand our attention, study, and daily application.

1. Facet #1: The Word of God presents us with the LAW of the Lord.
2. Facet #2: The Word of God presents us with the TESTIMONY of the Lord.
3. Facet #3: The Word of God presents us with the PRECEPTS of the Lord.
4. Facet #4: The Word of God presents us with the COMMANDS of the Lord.
5. Facet #5: The Word of God presents us with the FEAR of the Lord.
6. Facet #6: The Word of God presents us with the JUDGMENTS of the Lord.

David also gives us six characteristics of the Word of God that lifts it to a realm where no thought or philosophy of man could ever hope to compare or compete. Only God knows truth for sure because He is Truth.

1. The Word of God is PERFECT.
2. The Word of God is SURE.
3. The Word of God is RIGHT.
4. The Word of God is PURE.
5. The Word of God is CLEAN.
6. The Word of God is TRUE.

> *"All Scripture is inspired by God and profitable for teaching, for reproof, for correction, for training in righteousness; so that the man of God may be adequate, equipped for every good work"* (2 Timothy 3:16-17, NASB).

> *"For the word of God is living and active and sharper than any two-edged sword, and piercing as far as the division of soul and spirit, of both joints and marrow, and able to judge the thoughts and intentions of the heart"* (Hebrews 4:12, NASB).

David then goes on to describe six ways the Living Word actively impacts our lives. It gives us the sharpening tools to lead lives that please God and serve and witness to man.

1. The Word of God RESTORES THE SOUL.
2. The Word of God MAKES WISE THE SIMPLE (i.e., the naïve, open-minded).
3. The Word of God REJOICES THE HEART.
4. The Word of God ENLIGHTENS THE EYES.
5. The Word of God ENDURES FOREVER.
6. The Word of God IS ALTOGETHER RIGHTEOUS.

DAVID'S DEEP-SEATED ATTRACTION TO THE WORD OF GOD

David follows this up with his testimony as to why the Word of God is better than anything men value in this world.

Testimony #1: The value of God's Word is beyond all worldly riches.

> *"They are more desirable than gold, yes, than much fine gold..."* (Psalm 19:10, NASB).

> *"I have rejoiced in the way of Your testimonies, as much as in all riches"* (Psalm 119:14, NASB).

> *"The law of Your mouth is better to me than thousands of gold and silver pieces"* (Psalm 119:72, NASB).

"Therefore I love Your commandments above gold, yes, above fine gold"
(Psalm 119:127, NASB).

Testimony #2: The value of God's Word is beyond all worldly pleasures.

"....sweeter also than honey and the drippings of the honeycomb"
(Psalm 19:10, NASB).

"How sweet are Your words to my taste! Yes, sweeter than honey to my mouth"
(Psalm 119:103, NASB)!

Testimony #3: The value of God's Word is beyond all worldly advice.

"Moreover, by them Your servant is warned..." (Psalm 19:11, NASB).

"How can a young man keep his way pure? By keeping it according to Your word. With all my heart I have sought You; do not let me wander from Your commandments. Your word I have treasured in my heart, that I may not sin against You" (Psalm 119:9-11, NASB).

Testimony #4: The value of God's Word is beyond all worldly rewards.

"...in keeping them there is great reward" (Psalm 19:11, NASB).

"This book of the law shall not depart from your mouth, but you shall meditate on it day and night, so that you may be careful to do according to all that is written in it; for then you will make your way prosperous, and then you will have success"
(Joshua 1:8, NASB).

"But his delight is in the law of the LORD, and in His law he meditates day and night. He will be like a tree firmly planted by streams of water, which yields its fruit in its season and its leaf does not wither; and in whatever he does, he prospers" Psalm 1:2-3, NASB).

DAVID'S DESPERATE CONVICTION REGARDING THE WORD OF GOD

David recognizes nothing is hidden from God, and He is the only one who can take what we have done wrong and make it right.

"Who can discern his errors? Acquit me of hidden faults. Also keep back Your servant from presumptuous sins; let them not rule over me; then I will be blameless, and I shall be acquitted of great transgression"
(Psalm 19:12-13, NASB).

"And there is no creature hidden from His sight, but all things are open and laid bare to the eyes of Him with whom we have to do" (Hebrews 4:13, NASB).

"Be gracious to me, O God, according to Your lovingkindness; according to the greatness of Your compassion blot out my transgressions. Wash me thoroughly from my iniquity and cleanse me from my sin" (Psalm 51:1-2, NASB).

"Search me, O God, and know my heart; try me and know my anxious thoughts; and see if there be any hurtful way in me, and lead me in the everlasting way" (Psalm 139:23-24, NASB).

"The Bible will keep you from sin or sin will keep you from the Bible" (D.L. Moody).

DAVID'S DAILY DEVOTION TO THE GOD OF THE BIBLE

Our thoughts and words are a daily struggle. David desires to please God with his words:

"Let the words of my mouth and the meditation of my heart be acceptable in Your sight, O Lord, my rock and my Redeemer" (Psalm 19:14, NASB).

CONCLUSION

God is calling us to be *Christ-centered men* who have trusted in Jesus Christ alone for our salvation, and who choose to submit to Him as the ultimate authority of our lives.

God is also calling us to be *worshiping men* that respond in adoration and celebration to the infinite majesty of God.

God is calling us to be men of the Word. Are we?

Small Group Discussion

1. Get into groups of no more than five men.
2. Pick a leader to facilitate discussion and make sure everyone participates.
3. You have 15 minutes.
4. Topic: Regular Bible reading.
5. Discussion questions:
   a. Read the phrase below and the series of words that follow. Which of the words is your attention drawn to and why?
      i. The Word of God is: Perfect, Sure, Right, Pure, Clean, True.
   b. What can you do to become more Christ-centered? What will you commit to doing/changing this week?
   c. Do those closest to you see you as a man of the Word?
   d. What keeps you from engaging with the Word of God?

Mastering the Scriptures:
Principles for Effective Bible Study

The most important book for every aspect of our lives is the Bible. Unfortunately, it often sits on the bookshelf, rather than being a regular part of our lives. Many of us do not know how to approach it so we can fully understand its meaning and apply it to our lives.

> *"The words of wise men are like goads, and masters of these collections are like well-driven nails; they are given by one Shepherd. But beyond this, my son, be warned: the writing of many books is endless, and excessive devotion to books is wearying to the body" (Ecclesiastes 12:11-12, NASB).*

> *"All Scripture is inspired by God and profitable for teaching, for reproof, for correction, for training in righteousness; so that the man of God may be adequate, equipped for every good work" (2 Timothy 3:16-17, NASB).*

> *"For the word of God is living and active and sharper than any two-edged sword, and piercing as far as the division of soul and spirit, of both joints and marrow, and able to judge the thoughts and intentions of the heart"*
> *(Hebrews 4:12, NASB).*

THE GOAL OF EFFECTIVE BIBLE STUDY

The goal of effective Bible study is getting the mind of God into the attitudes and actions of men.

> *"For my thoughts are not your thoughts, neither are your ways my ways,' declares the Lord. 'As the heavens are higher than the earth, so are my ways higher than your ways and my thoughts than your thoughts'" (Isaiah 55:8-9, NIV).*

> *"Oh, the depth of the riches of the wisdom and knowledge of God! How unsearchable his judgments, and his paths beyond tracing out! Who has known the mind of the Lord? Or who has been his counselor?" (Romans 11:33-34, NIV)*

> *"The secret things belong to the LORD our God, but the things revealed belong to us and to our children forever, that we may follow all the words of this law" (Deuteronomy 29:29, NIV).*

How has God revealed His mind to us? Primarily through the Word of God. How then has His Word come to us? Through a series of important steps:

1. **Revelation:** The process by which God spoke His mind to men.
2. **Inspiration:** The method by which God Himself spoke through human authors His exact revelation to men. We believe in Verbal Plenary Inspiration:
   a. Verbal: Every word found in the Bible is given by God.
   b. Plenary: Everything in the Bible is authoritative.

      c. Inspiration: Everything in the Bible is divinely directed

3. **Transmission:** The miraculous and sacrificial preservation of the Scriptures throughout human history.
4. **Translation:** The careful translation of the original language manuscripts of Scripture into various languages.
5. **Interpretation:** The accurate understanding of the meaning of Scripture in light of its historical and grammatical context.
6. **Illumination:** The ministry of the Holy Spirit in the life of the believer to produce understanding and the proper response to Scripture.
7. **Application:** The careful attempt at demonstrating the Scripture's relevancy in human lives so a change in attitudes and actions occur.

THE METHOD OF EFFECTIVE BIBLE STUDY

The Bible is to be viewed as a consistent whole, and based on that, all verses interpreted in light of *other* verses, looking for the consistent truth God provides. We should not look for random verses that seem to say what we want them to say. When studying the Bible keep the following in mind:

1. **Historical context:** We study every portion of Scripture considering its historical and cultural context.
2. **Grammatical meaning:** We interpret Scripture considering the nuances of the words and grammar in the text.
3. **Exegesis (to draw meaning, rather than to insert meaning in):** This word comes from a Greek word meaning "to lead out" and speaks of pulling truths *out* of Scripture (*exegesis*) rather than reading opinions *into* Scripture (*eisegesis*). We draw our Biblical conclusions from the facts of Scripture (inductive study), rather than having pre-determined conclusions and attempting to find facts in the Bible to support those conclusions (deductive study).

A Simplified Guide for Effective Bible Study

1. **Step One: Preparation—Anticipating God's direction**
   a. Begin with P.R.A.Y.E.R. (Praising, Repenting, Asking, Yielding, Entreating, Rejoicing).
   b. Make a commitment to find the single meaning of the text.
   c. Proceed with caution, drawing conclusions from the facts of Scripture (inductive exegesis).

2. **Step Two: Observation—Asking the right questions**
   a. Study the background of the book.
   b. Read the entire book or passage multiple times, in different translations (i.e., NIV, ESV, NASB).
   c. Carefully examine the specific passage in many translations.
   d. Ask appropriate questions (Who? What? Where? When? How? Why?).
   e. Look up cross-references.
   f. Write down your observations.

3. **Step Three: Interpretation—Answering the right questions**
   a. Do particular word studies (synonyms, antonyms, figures of speech, idioms, repeated words and phrases, etc.).
   b. Watch for specific details in the grammar (tenses, voices, moods, person, number, prepositions, conjunctions, etc.).
   c. Write down what others say about the text.
   d. Begin problem solving, deciding on what seems to be the best view.

4. **Step Four: Application—Applying the right answers**
   a. Answer the question: "So what?" ("What should I do in response?")
   b. List commands to obey, promises to keep, truths to know, actions to take, sins to forsake, examples to follow, things to avoid, new thoughts about God.

5. **Step Five: Presentation—Announcing the Good News**
   a. Share what you have learned.
   b. Organize the presentation.
   c. Select appropriate illustrations.
   d. Scan or file all research and notes.

(For further study, read Appendix A: "Fundamentals of the Faith"; and Appendix C: "Guide to Daily Devotions," "Daily Bible Reading Chart," and "The Bible on Trial: Evidence for Its Reliability.")

(For further study, read "Mastering the Scriptures: A Self-Study Course in Effective Bible Study," by Dr. James M. Cecy, available at www.jaron.org and www.amazon.com.)

SESSION 6
Personal Purity as a
Priority for the Christian Man

> *Until a leader declares war against an evil habit that enslaves him, rendering him ineffective, he cannot be his best for God or be of any use to man.*

SESSION 6
Personal Purity as a
Priority for the Christian Man

Class discussion
The content below will be discussed during class. If you miss class this week, you are required to read them on your own time, prior to next week's class.

Application from the last session
Pick one thing you learned from the last session you can apply in your life as either an action item or a truth you should embrace.

_____

_____

Before class
____   Reviewed the names of your fellow MIAs
____   Continued your Solo Initiative
____   Read the Bible at least four times this week
____   My Life Focus: Completed tasks 4-5 (Appendix D)
____   Attended church (Sermon topic: _____)
____   Met with my Accountability Partner

Bible reading

Date	Book/Chapters	At least one thought from what you read

Accountability checklist

___ Asked accountability questions ___ Discussed what you are learning in class	___ Discussed Solo Initiative ___ Prayed

My prayer request:
Accountability partner's prayer request:
Time/Place of next meeting:

At the beginning of class

- Put on your name tag (Right side)
- Pick up your envelope if you turned in forms last week (Re-file forms in your manual)
- Drop off envelope if you are turning in any new forms
- Join a prayer group (3-4 men), praying with different men each week

Class schedule

- 20 minutes: Small group prayer
- 10 minutes: Attendance and announcements (e.g., missing chair, service projects)
- 20 minutes: Share testimonies
- 30 minutes: Teach and discuss "Walking in Holiness in an Ungodly World"
- 15 minutes: Small Group Discussion
- 10 minutes: Break
- 40 minutes: Teach and discuss "A Revival of Purity"
- 5 minutes: Review next week's assignments

Weekly prayer requests

Name	Request
Yours	

Calling a missing chair

"…You will be missed because your seat will be empty" (1 Samuel 20:18).

Missing chair:	
Phone number:	Email:
Contacted:	Status:

Testimonies

Name	Application

Teaching goal

That men will understand sexual purity is a universal struggle, requiring that we guard our minds, our bodies and each other as we strive to walk in holiness in an immoral world.

Walking in Holiness in an Ungodly World

Often in life the greatest challenge is not our inability to know the right thing to do; it is in doing it. We live in a world of constant temptation and if we do not have a strategy to combat it, we will find ourselves repeatedly succumbing to it. Godly purity and holiness require intentionality.

At our most base level man is motivated to seek pleasure. Without a plan and purpose to seek holiness our default position usually leads to the wrong choice. Do you have a strategy to pursue godliness?

"For this is the will of God, your sanctification; that is, that you abstain from sexual immorality; that each of you know how to possess his own vessel in sanctification and honor, not in lustful passion, like the Gentiles who do not know God; and that no man transgress and defraud his brother in the matter because the Lord is the avenger in all these things, just as we also told you before and solemnly warned you. For God has not called us for the purpose of impurity, but in sanctification. So, he who rejects this is not rejecting man but the God who gives His Holy Spirit to you" (1 Thessalonians 4:3-8, NASB).

"Do not love the world or anything in the world. If anyone loves the world, love for the Father is not in them. For everything in the world—the lust of the flesh, the lust of the eyes, and the pride of life—comes not from the Father but from the world. The world and its desires pass away, but whoever does the will of God lives forever" (1 John 2:15-17, NIV).

"Do not conform to the pattern of this world, but be transformed by the renewing of your mind. Then you will be able to test and approve what God's will is—his good, pleasing and perfect will" (Romans 12:2, NIV).

When they say "the world," what are they referring to?

_____

_____

Why is the love of "this world" bad?

_____

_____

How does the love of "the world" stand in contrast to the love of God?

_____

_____

How would you define the lust of the flesh? The lust of the eyes? The pride of life?

_____

_____

We have spent time discussing the Fruit of the Spirit. This fruit is the natural result of a life being yielded and submitted to the Holy Spirit's guidance. Right before the verses on spiritual fruit in Galatians are verses that could be called the Fruit of the Flesh, or the Fruit of the World.

> *"The acts of the flesh are obvious: sexual immorality, impurity and debauchery; idolatry and witchcraft; hatred, discord, jealousy, fits of rage, selfish ambition, dissensions, factions and envy; drunkenness, orgies, and the like. I warn you, as I did before, that those who live like this will not inherit the kingdom of God"* (Galatians 5:19-21, NIV).

What acts of the flesh from the above verses most often define your conduct?

_____

_____

Would you rather partner with a person who displays the Fruit of the Spirit or the Fruit of the World? Would it matter if that person were a spouse, family member, business partner or a person you see socially?

_____

_____

Do you most often attract people who are filled with the Fruit of the Spirit or the Fruit of the World? Why do you think that is?

_____

_____

> *"I do not understand what I do. For what I want to do I do not do, but what I hate I do"* (Romans 7:15, NIV).

> *"If anyone, then, knows the good they ought to do and doesn't do it, it is sin for them"* (James 4:17, NIV).

Examine yourself in the area of personal holiness to assess where you act in ways contrary to God's will. Consider why this is, and what you can do to confront it and defeat it.

If all your thoughts over a 24-hour period were broadcast to your friends and family, how would they respond?

_____

_____

Small Group Discussion

1. Get into groups of no more than five men.
2. Pick a leader to facilitate discussion and make sure everyone participates.
3. You have 15 minutes.
4. Topic: Purity is a key to holiness. How do you achieve it?
5. Discussion questions:
   a. Where do you find the biggest challenges to stay holy? What helps you overcome them?
   b. What standards you have established in your life for personal holiness?
   c. If you have strong level of accountability with another man, share how you helped create it. If not, what can you do to create strong and brotherly accountability?

A Revival of Purity

The world seems to be rejecting all moral standards, leaving us with little to hold onto when it comes to right and wrong. This is especially problematic in the area of sexual behavior. What is appropriate in popular culture is based solely on what anyone may desire to do.

God, however, is not confused on the subject. He has His standards clearly set for anyone who is willing to inquire. While the quest for personal purity runs contrary to the way society is headed, it is a quest God wants us to pursue. No society holds together long when it moves down the slippery slope towards sexual anarchy. Consider the words of the Apostle Paul, writing to people who lived in the midst of a deeply perverse culture:

> *"For this is the will of God, your sanctification; that is, that you abstain from sexual immorality; that each of you know how to possess his own vessel in sanctification and honor, not in lustful passion, like the Gentiles who do not know God; and that no man transgress and defraud his brother in the matter because the Lord is the avenger in all these things, just as we also told you before and solemnly warned you. For God has not called us for the purpose of impurity, but in sanctification. So, he who rejects this is not rejecting man but the God who gives His Holy Spirit to you" (1 Thessalonians 4:3-8, NASB).*

THREE COMMANDS FOR SEXUAL PURITY

The Apostle Paul is explicit that he is giving us God's specific and clear will on the subject of sexual purity. He ties these instructions directly to our sanctification (our holiness). They are not suggestions; they are lifestyle commands.

In verses 3-8 above, Paul provides three specific commands from God:

1. Lifestyle command #1: Abstain from sexual immorality (1 Thessalonians 4:3b).
2. Lifestyle command #2: Know how to acquire a mate (1 Thessalonians 4:4-5).
3. Lifestyle command #3: Do not transgress and defraud (1 Thessalonians 4:6).

Consider how you are complying with each of the above commands. Where are you having trouble, and what is the source of those troubles?

_____

_____

THREE REASONS FOR SEXUAL PURITY

In verses 6-8, the Apostle Paul gives reasons why a man should pursue sexual purity. These all center around God, whose view is clear on the subject.

1. Reason #1: God avenges immorality (4:6b).
2. Reason #2: God calls us to be pure (4:7).
3. Reason #3: God Himself is Holy and enables us to be pure (4:8).

Let's put it all together:

1. God wills that we be pure.
2. God calls us to be pure.
3. God enables us to be pure.

So then, what is the only issue?

1. Do we really want to be pure?

(See Appendix C: "Safeguarding My Personal Purity")

(For further study, read "The Purity War: A Biblical Guide to Living in an Immoral World" by Dr. James M. Cecy. Includes Study Guide & Personal Accountability Program. Available at www.jaron.org and www.amazon.com.)

SESSION 7
Growing as a Leader
of the Family

The best test of whether one is an effective leader in his family is to find out whether anyone is following.

SESSION 7
Growing as a Leader of the Family

Class discussion
The content below will be discussed during class. If you miss class this week, you are required to read them on your own time, prior to next week's class.

Application from the last session
Pick one thing you learned from the last session you can apply in your life as either an action item or a truth you should embrace.

_____

_____

Before class
____ Reviewed the names of your fellow MIAs
____ Continued your Solo Initiative
____ Read the Bible at least four times this week (See Bible Reading Chart, Appendix C)
____ My Life Focus: Completed Tasks 8-10 (Appendix D)
____ Attended church (Sermon topic: _____)
____ Met with my Accountability Partner

Before class Option A group only
____ Completed "Survey Regarding Your Wife"
____ Completed "Taking My Marital Pulse (Men Only Survey)"
____ Completed "Taking My Marital Pulse (Couples Survey)"

Bible reading

Date	Book/Chapters	At least one thought from what you read

Accountability checklist

___ Asked accountability questions ___ Discussed what you are learning in class	___ Discussed Solo Initiative ___ Prayed
My prayer request:	
Accountability partner's prayer request:	
Time/Place of next meeting:	

At the beginning of class

- Put on your name tag (Right side)
- Pick up your envelope if you turned in forms last week (Re-file forms in your manual)
- Drop off envelope if you are turning in any new forms
- Join a prayer group (3-4 men), praying with different men each week

Class schedule

All Together

- 20 minutes: Small group prayer
- 10 minutes: Attendance and announcements (e.g., missing chair, service projects)
- 10 minutes: Share testimonies

Option A: Married and Older Men

- 15 minutes: Introduction to the Marriage Surveys:
  - "Survey Regarding Your Wife"
  - "Taking My Marital Pulse (Men-Only Survey)"
  - "Taking My Marital Pulse (Couples Survey)"
- 15 minutes: Small Group Discussion
- 10 minutes: Break
- 30 minutes: Teach and discuss "The Biblical Foundation for Marriage"
- 20 minutes: Teach and discuss "Next Generation" and "The Next Generation Survey"

Option B: Unmarried Younger Men

- 35 minutes: Review "Growing as a Young Man of God"
- 15 minutes: Small Group Discussion
- 10 minutes: Break
- 30 minutes: Discussion of "Growing as a Young Man of God"

Class Back Together

- 15 minutes: Teach and discuss "Blessing the Generations"
- 5 minutes: Review next week's assignments

Weekly prayer requests

Name	Request
Yours	

Calling a missing chair

"…You will be missed because your seat will be empty" (1 Samuel 20:18).

Missing chair:	
Phone number:	Email:
Contacted:	Status:

Testimonies

Name	Application

Teaching goal : Option A—For married men

That men realize that next to their relationship with the Lord, no relationships are more important than those with their immediate family.

Teaching goal : Option B—For single men

That younger men understand they are currently making decisions not only defining who they are now, but who they will become in the future. God has a plan and purpose for their life that is the only true path to contentment.

The Biblical Foundation for Marriage

"I will walk within my house in the integrity of my heart" (Psalm 101:2, NASB).

FROM THE BEGINNING

"So the man gave names to all the livestock, the birds in the sky and all the wild animals. But for Adam no suitable helper was found. So the LORD God caused the man to fall into a deep sleep; and while he was sleeping, he took one of the man's ribs and then closed up the place with flesh. Then the LORD God made a woman from the rib he had taken out of the man, and he brought her to the man. The man said, 'This is now bone of my bones and flesh of my flesh; she shall be called 'woman,' for she was taken out of man.' That is why a man leaves his father and mother and is united to his wife, and they become one flesh. Adam and his wife were both naked, and they felt no shame" (Genesis 2:20-25, NIV).

Adam noticed something significant was missing from his life. What was it?

_____

To establish this new relationship, what is man instructed to do?

_____

What does this passage tell us about the strength of the unity intended for this relationship?

_____

What does this passage tell us about the intimacy intended?

_____

MARRIAGE IS INTENDED TO BE PERMANENT

"Some Pharisees came to him to test him. They asked, 'Is it lawful for a man to divorce his wife for any and every reason?' 'Haven't you read,' he replied, 'that at the beginning the Creator 'made them male and female,' and said, 'For this reason a man will leave his father and mother and be united to his wife, and the two will become one flesh'? So they are no longer two, but one flesh. Therefore what God has joined together, let no one separate" (Matthew 19:3-6, NIV).

What standard is set out in Scripture for the length of a marriage?

_____

THE STRUCTURE OF THE MARRIAGE RELATIONSHIP

"Submit to one another out of reverence for Christ. Wives, submit yourselves to your own husbands as you do to the Lord. For the husband is the head of the wife as Christ is the head of the church, his body, of which he is the Savior. Now

as the church submits to Christ, so also wives should submit to their husbands in everything. Husbands, love your wives, just as Christ loved the church and gave himself up for her to make her holy, cleansing her by the washing with water through the word, and to present her to himself as a radiant church, without stain or wrinkle or any other blemish, but holy and blameless. In this same way, husbands ought to love their wives as their own bodies. He who loves his wife loves himself. After all, no one ever hated their own body, but they feed and care for their body, just as Christ does the church—for we are members of his body. 'For this reason a man will leave his father and mother and be united to his wife, and the two will become one flesh.' This is a profound mystery—but I am talking about Christ and the church. However, each one of you also must love his wife as he loves himself, and the wife must respect her husband"
(Ephesians 5:21-33, NIV).

Today the word "submission" has a negative connotation, taking on the concept of forced servitude. That's not the Biblical meaning intended. Willing submission is the key to relationships throughout Scripture. God is the pinnacle of all authority; it is at His throne all submission starts and flows.

What does the passage indicate is the first area in which to practice submission?

_____

The Greek word used in the New Testament for submission is *hupotasso*, which means "placement, position, status or ranking under another." The same word is used to describe submitting to the government or those in authority in the church. The Biblical concept of submission implies a *choice* being made. It is seen as placing yourself voluntarily under God's designed authority. It involves faith in God and God's word. Submission should rightly be seen as distinct from obedience (*hupakouo*), in which a person has no real choice. In Scripture, slaves were commanded to obey masters. No questioning. No collaborating. Just do it!

Before you start worrying about whether your wife is submissive, you need to assess your *own role* in your marriage. Have you earned the right to lead? Would you want to submit to you?

What does the passage above say about the duties of the husband?

_____

To whom are you to submit?

_____

The first aspect to address is how submitted you are to godly authority. Is your wife being asked to follow someone serving God, or is she being asked to join your personal rebellion against God and His direction in your life? How legitimate is your leadership? It is only as legitimate as it is under the greater authority of Jesus Christ and the leading of the Holy Spirit. Your first job is to straighten up yourself, before you expect others to follow you. You are to show the same care and sacrifice for your wife as Christ showed for His church.

You are to be the very definition of a servant-leader. You are to love (selflessly sacrifice for) your wife and family. This implies your goal is to see to their needs *before* your own. Your focus is on their best interests in all things. Do you seek your wife's input and opinion on important matters, especially those involving your marriage and your family? Your wife should feel like a cherished and esteemed partner, never used or taken for granted.

How do you think your wife would submit to a man who consistently demonstrated self-sacrifice towards her best interests?

_____

_____

If you have children, the issue of submission can become even more significant for your wife. How does she feel about your spiritual leadership in the home? Should she trust the spiritual guidance of the children to your words and actions? Who is the spiritual leader in the home? If the answer is not clearly you, there is immediate work to be done.

How does your wife know she is loved and cherished? What are some things you can do immediately to improve the situation?

_____

_____

Beyond submission, what instruction is given to the wife in Ephesians, Chapter 5?

_____

_____

She is to respect you. How easy are you making that instruction for her to follow? Have you ever been in a position where you had the difficult challenge of following someone you did not respect? Your job is to act in a way that earns and deserves your wife's respect.

If you have children, what type of example are you providing? When they grow up would they want the type of marriage they see in your relationship? Do you want your grandchildren to be raised by someone like you? Would you want your daughter to look for someone like you?

A good first step is to complete the surveys in this session's materials. They will help you find blind spots and get your marriage headed in a direction that benefits both you and your wife. Next to your walk with God, your marriage relationship is the most important relationship you have. Do you want a good relationship that both you and your wife enjoy and cherish, or do you want a relationship that is a constant battle, filled with stress and discontentment?

(For further study, read "The Taste Test for Godly Speech," in Appendix C.)

> ## *The greatest thing a father can do for his children is to love their mother.*

Option A: Survey Regarding Your Wife

[If you are unmarried and not engaged you may skip this assignment]

Ask your wife the following questions. Use this information and plan at least two dates with your wife before MIA ends. It might make for some interesting dialogue if you try to guess the answers *before* asking your wife.

1. What is her favorite meal?
   _____

2. What is her favorite dessert?
   _____

3. What is her favorite restaurant?
   _____

4. What is her favorite holiday?
   _____

5. What was her favorite subject in school?
   _____

6. What is her favorite movie?
   _____

7. Who is her favorite actor?
   _____

8. Who is her favorite actress?
   _____

9. What is her favorite singer/group?
   _____

10. What is her favorite song?
    _____

11. What is her favorite place to go to be alone?
    _____

12. What is her favorite book (other than the Bible)?
    _____

13. What was her favorite vacation?

_____

14. If she could take a vacation anywhere where would she go?

_____

15. What is something she considers especially romantic?

_____

16. What is her favorite sport?

_____

17. What is her favorite TV show?

_____

18. What is one thing that makes her laugh?

_____

19. What is one thing that makes her cry?

_____

20. What is the best present she ever received?

_____

21. What is her favorite book in the Bible?

_____

22. When does she feel most content?

_____

23. When does she feel the most anxious?

_____

24. If she could accomplish one major thing in the next 12 months what would it be?

_____

25. If she could change one thing about you what would it be?

_____

26. What are three things you should be praying about for her?

_____

27. What one question didn't you ask that she wishes you did? (Then ask it!)

_____

Taking My Marital Pulse (Men-Only Survey)

As we reflect on God's plan for marriage, answer the questions below. If you are not married, reflect on the value of each point, evaluating how you would score at this point in your life. You will not be asked to disclose your answers unless you want to.

	As a husband I am...	Scripture	Winning		Struggling		Losing	
1.	Making sure we have a healthy sex life.	Proverbs 5:15-19	10 9 8		7 6 5 4		3 2 1	
2.	Treating my wife as a precious gift from God.	Proverbs 18:22; 19:13-14; 31:10	10 9 8		7 6 5 4		3 2 1	
3.	Acknowledging and rewarding my wife for her hard work.	Proverbs 31:27-28	10 9 8		7 6 5 4		3 2 1	
4.	Giving my wife the praise she deserves.	Proverbs 31:28-31	10 9 8		7 6 5 4		3 2 1	
5.	Loving my wife as Christ loves the Church.	Ephesians 5:25-30	10 9 8		7 6 5 4		3 2 1	
6.	Sacrificing for my wife.	Ephesians 5:25-30	10 9 8		7 6 5 4		3 2 1	
7.	Loving my wife as my own body.	Ephesians 5:25-30	10 9 8		7 6 5 4		3 2 1	
8.	Nourishing and cherishing my wife.	Ephesians 5:25-30	10 9 8		7 6 5 4		3 2 1	
9.	Not embittered, but generously forgiving my wife.	Colossians 3:19	10 9 8		7 6 5 4		3 2 1	
10.	Living with my wife in an understanding way.	1 Peter 3:7	10 9 8		7 6 5 4		3 2 1	
11.	Appreciating my wife's physical limitations.	1 Peter 3:7	10 9 8		7 6 5 4		3 2 1	
12.	Understanding and respecting her emotional differences.	1 Peter 3:7	10 9 8		7 6 5 4		3 2 1	
13.	Honoring her as a joint heir in Christ.	1 Peter 3:7	10 9 8		7 6 5 4		3 2 1	
14.	A one woman man, that woman being my wife.	Genesis 2:24	10 9 8		7 6 5 4		3 2 1	
15.	Never looking at another woman lustfully.	Matthew 5:27-28	10 9 8		7 6 5 4		3 2 1	
16.	Never looking at sexually explicit materials.	Matthew 5:27-28	10 9 8		7 6 5 4		3 2 1	

	Additional Questions	Excellent	Good	Poor
1.	I would rate my marriage as:	10 9 8	7 6 5 4	3 2 1
2.	My wife would rate our marriage as:	10 9 8	7 6 5 4	3 2 1
3.	I would rate the communication in our marriage as:	10 9 8	7 6 5 4	3 2 1
4.	I would rate my spiritual leadership in the home as:	10 9 8	7 6 5 4	3 2 1
5.	I would rate my family life as:	10 9 8	7 6 5 4	3 2 1
6.	My wife would rate our family life as:	10 9 8	7 6 5 4	3 2 1

I will focus on improving my marriage in the following areas:

_____

_____

_____

_____

_____

_____

_____

_____

_____

_____

_____

_____

_____

_____

SHARE THESE COMMITMENTS WITH YOUR ACCOUNTABILITY PARTNER

Taking My Marital Pulse (Couples Survey)

(A Discussion Agenda for Married Couples)

Find some time when you and your wife can sit and discuss without any interruptions. Focus on making it a dialogue, where you listen more than you talk. Be sure both of you participate in the discussion. While we will discuss general aspects of the survey in class, no one will be asked to disclose anything specific. This assignment is between the two of you.

1.	Have we been enjoying each other?	9.	Are we having family time together?
2.	Have we been eating dinner together?	10.	Have we been playing together?
3.	Have we been protecting our day off?	11.	Have we been romancing each other?
4.	Have we been praying together?	12.	Have we lost the joy of our sexual union?
5.	Have we been holding a grudge or harboring bitterness?	13.	Have we gone on a meaningful date recently?
6.	How does our relationship reflect the love of Christ?	14.	Are we on the same page when it comes to matters of finance?
7.	Have we been too busy to focus on each other?	15.	Are we on the same page when it comes to issues involving the kids?
8.	Have we been going to bed at the same time?	16.	Have we been meeting each other's needs?

What are we going to do *this week* to build our marriage (State specific action steps)?

_____

_____

As your husband, I will do the following to address issues identified above:

1. _____
2. _____
3. _____

As your wife, I will do the following to address issues identified above:

1. _____
2. _____
3. _____

DO NOT SHARE THESE COMMITMENTS WITH YOUR ACCOUNTABILTY PARTNER. THEY ARE PERSONAL, FOR YOU AND YOUR WIFE.

Small Group Discussion

1. Get into groups of no more than five men.
2. Pick a leader to facilitate discussion and make sure everyone participates.
3. You have 15 minutes.
4. Topic: Managing your marriage.
   a. Those who have never been married are encouraged to discuss from the standpoint of what they have observed in the marriages they are close to (without saying who they are referencing).
5. Discussion questions:
   a. Option A materials (without disclosing private matters between you and your wife)
      i. Were there any questions you asked your wife where her answer surprised you? Why was it (or why was it not) surprising? What might change in your relationship because of these answers?
      ii. Marital Pulse: How did you feel after answering these? Are there are areas you want to grow in? How are you going to accomplish growth?
      iii. Couples survey: Share about what you learned by discussing these with your wife.

The Next Generation

"My child arrived just the other day; he came to the world in the usual way. But there were planes to catch and bills to pay; he learned to walk while I was away."
(Sandy and Harry Chapin, "Cat's in the Cradle")

THE NEED FOR MEN AS FAMILY LEADERS

One of the most dramatic changes in society over the last 50 years has been the diminishing or even elimination of the father's role in the family unit. The progressive movement's demand for a gender-neutral society not only defies reality, but it also threatens to unravel one of the fundamental building blocks of a healthy culture, the Biblical family unit (i.e., a mother and father). For some families, the absence of a father is an unfortunate physical reality. Sadder still are the families with a father physically present, but devoid of emotional and spiritual leadership.

The nuclear family has blown up, and the fallout has left generations of children with no strong male role model. Studies have shown if children have the influence of a committed father in the home, they are more likely to succeed in life. Fatherlessness (physically and/or emotionally) places a double-burden on the mother, who must be the mother as well as play a role she is not equipped to play—that of father. How are you doing playing your role?

OUR SPECIFIC PLANS FOR OUR CHILDREN

For too many men, their interactions with their kids involve ordering them around and criticizing them. If this applies to you, is it any surprise your children avoid interacting with you? Would you want to follow a father like you?

What type of healthy relationship would you like with your children?

_____

_____

What type of people are you trying to raise your children to be?

_____

_____

AUTHORITY EXERCISED THROUGH SERVANT-LEADERSHIP

"Children, obey your parents in the Lord, for this is right. Honor your father and mother—which is the first commandment with a promise—that it may go well with you and that you may enjoy long life on the earth" (Ephesians 6:1-3, NIV).

What is your role in relationship to your children who are commanded by God obey you? You are to be a servant-leader, loving and caring for them sacrificially, taking on the challenge to raise them to be responsible adults who love the Lord and serve mankind. Ultimately, how they turn out is their choice, but you have a role to play in shaping them to become a man or woman of God, vital to His kingdom work.

GENERATIONAL DISCIPLESHIP

Part of being a servant-leader and providing loving discipline is in our understanding of the multi-generational aspect of discipleship. In 2 Timothy, the Apostle Paul provides us with a model of what this looks like:

> *"And the things you have heard me say in the presence of many witnesses entrust to reliable people who will also be qualified to teach others"* (2 Timothy 2:2, NIV).

REARING CHILDREN WITH WISDOM AND DISCIPLINE

> *"Listen, my sons, to a father's instructions; pay attention and gain understanding. I give you sound learning, so do not forsake my teaching" (Proverbs 4:1-2, NIV).*

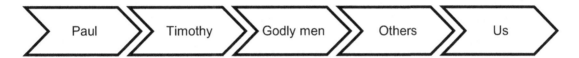

> *"The heart of the problem is a problem of the heart" (Warren Wiersbe).*

We need to be concerned about our children's hearts.

> *"For it is from within, out of a person's heart, that evil thoughts come—sexual immorality, theft, murder, adultery, greed, malice, deceit, lewdness, envy, slander, arrogance and folly" (Mark 7:21, NIV).*

> *"The good man brings good things out of the good stored up in his heart, and the evil man brings evil things out of the evil stored up in his heart. For the mouth speaks what the heart is full of" (Luke 6:45, NIV).*

What are you doing to develop the right type of heart in your children? Do you *punish* or *discipline* your children? There is a significant difference between the two. Punishment is punitive in nature and is designed to inflict some type of unwelcome consequence for behavior judged unacceptable by the parent. It focuses on the external conduct almost exclusively. It usually ends when the punishment is completed, with the child sorry they got caught, but no real life-lesson learned, other than to do a better job of avoiding detection next time.

Discipline is a quite different matter. It focuses on the heart of the matter, more than on the external action. There is often punishment involved, but it is only one step in the process. Think of discipline as a form of discipleship. The important part of the discipline process is to deal with the heart and to make sure that, in the end, your child has learned from the experience and your relationship with your child is enhanced, and not wounded by the experience.

Why do we so often opt for punishment rather than discipline in dealing with our children?

_____

_____

INFLUENCES ON OUR CHILDREN

> *"For He established a testimony in Jacob, and appointed a law in Israel, which He commanded our fathers, that they should teach them to their children, That the generation to come might know, even the children yet to be born, that they may arise and tell them to their children…" (Psalms 78:5-6, NASB).*

AVOIDING BECOMING A FRUSTRATING FATHER

> *"Fathers, do not embitter your children, or they will become discouraged" (Colossians 3:21, NIV).*

> *"Fathers, do not exasperate your children; instead, bring them up in the training and instruction of the Lord" (Ephesians 6:4, NIV).*

List ways you exasperate your children:

_____

_____

THE ROLE OF GRANDPARENTS

Grandparents also have a role to play when it comes to their grandchildren. If you have grandchildren, how are you interacting with them in regard to spiritual matters? Sometimes grandparents may have a more willing audience than parents when it comes to spiritual matters.

What are you doing to impact your grandchildren?

_____

_____

Our witness begins in the home.

The Next Generation Survey

The following questions are for fathers. If you are not yet a father, base your answers on the expectations and aspirations for yourself as a potential or future father. Rank your answers on a scale of "Never" (0) to "Always" (5).

1.	I discipline my children with a desire for it to be a learning experience.	0	1	2	3	4	5
2.	My children see me showing affection towards my wife.	0	1	2	3	4	5
3.	My children see and hear me praying.	0	1	2	3	4	5
4.	We have devotional family time.	0	1	2	3	4	5
5.	We eat meals together as a family at least three times a week.	0	1	2	3	4	5
6.	I admit to my children when I make a mistake.	0	1	2	3	4	5
7.	I listen to my children when they talk to me, giving them my undivided attention.	0	1	2	3	4	5
8.	I spend a quantity of quality time with my children each week.	0	1	2	3	4	5
9.	My children are not developing prejudices of others by observing me.	0	1	2	3	4	5
10.	I avoid doing things that exasperate my children.	0	1	2	3	4	5
11.	I seek out opportunities to compliment my children when they do a good job.	0	1	2	3	4	5
12.	I know the names of my children's teachers.	0	1	2	3	4	5
13.	I attend my children's sporting events and performances of various kinds.	0	1	2	3	4	5
14.	I never talk badly about my parents or in-laws in front of my children.	0	1	2	3	4	5
15.	When my children are struggling, I am right there helping them.	0	1	2	3	4	5
16.	I know the names of my children's best friends.	0	1	2	3	4	5
17.	I require my children to do chores and hold them accountable for doing them.	0	1	2	3	4	5
18.	I discuss with my children what they are learning in church.	0	1	2	3	4	5
19.	I am aware of what movies, TV, internet and video my children are watching.	0	1	2	3	4	5
20.	Our house is a welcoming place for our children to bring their friends.	0	1	2	3	4	5
21.	My wife and I are mostly in agreement regarding training our children.	0	1	2	3	4	5
22.	I do not play favorites among my children.	0	1	2	3	4	5
23.	I continue to foster a good relationship with my kids' grandparents.	0	1	2	3	4	5
24.	I feel free to be "child-like and silly" when I play with my children. I am fun!	0	1	2	3	4	5
25.	My children feel that they can talk to me about any issues they are facing.	0	1	2	3	4	5
26.	My children know that Christ plays an important role in our family's decisions.	0	1	2	3	4	5
27.	My children do not see inconsistencies between the things I say and do.	0	1	2	3	4	5

Which of the above concerned me the most? What do I need to do to improve my score?

_____

SHARE YOUR COMMITMENT WITH YOUR ACCOUNTABILITY PARTNER.

Blessing the Generations

"Bless," "blessed," and "blessing" are such familiar words, but what do they really mean?

THE AARONIC BLESSING

> *"Then the LORD spoke to Moses, saying, 'Speak to Aaron and to his sons,*
> *saying, 'Thus you shall bless the sons of Israel. You shall say to them:*
> *The LORD bless you, and keep you;*
> *The LORD make His face shine on you,*
> *And be gracious to you;*
> *The LORD lift up His countenance on you,*
> *And give you peace'" (Numbers 6:22-26, NASB).*

1. **Blessing #1: "May the LORD bless you" (Numbers 6:24).**
   a. Bless = Hebrew: *barak* = to kneel.
   b. A related word *berakhah* means to present a gift—on their level.
   c. Our blessing: "May the LORD bless you" (Numbers 6:24).
   d. What we are really saying: "May the LORD show Himself real to you."

2. **Blessing #2: "May the LORD keep you" (Numbers 6:24).**
   a. Keep = Hebrew: *shamar* = to guard, protect, keep careful watch over (i.e., put a hedge of protection around).
   b. Our blessing: "May the LORD keep you" (Numbers 6:24).
   c. What we are saying: "May the LORD put a hedge of protection around you."
   d. "...deliver US (me and others) from evil..."

3. **Blessing #3: "May the LORD make His face shine on you" (Numbers 6:25).**
   a. Face = Hebrew: *paniym* = plural word meaning faces (e.g., the many faces, attributes of God....the fullness of His presence).
   b. Our blessing: "May the LORD make His face shine on you" (Numbers 6:25).
   c. What we are really saying: "May the LORD light your life with the fullness of His glorious character."

4. **Blessing #4: "May the LORD be gracious to you" (Numbers 6:25).**
   a. Gracious = Hebrew: *channa* = God's favor, mercy and pity.
   b. Focuses on the need for God's protection.
   c. We are in danger of hell, God provides the grace for salvation.
   d. We are in danger of sin, God provides us the grace for sanctification.
   e. Our blessing: "May the LORD be gracious to you" (Numbers 6:25).
   f. What we are really saying: "May the Lord show His saving power to you."

5. **Blessing #5: "May the LORD lift up His countenance on you" (Numbers 6:26).**
   a. "...the LORD turn His face toward you..."
   b. "lift up His countenance" = Hebrew: *nasa paniym* = "lift up His faces" (plural)
   c. Pictures someone lifting up their chin when sad and disappointed, and saying "Look at me. Do you know how much I love you?"
   d. Our blessing: "May the LORD lift up His countenance on you" (Numbers 6:26).
   e. What we are really saying: "May the LORD show how pleased He is with you."

6. **Blessing #6: "May the LORD give you His peace" (Numbers 6:26).**
   a. Peace = Hebrew: *shalom* = wholeness or completion.
   b. "May you accept the wholeness and completion God provides."
   c. 1 Thessalonians 5:23 – "Now may the God of peace Himself sanctify you entirely; and may your spirit and soul and body be preserved complete, without blame at the coming of our Lord Jesus Christ."
   d. Give = Hebrew: *siym,* or sometimes *suym* = to put something or someone in its proper place (cf. Psalm 23).
   e. Our blessing: "May the LORD give you His peace" (Numbers 6:26).
   f. What we are really saying: "May the LORD bring you His wholeness."

CONCLUDING CHALLENGE

1. Make a list of people you want to bless (e.g., family, friends, etc.).
2. Pray over them and bless them.

A Generational Prayer of Blessing (Adapted from Numbers 6:24-26)

Pray this prayer over each of your children and grandchildren:

May the LORD bless you and show Himself real to you.

May the LORD keep you and put a hedge of protection around you.

May the LORD make His face shine on you and light your life with the fullness of His glorious character.

May the LORD be gracious to you and show His saving power to you.

May the LORD lift up His countenance on you and show how pleased He is with you.

May the LORD give you His peace and bring you His wholeness.

This is my prayer for you and the generations to follow. In the strong and mighty name of Jesus Christ, Our Lord and Savior.

Option B: Growing as a Young Man of God (Titus 2:6)

INTRODUCTION

Who are you today? How do those that know you see you? More importantly, who are you becoming? What do the answers to these three questions tell you? You can give lip service to the questions, but if you examine how you spend your time, the choices you make, and who you're trying to impress, the truth will start to emerge. In many ways, the current "You" is simply the accumulation of the choices you have made over your life.

While you cannot change the past, you have unlimited opportunity to start becoming the person God wants you to be. So, the logical questions are, who do you want to be, and where do you find help in charting your course? The answer is straightforward and not surprising: The Bible.

In every stage of life, we can find direction and inspiration in God's Word. The Apostle Paul gives Titus straightforward instructions to men and women, young and old, in order to teach and equip them.

<u>For Older Men</u>
"…to be temperate, dignified, sensible, sound in faith, in love, in perseverance…"
(Titus 2:2, NASB)

<u>For Older Women</u>
"…to be reverent in their behavior, not malicious gossips nor enslaved to much wine, teaching what is good…" *(Titus 2:3-4, NASB)*

<u>For Younger Women</u>
"…to love their husbands, to love their children, to be sensible, pure, workers at home, kind, being subject to their own husbands, that the word of God will not be dishonored" *(Titus 2:4-5, NASB).*

EQUIPPING YOUNG MEN

The qualities above are certainly things to recommend to each group. People with those characteristics are the people you can use to build strong families and churches. So, what should be taught to young men?

"Likewise urge the young men to be sensible; in all things show yourself to be an example of good deeds, with purity in doctrine, dignified, sound in speech which is beyond reproach, so that the opponent will be put to shame, having nothing bad to say about us" (Titus 2:6-8, NASB).

What does the Apostle Paul instruct Titus to do with young men? To *urge* them. Not simply to suggest these things or add them to a list of things to do. Rather, to clearly emphasize the need to focus on these things and apply them to their lives.

What is the first thing he is urging them to be? To be *sensible*. Being sensible means to focus oneself to give full, rational and reasonable thought to one's actions. What are things young men should be taught to embrace and be an example of?

> Doing good deeds—Pure doctrine—Being dignified—
> Sound speech—Being beyond reproach

What do the above look like when pursued and lived out in your day-to-day life?

What does the Apostle Paul say will be the effect of adopting those characteristics in a young man's life? That no one will be able to say negative things about you, and if they do, they will be put to shame by the truth of your exemplary life. Additionally, blessings come to you as set forth by Jesus in the Beatitudes:

> *"Blessed are you when people insult you and persecute you, and falsely say all kinds of evil against you because of me. Rejoice and be glad, for your reward in heaven is great; for in the same way they persecuted the prophets who were before you" (Matthew 5:11-12, NASB).*

THE CHALLENGES OF YOUTH

Life is full of transitions. The level of your maturity at each stage of life reflects how well you make difficult choices and transitions. Sometimes you chose the Lord's way and other times your own way. Choosing the Lord's way is a challenge for many youth (and to be honest, older people too). Proverbs provides wisdom in addressing many of life's challenges:

> *"The glory of young men is their strength, and the honor of old men is their gray hair" (Proverbs 20:29, NASB).*

What are some of the strengths we think young men should utilize in effective service for the Lord?

> Physical strength—Purpose—Endurance—Passion—Vision—Enthusiasm—Conviction

When properly managed, how can each of the above be powerful tools for serving the Lord?

The Bible is full of stories of young men used mightily by God. Which of the young men below do you especially admire, and how can you apply their lessons to your own walk?

1. Young David, the Shepherd (1 Samuel 17)
2. Young Gideon, the Judge of Israel (Judges 6-8)
3. Young Jeremiah, the Prophet (Jeremiah 1)
4. Young John, the Apostle (John 19:25-27)
5. Young Timothy, the Missionary-Pastor (1 Timothy 4:12)
6. Young Titus, the Missionary (Titus 2:7-8)

Young men can allow reckless emotions to get them in all sorts of trouble. You have the twin challenges of hormones and the fact that the frontal cortex (which controls impulse control) is not yet fully developed. This means you have to be deliberate and thoughtful in your decisions. The first thought you have on how to handle a situation may not be your best thought. Reflection and deliberation are tools you need to learn to employ.

What can we learn from Solomon's words regarding youthful lusts?

> *"Rejoice, young man, during your childhood, and let your heart be pleasant during the days of young manhood. And follow the impulses of your heart and the desires of your eyes. Yet know that God will bring you to judgment for all these things. So, remove vexation from your heart and put away pain from your body, because childhood and the prime of life are fleeting"*
> *(Ecclesiastes 11:9-10, NASB).*

Solomon is saying to enjoy youth, but to be aware that choices made are not without consequences, so consider them carefully. The consequences of decisions made today follow you throughout life.

> *"…vigorous young men stumble badly…" (Isaiah 40:30, NASB).*

The Apostle Paul understands the competing impulses that accompany youth, and he warns young Timothy to be on guard. Timothy was dedicated to the Lord and Paul had tremendous trust and faith in him, but he still felt compelled to remind Timothy.

> *"Now flee from youthful lusts and pursue righteousness, faith, love and peace, with those who call on the Lord from a pure heart" (2 Timothy 2:22, NASB).*

A YOUNG MAN'S NEEDS

Ask yourself: "What kind of character am I developing in my life? Is my character firmly anchored in Biblical truths, or is it based on a shallow pool of me, myself and I?" The following are the two basic needs every young man should learn to embrace:

Need #1: To Flee Foolish Passions

Young men need to flee from being impulsive and reckless. The essence of maturity is the ability to delay gratification (i.e., to wait), and to weigh the consequences before we commit the act. It is not always a matter of *delaying* gratification, but also saying "no" to certain gratifications that will *never* honor the Lord. Keep in mind, it is not only what we *avoid*, but also what we *pursue* in life that defines us.

Young men need to flee from being overly confident. There's an old expression that says "do not have your mouth write checks that you have no intention or ability to have cashed."

Simon Peter was often an example of misplaced braggadocio:

> *"Lord, with You I am ready to go both to prison and to death! I say to you, Peter, the cock will not crow today until you have denied three times that you know Me"* (Luke 22:34, NASB).

Young men need to flee from major swings in attitude and behavior. Emotions are fine when they are under control. However, when unrestrained, they often lead to trouble. Emotions can betray us at every turn. Always stop and ask yourself where your emotions are coming from. Do you truly understand the facts and circumstances, and are your emotions operating in a way that is rational? Many times, turning and walking away is the best course of action. Learning how to de-accelerate emotionally charged situations will reap many benefits.

> *"A gentle answer turns away wrath, but a harsh word stirs up anger"* (Proverbs 15:1, NASB).

Young men need to flee from being naïve. No one is more confident at times than a young man who lacks both knowledge and experience and is still ready to charge headfirst into the hornets' nest. You can save yourselves a lot of heartache by admitting what you don't know. You need to consider the sources you are drawing your view of the world from.

> *"There is a way that appears to be right, but in the end it leads to death"* (Proverbs 14:12, NASB).

> *"And I saw among the naïve, and discerned among the youths a young man lacking sense…"* (Proverbs 7:7, NASB).

Note: Naïve = Hebrew: *pethi* = naïve, open-minded, which is not the same as being fair-minded, but rather empty-headed.

> *"The naïve believes everything, but the sensible man considers his steps"* (Proverbs 14:15, NASB).

> *"The prudent sees the evil and hides himself, but the naïve go on, and are punished for it"* (Proverbs 22:3, NASB).

> *"A prudent man sees evil and hides himself, the naïve proceed and pay the penalty…"* (Proverbs 27:12, NASB).

> *"The naïve inherit foolishness, but the sensible are crowned with knowledge"* (Proverbs 14:18, NASB).

The poster child for naïve behavior in youth is the younger son in the parable of the Prodigal

Son (Luke 15). In what way was he naïve in the choices he made?

Need #2: To Pursue Godly Wisdom

As we saw from the instructions to young men in Titus, it is key to be sensible in our actions. The phrase "to be sensible" (Greek "*sophroneo*") means to act wisely, to be sober-minded, to use common sense, to be of right mind, to be prudent. The word for prudent in Hebrew is "*ormah*," which means, "to strip, to make naked, to peel off the layers of a problem, to get to the core issue." This is the opposite of going off emotionally half-cocked.

> *"The prudent sees the evil and hides himself but the naïve go on, and are punished for it" (Proverbs 22:3, NASB).*

> *"The naïve inherit foolishness, but the sensible are crowned with knowledge" (Proverbs 14:18, NASB).*

Here are some truths about prudence and the role it plays in maturing and becoming the man the Lord wants you to be:

1. Prudence is a comprehensive quality that overrules the weakness of your youth.
2. Prudence is an all-encompassing attribute to make you a spiritually fit young man.
3. Prudence is a lifelong pursuit that will help you become a spiritually fit older man.

David was considered a prudent man, "a mighty man of valor, one prudent in speech…and the Lord was with him…" (1 Samuel 16:18).

WHERE DO YOUNG MEN LEARN TO BE SENSIBLE?

Young men learn to be sensible from the Word of God. If you anchor your attitudes, convictions, conduct and desires in the Word of God you are on the right path to being sensible and prudent. Sometimes the Book of Proverbs is referred to as "The Young Man's Guidebook to Right Living."

> *"How can a young man keep his way pure? By keeping it according to your Word" (Psalm 119:9, NASB).*

The New Testament contains a tremendous amount of rich advice, much of which can be found in the Book of James. In fact, spending a month reading Proverbs and James is an extremely beneficial exercise. Read both of these books and as you do, write down how it speaks to you as a young man. You will be amazed at the insights.

> *"…if any of you lacks wisdom, let him ask of God, who gives to all generously and without reproach, and it will be given to him" (James 1:5, NASB).*

Young men learn to be sensible from the *people* of God (Role models, mentors and accountability partners). Role models, mentors and accountability partners are necessary components of a thriving Christian walk. It starts with parents. They are the most impactful and important role models, for good or bad.

> *"Hear, my son, your father's instruction and do not forsake your mother's teaching; Indeed, they are a graceful wreath to your head and ornaments about your neck" (Proverbs 1:8-9, NASB).*

Remember the words of the Apostle Paul to Timothy: "Likewise urge (Greek: *parakaleo* = exhort, encourage, come alongside to help) the young men to be sensible..." This is the idea of mentoring. The older men (more mature in the faith) are directed to mentor the younger men. This instruction should cause you to ask some important questions: Who do I consider a mentor? Who am I allowing to disciple me; building his wisdom and experience into me? Who am I mentoring? Who is younger in the faith than me, that I can provide godly wisdom to from my own experiences? Sometimes it is the challenge of mentoring brings about more growth than even being mentored by someone else. Remember:

God wants to mold the young men in our midst.
He is recruiting all of us to be a part of His training program.

> *"...in all things show yourself to be an example of good deeds, with purity in doctrine, dignified, sound in speech which is beyond reproach, so that the opponent will be put to shame, having nothing bad to say about us"*
> *(Titus 2:7-8, NASB).*

> *"Iron sharpens iron, so one man sharpens another" (Proverbs 27:17, NASB).*

When God alludes to us as an army, He is not speaking as metaphorically as we might want to believe. John Wesley captured this truth when he declared that if he had a hundred men who fear nothing but sin and desire nothing but God, he could change the world.

There is a three-legged stool when it comes to these positive influences in your life. The first two legs are role models and mentors, but they don't do the complete job. The third leg is an accountability partner. An accountability partner is the person you let into your life, talking about the things you won't share, except in the safest of relationships (For additional information on the value and importance of accountability please see Appendix C).

> *"Therefore, confess your sins to one another and pray for one another, that you may be healed. The prayer of a righteous person has great power as it is working" (James 5:16, NASB).*

> *"Two are better than one, because they have a good reward for their toil. For if they fall, one will lift up his fellow. But woe to him who is alone when he falls and*

has not another to lift him up! Again, if two lie together, they keep warm, but how can one keep warm alone" (Ecclesiastes 4:9-11, NASB)?

"Bear one another's burdens, and so fulfill the law of Christ"
(Galatians 6:2, NASB).

Prayer of Dedication

"Heavenly Father, give us young men who are sensible, prudent, holy and pure, who are men of the Word and men of integrity and who are mighty in Spirit and champions for the Lord. We dedicate these young men to You. We dedicate ourselves to You as the older men in these young men's lives. Give us the wisdom to teach Your ways to them and to live our faith before them. In the strong and mighty Name of our Lord and Savior Jesus Christ. Amen."

Note: This class is an excellent opportunity for you as a young man to square up your life and put it on a course towards maturity God desires. The process of preparing your My Life Focus (Appendix D) can be an absolute watershed moment in your life. Take the questions seriously. Create a workable plan and be deliberate in its implementation. It is the formula for a life of contentment rather than a life of regret.

Small Group Discussion

1. Get into groups of no more than five men.
2. Pick a leader to facilitate discussion and make sure everyone participates.
3. You have 15 minutes.
4. Topic: Becoming a Young Man of God.
5. Discussion questions:
   a. What are three things you can do to be more sensible and prudent in your interactions on a daily basis?
   b. Name a person you consider a good role model. Have you told them?
   c. Name a person you consider a mentor. How can you deepen this relationship?
   d. Is there a younger man around you that you can serve as a mentor?
   e. What steps can you take to keep accountability an active part of your life after Men in Action is over?

SESSION 8
My Work, My Mission

SESSION 8
My Work, My Mission

Class discussion
The content below will be discussed during class. If you miss class this week you are required to read them on your own time, prior to next week's class.

Application from the last session
Pick one thing you learned from the last session you can apply in your life as either an action item or a truth you should embrace.

_____

_____

Before class
____ Continued your Solo Initiative
____ Read the Bible at least four times this week
____ Prepared My Life Focus (end of last week's materials)
____ Reviewed and rated the Case Studies (see class materials below)
____ Attended church (Sermon topic: _____)
____ Met with my Accountability Partner

Bible reading

Date	Book/Chapters	At least one thought from what you read

Accountability checklist

___ Asked accountability questions ___ Discussed what you are learning in class	___ Discussed Solo Initiative ___ Prayed

My prayer request:
Accountability partner's prayer request:
Time/Place of next meeting:

(Have you attended a men's event or done a service project yet?)

At the beginning of class

- Put on your nametag (Right side)
- Pick-up your envelope if you turned in forms last week (Re-file forms in your manual).
- Drop off envelope if you are turning in any new forms.
- Get into prayer groups (Pray with different men each week).

Class schedule

- 20 minutes: Small group prayer
- 10 minutes: Attendance and announcements (e.g., missing chair, service projects)
- 20 minutes: Share testimonies
- 30 minutes: Discuss "Selecting a Meaningful Career"
- 10 minutes: Break
- 20 minutes: Discuss "Employing a Person: The Five C's of Effective Recruiting"
- 15 minutes: Small Group Discussion
- 20 minutes: Discuss "The Art and Science of Delegation"
- 5 minutes: Review next week's assignments

Weekly prayer requests

Name	Request
Yours	

Calling a missing chair
"…You will be missed because your seat will be empty" (1 Samuel 20:18).

Missing Chair:	
Phone Number:	Email:
Contacted:	Status:

Testimonies

Name	Application

Teaching goal
That men understand there is no curtain that separates their work-life from the rest of their walk as a Christian. Their witness in the workplace is as key as it is anywhere else.

Selecting a Meaningful Career

While a necessity, work should be more than simply a way to prevent homelessness and starvation. As Christians, we are called to adopt a Kingdom view of work. While serving the employer is an important and legitimate part of your mission, the Christian's mission at work includes an attitude that leads to a more important and fulfilling work experience. Understanding and adopting this attitude leads to a more important and fulfilling work experience. Work is not the result of the sinful fall of man, but pre-existed the fall:

> *"Then the Lord God took the man and put him into the Garden of Eden to cultivate it and keep" (Genesis 2:15, NASB).*

In creating all things "good", God assigned man to work from the beginning. It was not until sin entered the Garden that work became hard.

> *"Cursed is the ground because of you; in toil you will eat of it all the days of your life" (Genesis 3:17b, NASB).*

In many ways, work became a chore rather than a natural pleasure. However, we should remember everything in existence is because God worked for six days. In fact, as Jesus told the Jews, God *continues* to work.

> *"…My Father is always at his work to this very day, and I too, am working."* (John 5:16, NIV).

If work is something God values and engages in Himself, we should embrace it as something we are *allowed* to do rather than something we are *forced* to do. Just because work was impacted by the curse does not mean work is a bad thing. In fact, the Bible tells us quite the opposite. The Bible is full of principles about work.

1. **Principle #1:** Work as if the Lord is your immediate supervisor.

   > *"Whatever you do, work at it with all your heart, as working for the Lord, not for human masters" (Colossians 3:23, NIV).*

2. **Principle #2:** Work is a necessity to meet one's daily needs.

   > *"For even when we were with you, we gave you this rule: 'The one who is unwilling to work shall not eat'" (2 Thessalonians 3:10, NIV).*

   > *"Anyone who does not provide for their relatives, and especially for their own household, has denied the faith and is worse than an unbeliever"* (1 Timothy 5:8, NIV).

3. **Principle #3:** Your work is part of your witness to others on behalf of the Lord.

    "In the same way, let your light shine before others, that they may see your good deeds and glorify your Father in heaven" (Matthew 5:16, NIV).

    "…and to make it your ambition to lead a quiet life: You should mind your own business and work with your hands, just as we told you, so that your daily life may win the respect of outsiders and so that you will not be dependent on anybody" (1 Thessalonians 4:11-12, NIV).

    "For we are God's handiwork, created in Christ Jesus to do good works, which God prepared in advance for us to do" (Ephesians 2:10, NIV).

4. **Principle #4:** Honesty in one's labors is the calling card of the Christian.

    "Whoever can be trusted with very little can also be trusted with much, and whoever is dishonest with very little will also be dishonest with much" (Luke 16:10, NIV).

    "One who is slack in his work is the brother to one that destroys" (Proverbs 18:9, NIV).

5. **Principle #5:** Seek work that is enjoyable, fulfilling, and allows you to serve the Lord.

    "A person can do nothing better than to eat and drink and find satisfaction in their own toil. This, too, I see is from the Hand of God, for without him, who can eat or find enjoyment? To the person who pleases him, God gives wisdom, knowledge and happiness, but to the sinner he gives the task of gathering and storing up wealth to hand it over to the one who pleases God. This too is meaningless, a chasing after the wind" (Ecclesiastes 2:24-26, NIV).

    "So I saw that there is nothing better for a person than to enjoy their work, because that is their lot. For who can bring him to see what will happen after them?" (Ecclesiastes 3:22, NIV)

List the usual reasons why one seeks employment.

_____

_____

How does your witness influence your work?

_____

_____

What skills/aptitude do you have that relate to job performance?

_____

_____

What type of job tasks do you enjoy doing?

_____

_____

What experience and education do you have that relate to employment?

_____

_____

Given your skills, area of enjoyment, education, and experience, what type of work is the best fit for you?

_____

_____

What work are you currently doing, and how does it relate to your answer above?

_____

_____

If your current work does not line up with your best employment fit, suggest some ways to move from where you are to where you are better suited.

_____

_____

You should view your workplace as a place to display your witness. Being directly verbal about your faith is limited in many jobs these days. However, our witness goes well beyond just what we say. It also has to do with how we are viewed by others through our _actions_.

Ask yourself this question: "If my co-workers were asked to describe me using ten adjectives, how many of them would be related to the list of the Fruit of the Spirit?" That is the real test of a faithful witness: love, joy, peace, patience, kindness, goodness, faithfulness, gentleness, and self-control.

Employing a Person: The Five C's of Effective Recruiting

You must select (or hire) someone for a position of responsibility. What are the standards they must meet to stay in that position? These five questions also work well when evaluating someone you intend to follow.

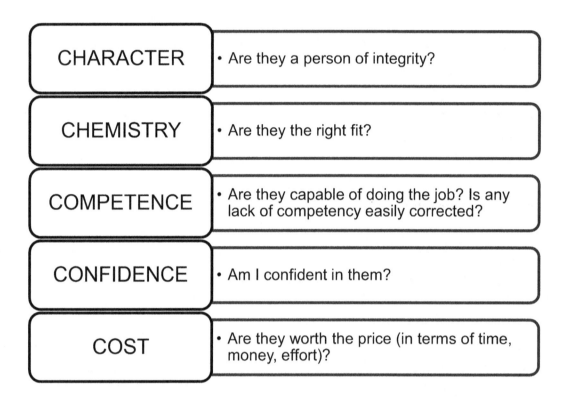

CHARACTER	• Are they a person of integrity?
CHEMISTRY	• Are they the right fit?
COMPETENCE	• Are they capable of doing the job? Is any lack of competency easily corrected?
CONFIDENCE	• Am I confident in them?
COST	• Are they worth the price (in terms of time, money, effort)?

Small Group Discussion

1. Get into groups of no more than five men.
2. Pick a leader to facilitate discussion and make sure everyone participates.
3. You have 15 minutes.
4. Topic: Developing a meaningful career.
5. Discussion question
    a. How do you select an occupation and a place to work? What are your goals for your career?
    b. Which of the Five C's of Effective Recruiting is the highest priority?

The Art and Science of Delegation

THE ART OF DELEGATION: A BIBLICALLY SUPPORTED MANAGEMENT TOOL

Delegation is an important management skill that requires constant development. It is more than the art of recruiting and wooing willing workers. It is the science of utilizing effective principles that are transferrable, measurable, and repeatable.

Delegation is also Biblical. The Bible emphasizes that people cannot do all the work themselves. A leader makes himself more effective through delegation. In Exodus 18, Moses was rebuked for not delegating. Jesus had many followers and a handpicked set of disciples. The Apostle Paul delegated all the time as evidenced by what we find in his letters. Pastors are not to do all the work, but rather equip God's *people* to do the work.

DUMPING VS. DELEGATING

Delegating is not code for "making your problem someone else's problem." There is a difference between dumping work and properly delegating work. In dumping, you drop work on another without proper training, oversight, or support. The attitude is that it is no longer *my* concern, but now it is *their* concern.

Delegation involves making sure the person being delegated to has the proper training, tools, and understanding to do the job, and to do it well. The person doing the delegation keeps an open door for questions and continues any necessary oversight, with the attitude being that I am still responsible for what I have delegated.

"Delegating work works, provided the one delegating works too" (Robert Half).

EFFECTIVE VS. INEFFECTIVE DELEGATION

Delegation is not simply about reducing your workload. It is about creating a multitude of positive outcomes. One outcome is freeing up your time so you can dedicate yourself to the tasks you need to do. Proper delegation saves time, develops people, grooms' successors, motivates, empowers, equips others, and in the end makes the whole team more effective. It also helps you clarify and refine your own priorities and tasks.

Ineffective delegation causes frustration, de-motivates, confuses, prevents tasks from being completed, discourages, and causes the organization to be dependent on new people from the outside (because you have not developed talent internally). Often those delegated to are unclear on not only *how to do* what they have been assigned, but also *what* they have been asked to do, and *why* they have been asked to do it.

Too often, the person in charge is unwilling to delegate because they do not want to release any of their authority and want all the credit when things go well. This also enables the ineffective delegator to lay the blame on someone else if it does not go well.

"No person will make a great businessman who wants to do it all himself or get all the credit" (Andrew Carnegie).

THE TEN STEPS OF SUCCESSFUL DELEGATION

1. **Identify the task**
   a. Start by defining the task. What are you wanting to accomplish? What is the outcome you seek?
   b. Confirm in your own mind that the task is appropriate to be delegated. Remember to ask yourself if those you report to would approve of you delegating this particular assignment. You are not passing the buck, but rather sharing the workload.

2. **Clarify the task**
   a. Be clear about what exactly you are asking to be done. Think it all through (Who? What? Where? When? How? Why?).
   b. Be clear. Be concise. If you do not have a handle on these tasks, you run the risk the job will not be completed or completed satisfactorily.

3. **Select the individual or team**
   a. Do you have a qualified individual or individuals to handle the assignment?
   b. What are your reasons for delegating? Is the individual/team being assigned because of their expertise, or because it is more of a training exercise? The reasons will help determine the level of involvement from you.
   c. Ask yourself about the benefits and risks associated with your choice.

4. **Assess ability and training needs**
   a. What is the skill-set of the person or persons being assigned the task?
   b. What additional training or resources need to be provided in order to achieve the desired outcome?
   c. When workers believe their efforts result in their ongoing development (of skills, responsibilities, etc.), they are more inclined to stay instead of leaving for another opportunity.

5. **Explain the reasons for delegation**
   a. Help them understand why the job is being assigned, both from your perspective as well as theirs.
   b. They need to understand why they are being asked to do the work rather than you. Explain why the work is important and its relevance to the bigger picture.
   c. Be clear on the authority being given to complete the delegated task.

6. **State the expected results**
   a. Nothing is as important as being clear on this step. Be clear on what success looks like. What do you want, and what do you expect?

b. If details are important in completing the work, be clear on these details. How will everyone know it has been successfully completed?

c. Be sure to encourage questions, and that your answers are clear.

7. **Assess the resources required to complete the work**

a. The first resource to consider is whether the person being delegated to has the time necessary to take on the assignment. It may require rearranging their workload and priorities.

b. What materials, workforce requirements, and financial support will be necessary for the person or team to be successful?

c. Where do they go to obtain necessary resources?

8. **Work out a time schedule with mileposts in advance**

a. Figure out when the task must be completed, and then work backwards, identifying the points at which progress should be assessed.

b. With more complex tasks, mileposts should be established along the way so you can evaluate how things are going and make adjustments when necessary.

c. Methods of checking and controlling must be clearly stated and understood by the other person, or this monitoring will seem like interference or lack of trust.

9. **Communicate often and provide support when necessary**

a. Set up a means of reporting that works for everyone involved.

b. Agree on how and when you will communicate (phone, email, memo, face-to-face, etc.), and always remember that communication is a two-way street. You not only need to be informed, but the person you have delegated to needs to be able to receive timely answers to inquiries made.

10. **Give feedback during the process and on the final results**

a. Do not be like the husband who said, "I told you I loved you on the day we were married and if anything changes I will let you know." Let the person know how they are doing along the way and whether they have achieved the expected goals at the end of the project. If not, review with them why things did not go according to plan, and deal with the issues together.

Remember, this effort is both a team-building exercise and an effort to develop leaders for the future. A good supervisor is always training those who can step up and do their job (or a similar job) in the future.

> *"You can delegate authority, but you can never delegate responsibility for delegating a task to someone else. If you picked the right man, fine, but if you picked the wrong man, the responsibility is yours – not his" (Richard Kravfe).*

> *"The best executive is the one who has sense enough to pick good men to do what he wants done, and self-restraint enough to keep from meddling with them while they do it" (Theodore Roosevelt).*

The goal is the successful completion of the delegated task. However, sometimes the result is less than optimal. Much can be learned from failure, provided that the failure was not due to lack of effort. So make sure to always debrief. Create an atmosphere where fear of failure is not something to be avoided.

Building a Life Focus Statement

Your teacher will provide any materials for the My Life Focus exercise.

SESSION 9
Understanding
My Spiritual Gifts

Effective leaders are self-educators.

SESSION 9
Understanding My Spiritual Gifts

Class discussion

The content below will be discussed during class. If you miss class this week, you are required to read them on your own time, prior to next week's class.

Application from the last session

Pick one thing you learned from the last session you can apply in your life as either an action item or a truth you should embrace.

_____

_____

Before class

____ Reviewed the names of your fellow MIAs
____ Continued your Solo Initiative
____ Read the Bible at least four times this week
____ My Life Focus: Completed tasks 11-14 (Appendix D)
____ Completed the 1st Spiritual Gift Survey (See session materials)
____ Your wife (or if you do not have a wife, a person who knows you well) completed the 2nd Spiritual Gift Survey
____ Attended church (Sermon topic: _____)
____ Met with my Accountability Partner

Bible reading

Date	Book/Chapters	At least one thought from what you read

Accountability checklist

___ Asked accountability questions	___ Discussed Solo Initiative
___ Discussed what you are learning in class	___ Prayed

My prayer request:
Accountability partner's prayer request:
Time/Place of next meeting:

(Have you attended a men's event or done a service project yet?)

At the beginning of class

- Put on your name tag (Right side)
- Pick up your envelope if you turned in forms last week (Re-file forms in your manual)
- Drop off envelope if you are turning in any new forms
- Join a prayer group (3-4 men), praying with different men each week

Class schedule

- 20 minutes: Small group prayer
- 10 minutes: Attendance & announcements (e.g., missing chair, service projects)
- 20 minutes: Share testimonies
- 40 minutes: Teach and discuss "Regarding Spiritual Gifts"
- 10 minutes: Break
- 35 minutes: Complete Spiritual Gifts Exercise
- 10 minutes: Discuss "My Life Focus"
- 5 minutes: Go over next week's assignment

Weekly prayer requests

Name	Request
Yours	

Calling a missing chair
"…You will be missed because your seat will be empty" (1 Samuel 20:18).

Missing chair:	
Phone number:	Email:
Contacted:	Status:

Testimonies

Name	Application

Teaching goal
That men would understand God has equipped them to serve and begin to explore how they use their gifting to serve as part of the Body of Christ.

Spiritual Gifts Survey: Instruction Sheet

The goal of this survey is to see how the various gifts work in concert to empower the church to collectively minister to the needs of those in the body.

This survey evaluates nine of the more common spiritual gifts. The survey is useful for class discussion and personal evaluation. The list of spiritual gifts in this exercise is not an exhaustive list of all potential spiritual gifts (The Bible itself is not clear that there is some finite list).

The survey consists of several statements about ideas, attitudes and behaviors that may or may not be true about you. Each statement should be evaluated as to how representative it is of you.

Scoring is on a 7-point scale. Giving yourself a "1" means the statement fits you perfectly. Giving yourself a "4" means the statement is correct about as often as it is incorrect. A score of "7" means the statement does not describe you at all. Scores of 2, 3, 5, and 6 are just gradations, meaning the statement is more or less true. Be careful not to start scoring a "4" for everything because you cannot decide.

There is no right or wrong answer to any of the questions. In each instance, assign your score in terms of what your opinion is *now*. The answers are a personal description of you, not someone you aspire to be. If you feel you are good at something, score yourself accordingly. It may be hard to give yourself a "1" when the question is "I am a very humble, self-effacing person in my interactions with others," but if it is true, then give it a score of "1".

Respond without over-thinking the questions. Your first impression is usually your best impression. This inventory is designed to give you a general idea of what your spiritual gifts are. You may find you have one dominant gift and a couple of subordinate gifts.

You have two copies of the Spiritual Gifts Survey. Use one copy and complete the survey yourself. Give the second copy to your wife (or a friend) and have them complete the survey with you as the subject. Do not look at each other's scores until you both have completed the survey.

Once both of you have completed the survey, write your respective scores for each question on the Spiritual Gifts Assessment Scoring document. There are ten questions for each of the nine gifts used in the survey (Administration, Teaching, Exhortation, Faith, Giving, Leadership, Mercy, Prophecy and Serving/Helps).

For another free spiritual gift survey go to: *www.gifts.churchgrowth.org*.

Spiritual Gifts Survey (Your Questions)

		Often True		Sometimes True			Rarely True	
1.	I am by nature a careful steward of my resources.	1	2	3	4	5	6	7
2.	When others are having discomfort I suffer with them.	1	2	3	4	5	6	7
3.	When people say that something cannot be done or is impossible, I feel the burden to believe it and trust God for it.	1	2	3	4	5	6	7
4.	My main desire in communicating God's Word is to get people to humble themselves before God.	1	2	3	4	5	6	7
5.	I desire that the people I am teaching experience the truth to the extent that I have in my own personal study.	1	2	3	4	5	6	7
6.	Advice and/or decisions I have given stand as the final decision of a group.	1	2	3	4	5	6	7
7.	I have a good record of achieving my set goals.	1	2	3	4	5	6	7
8.	I enjoy managing programs more than people.	1	2	3	4	5	6	7
9.	When I see a need I feel an immediate obligation to meet it.	1	2	3	4	5	6	7
10.	I always feel compelled to prescribe a step by step plan of action for the solution of problems.	1	2	3	4	5	6	7
11.	I believe God uses me as a channel of His resources.	1	2	3	4	5	6	7
12.	I tend to enjoy the process more than the results in a plan of action.	1	2	3	4	5	6	7
13.	One result that I look for in presenting God's truth is true repentance.	1	2	3	4	5	6	7
14.	I identify with people and their problems to the degree that I am sometimes affected by them personally.	1	2	3	4	5	6	7
15.	When I communicate the Word of God, I consistently look for ways to illustrate truth.	1	2	3	4	5	6	7
16.	I enjoy associating with those who display a definite direction in their life.	1	2	3	4	5	6	7
17.	I concentrate more on doing practical things that need to be done rather than on why they should be done.	1	2	3	4	5	6	7
18.	I have discovered that I do not have to wait for clear evidence and confirmation before making a decision.	1	2	3	4	5	6	7
19.	I feel that I am able to trust God in difficult circumstances without hesitation or indecision.	1	2	3	4	5	6	7
20	I find it relatively easy and enjoyable to spend much time in intense study and research of the Bible.	1	2	3	4	5	6	7
21.	I find myself setting goals and objectives for myself and my ministry as a believer.	1	2	3	4	5	6	7
22.	I usually have a great deal of joy in just "doing things" that need to be done no matter how small or trivial the task.	1	2	3	4	5	6	7
23.	I am able to motivate people to establish spiritual goals.	1	2	3	4	5	6	7

		Often True		Sometimes True			Rarely True	
24.	I would rather provide the necessary materials needed than perform some manual task.	1	2	3	4	5	6	7
25.	I am gripped by the awesomeness of the message I am proclaiming.	1	2	3	4	5	6	7
26.	I like to see others organized.	1	2	3	4	5	6	7
27.	People regularly express their appreciation of my presence when they are undergoing extreme difficulty.	1	2	3	4	5	6	7
28.	When sharing with people, I have a special sensitivity as to what to say or what not to say.	1	2	3	4	5	6	7
29.	I would rather deal with someone having problems personally, instead of sending them to someone else for help.	1	2	3	4	5	6	7
30.	The successful operation of an activity gives me great satisfaction.	1	2	3	4	5	6	7
31.	I feel a burden to encourage people to trust God when I see them defeated and discouraged.	1	2	3	4	5	6	7
32.	I would rather do a particular task than spend time counseling with people.	1	2	3	4	5	6	7
33.	I love to prove and answer Biblical issues and questions.	1	2	3	4	5	6	7
34.	I am irritated about wrong practices or doctrinal error whenever I sense it.	1	2	3	4	5	6	7
35.	When I hear of someone in need, I immediately think of offering material assistance.	1	2	3	4	5	6	7
36.	When someone is not doing a job well, I am concerned about making him effective in what he is doing.	1	2	3	4	5	6	7
37.	I would rather show someone else how to do a task than do it myself.	1	2	3	4	5	6	7
38.	I find myself responding immediately to financial needs by sharing my resources without a great deal of planning to do so.	1	2	3	4	5	6	7
39.	I like to help people personally regardless of their character or point of view.	1	2	3	4	5	6	7
40.	I find that it is not necessary for me to have a 'job description" when I am asked to do a particular task.	1	2	3	4	5	6	7
41.	People express to me how much I have helped or encouraged them in time of need.	1	2	3	4	5	6	7
42.	I believe I have a pioneering spirit and am not easily discouraged.	1	2	3	4	5	6	7
43.	I find that I see past the surface of an activity to the broader picture of details and results.	1	2	3	4	5	6	7
44.	When I hear a question or problem, I am anxious to both find and give a Biblical answer.	1	2	3	4	5	6	7
45.	When I speak God's Word I feel compelled to call for commitment from my audience.	1	2	3	4	5	6	7
46.	When I give money to someone for something, I desire to avoid letting anyone know what I did.	1	2	3	4	5	6	7

		Often True		Sometimes True			Rarely True	
47.	People often say to me that I have an ability to explain difficult Biblical passages to them usually giving scriptural reasons.	1	2	3	4	5	6	7
48.	Other believers share with me that I have the ability to communicate God's Word with great boldness and conviction.	1	2	3	4	5	6	7
49.	When I am confronted by an obstacle, I tend to see it in terms of God's resources instead of my own resources.	1	2	3	4	5	6	7
50.	I think of creative ways to minister and help those who are suffering.	1	2	3	4	5	6	7
51.	I easily spot weaknesses and strengths in organizational planning.	1	2	3	4	5	6	7
52.	I feel a special burden to relieve others of their duties in order to free them to do their most important work.	1	2	3	4	5	6	7
53.	I sense a great deal of identification with people having personal and emotional problems, but I am not weighed down by these.	1	2	3	4	5	6	7
54.	In a group situation when tension turns to stress, I am the one who is looked to for direction.	1	2	3	4	5	6	7
55.	I find myself wanting time to be budgeted properly.	1	2	3	4	5	6	7
56.	When I hear of someone who needs help, I immediately offer my services if it is possible.	1	2	3	4	5	6	7
57.	I am able to give directions to others and make decisions for them, which involves persuading them to my way of thinking.	1	2	3	4	5	6	7
58.	I have a desire to persuade others to move toward achieving group objectives.	1	2	3	4	5	6	7
59.	I get really excited when I see a worthwhile project that I can underwrite, counting it a great honor and privilege.	1	2	3	4	5	6	7
60.	I would rather explain the meaning of a word than simply share a verse by quoting it to someone.	1	2	3	4	5	6	7
61.	I feel the urgency to communicate the message of God zealously.	1	2	3	4	5	6	7
62.	When confronted with an opportunity to advance God's work, I feel compelled to seize it without hesitating.	1	2	3	4	5	6	7
63.	I find that when visiting those who are suffering it brings me joy rather than depressing me.	1	2	3	4	5	6	7
64.	I have an effective prayer ministry in my life with many wonderful answers to prayer that from a human point of view seem impossible or unlikely.	1	2	3	4	5	6	7
65.	I have a strong sense of compassion toward needy people.	1	2	3	4	5	6	7
66.	I find myself constantly thinking of decisions that need to be made in giving overall direction to a group or organization.	1	2	3	4	5	6	7
67.	I see myself more in a supportive role to others than in public ministry.	1	2	3	4	5	6	7
68.	When someone shares a problem with me, I am able to help them from the Word of God and motivate them to act on it.	1	2	3	4	5	6	7

		Often True		Sometimes True			Rarely True	
69.	I am so confident that God will meet my needs that I give to Him sacrificially and consistently.	1	2	3	4	5	6	7
70.	When I discover Biblical truth, I automatically begin to think of ways that it could be presented in an intelligible and interesting way.	1	2	3	4	5	6	7
71.	I have proclaimed God's truth in a way that goes against the majority opinion.	1	2	3	4	5	6	7
72.	I enjoy management as it relates to working closely with people.	1	2	3	4	5	6	7
73.	I have influenced others to accomplish a particular task or Biblical purpose.	1	2	3	4	5	6	7
74.	I have the ability to visualize circumstance and solutions that other believers cannot see.	1	2	3	4	5	6	7
75.	I am anxious to discover those who are suffering or bereaved.	1	2	3	4	5	6	7
76.	I find it easy to move from a discussion of things in general to a discussion of spiritual things.	1	2	3	4	5	6	7
77.	I find that I refer to the Word of God when I minister to others, I resort much more to the Word of God than my personal experiences.	1	2	3	4	5	6	7
78.	People seem to depend upon me to decide the process by which groups carry out their work.	1	2	3	4	5	6	7
79.	I am more satisfied with how a person has been helped by what I did than by simply doing the job needed.	1	2	3	4	5	6	7
80.	I have been willing to maintain a lower standard of living in order to benefit God's work.	1	2	3	4	5	6	7
81.	I enjoy imparting scriptural principles to others.	1	2	3	4	5	6	7
82.	I enjoy organizing ideas, people, resources, and time for more effective ministry.	1	2	3	4	5	6	7
83.	I find it easy to convey truth to others.	1	2	3	4	5	6	7
84.	I find it easy to lend or give things away.	1	2	3	4	5	6	7
85.	I enjoy talking to people about their spiritual development.	1	2	3	4	5	6	7
86.	People express confidence in goals that I have set.	1	2	3	4	5	6	7
87.	People with problems seem to beat a path to my doorstep.	1	2	3	4	5	6	7
88.	I have felt compelled to warn people of the impending consequences of sin.	1	2	3	4	5	6	7
89.	People often express to me that I minister to them through my helpful spirit.	1	2	3	4	5	6	7
90.	Other people are often challenged by my ability to trust God.	1	2	3	4	5	6	7

Before totaling your scores, list the order you would *expect* your gifts to manifest, where "1" is most likely, and "9" is least likely.

	Gift	Rank Order
1.	Administration	
2.	Teaching	
3.	Exhortation	
4.	Faith	
5.	Giving	
6.	Leadership	
7.	Mercy	
8.	Prophecy	
9.	Serving/Helps	

Disclaimer: This survey was adapted from a variety of unknown sources.

Spiritual Gifts Survey (Spouse/Other)

		Often True		Sometimes True			Rarely True	
1.	I am by nature a careful steward of my resources.	1	2	3	4	5	6	7
2.	When others are having discomfort I suffer with them.	1	2	3	4	5	6	7
3.	When people say that something cannot be done or is impossible, I feel the burden to believe it and trust God for it.	1	2	3	4	5	6	7
4.	My main desire in communicating God's Word is to get people to humble themselves before God.	1	2	3	4	5	6	7
5.	I desire that the people I am teaching experience the truth to the extent that I have in my own personal study.	1	2	3	4	5	6	7
6.	Advice and/or decisions I have given stand as the final decision of a group.	1	2	3	4	5	6	7
7.	I have a good record of achieving my set goals.	1	2	3	4	5	6	7
8.	I enjoy managing programs more than people.	1	2	3	4	5	6	7
9.	When I see a need I feel an immediate obligation to meet it.	1	2	3	4	5	6	7
10.	I always feel compelled to prescribe a step by step plan of action for the solution of problems.	1	2	3	4	5	6	7
11.	I believe God uses me as a channel of His resources.	1	2	3	4	5	6	7
12.	I tend to enjoy the process more than the results in a plan of action.	1	2	3	4	5	6	7
13.	One result that I look for in presenting God's truth is true repentance.	1	2	3	4	5	6	7
14.	I identify with people and their problems to the degree that I am sometimes affected by them personally.	1	2	3	4	5	6	7
15.	When I communicate the Word of God, I consistently look for ways to illustrate truth.	1	2	3	4	5	6	7
16.	I enjoy associating with those who display a definite direction in their life.	1	2	3	4	5	6	7
17.	I concentrate more on doing practical things that need to be done rather than on why they should be done.	1	2	3	4	5	6	7
18.	I have discovered that I do not have to wait for clear evidence and confirmation before making a decision.	1	2	3	4	5	6	7
19.	I feel that I am able to trust God in difficult circumstances without hesitation or indecision.	1	2	3	4	5	6	7
20	I find it relatively easy and enjoyable to spend much time in intense study and research of the Bible.	1	2	3	4	5	6	7
21.	I find myself setting goals and objectives for myself and my ministry as a believer.	1	2	3	4	5	6	7
22.	I usually have a great deal of joy in just "doing things" that need to be done no matter how small or trivial the task.	1	2	3	4	5	6	7
23.	I am able to motivate people to establish spiritual goals.	1	2	3	4	5	6	7

		Often True		Sometimes True			Rarely True	
24.	I would rather provide the necessary materials needed than perform some manual task.	1	2	3	4	5	6	7
25.	I am gripped by the awesomeness of the message I am proclaiming.	1	2	3	4	5	6	7
26.	I like to see others organized.	1	2	3	4	5	6	7
27.	People regularly express their appreciation of my presence when they are undergoing extreme difficulty.	1	2	3	4	5	6	7
28.	When sharing with people, I have a special sensitivity as to what to say or what not to say.	1	2	3	4	5	6	7
29.	I would rather deal with someone having problems personally, instead of sending them to someone else for help.	1	2	3	4	5	6	7
30.	The successful operation of an activity gives me great satisfaction.	1	2	3	4	5	6	7
31.	I feel a burden to encourage people to trust God when I see them defeated and discouraged.	1	2	3	4	5	6	7
32.	I would rather do a particular task than spend time counseling with people.	1	2	3	4	5	6	7
33.	I love to prove and answer Biblical issues and questions.	1	2	3	4	5	6	7
34.	I am irritated about wrong practices or doctrinal error whenever I sense it.	1	2	3	4	5	6	7
35.	When I hear of someone in need, I immediately think of offering material assistance.	1	2	3	4	5	6	7
36.	When someone is not doing a job well, I am concerned about making him effective in what he is doing.	1	2	3	4	5	6	7
37.	I would rather show someone else how to do a task than do it myself.	1	2	3	4	5	6	7
38.	I find myself responding immediately to financial needs by sharing my resources without a great deal of planning to do so.	1	2	3	4	5	6	7
39.	I like to help people personally regardless of their character or point of view.	1	2	3	4	5	6	7
40.	I find that it is not necessary for me to have a 'job description" when I am asked to do a particular task.	1	2	3	4	5	6	7
41.	People express to me how much I have helped or encouraged them in time of need.	1	2	3	4	5	6	7
42.	I believe I have a pioneering spirit and am not easily discouraged.	1	2	3	4	5	6	7
43.	I find that I see past the surface of an activity to the broader picture of details and results.	1	2	3	4	5	6	7
44.	When I hear a question or problem, I am anxious to both find and give a Biblical answer.	1	2	3	4	5	6	7
45.	When I speak God's Word I feel compelled to call for commitment from my audience.	1	2	3	4	5	6	7
46.	When I give money to someone for something, I desire to avoid letting anyone know what I did.	1	2	3	4	5	6	7

		Often True		Sometimes True			Rarely True	
47.	People often say to me that I have an ability to explain difficult Biblical passages to them usually giving scriptural reasons.	1	2	3	4	5	6	7
48.	Other believers share with me that I have the ability to communicate God's Word with great boldness and conviction.	1	2	3	4	5	6	7
49.	When I am confronted by an obstacle, I tend to see it in terms of God's resources instead of my own resources.	1	2	3	4	5	6	7
50.	I think of creative ways to minister and help those who are suffering.	1	2	3	4	5	6	7
51.	I easily spot weaknesses and strengths in organizational planning.	1	2	3	4	5	6	7
52.	I feel a special burden to relieve others of their duties in order to free them to do their most important work.	1	2	3	4	5	6	7
53.	I sense a great deal of identification with people having personal and emotional problems, but I am not weighed down by these.	1	2	3	4	5	6	7
54.	In a group situation when tension turns to stress, I am the one who is looked to for direction.	1	2	3	4	5	6	7
55.	I find myself wanting time to be budgeted properly.	1	2	3	4	5	6	7
56.	When I hear of someone who needs help, I immediately offer my services if it is possible.	1	2	3	4	5	6	7
57.	I am able to give directions to others and make decisions for them, which involves persuading them to my way of thinking.	1	2	3	4	5	6	7
58.	I have a desire to persuade others to move toward achieving group objectives.	1	2	3	4	5	6	7
59.	I get really excited when I see a worthwhile project that I can underwrite, counting it a great honor and privilege.	1	2	3	4	5	6	7
60.	I would rather explain the meaning of a word than simply share a verse by quoting it to someone.	1	2	3	4	5	6	7
61.	I feel the urgency to communicate the message of God zealously.	1	2	3	4	5	6	7
62.	When confronted with an opportunity to advance God's work, I feel compelled to seize it without hesitating.	1	2	3	4	5	6	7
63.	I find that when visiting those who are suffering it brings me joy rather than depressing me.	1	2	3	4	5	6	7
64.	I have an effective prayer ministry in my life with many wonderful answers to prayer that from a human point of view seem impossible or unlikely.	1	2	3	4	5	6	7
65.	I have a strong sense of compassion toward needy people.	1	2	3	4	5	6	7
66.	I find myself constantly thinking of decisions that need to be made in giving overall direction to a group or organization.	1	2	3	4	5	6	7
67.	I see myself more in a supportive role to others than in public ministry.	1	2	3	4	5	6	7
68.	When someone shares a problem with me, I am able to help them from the Word of God and motivate them to act on it.	1	2	3	4	5	6	7

		Often True		Sometimes True			Rarely True	
69.	I am so confident that God will meet my needs that I give to Him sacrificially and consistently.	1	2	3	4	5	6	7
70.	When I discover Biblical truth, I automatically begin to think of ways that it could be presented in an intelligible and interesting way.	1	2	3	4	5	6	7
71.	I have proclaimed God's truth in a way that goes against the majority opinion.	1	2	3	4	5	6	7
72.	I enjoy management as it relates to working closely with people.	1	2	3	4	5	6	7
73.	I have influenced others to accomplish a particular task or Biblical purpose.	1	2	3	4	5	6	7
74.	I have the ability to visualize circumstance and solutions that other believers cannot see.	1	2	3	4	5	6	7
75.	I am anxious to discover those who are suffering or bereaved.	1	2	3	4	5	6	7
76.	I find it easy to move from a discussion of things in general to a discussion of spiritual things.	1	2	3	4	5	6	7
77.	I find that I refer to the Word of God when I minister to others, I resort much more to the Word of God than my personal experiences.	1	2	3	4	5	6	7
78.	People seem to depend upon me to decide the process by which groups carry out their work.	1	2	3	4	5	6	7
79.	I am more satisfied with how a person has been helped by what I did than by simply doing the job needed.	1	2	3	4	5	6	7
80.	I have been willing to maintain a lower standard of living in order to benefit God's work.	1	2	3	4	5	6	7
81.	I enjoy imparting scriptural principles to others.	1	2	3	4	5	6	7
82.	I enjoy organizing ideas, people, resources, and time for more effective ministry.	1	2	3	4	5	6	7
83.	I find it easy to convey truth to others.	1	2	3	4	5	6	7
84.	I find it easy to lend or give things away.	1	2	3	4	5	6	7
85.	I enjoy talking to people about their spiritual development.	1	2	3	4	5	6	7
86.	People express confidence in goals that I have set.	1	2	3	4	5	6	7
87.	People with problems seem to beat a path to my doorstep.	1	2	3	4	5	6	7
88.	I have felt compelled to warn people of the impending consequences of sin.	1	2	3	4	5	6	7
89.	People often express to me that I minister to them through my helpful spirit.	1	2	3	4	5	6	7
90.	Other people are often challenged by my ability to trust God.	1	2	3	4	5	6	7

Before totaling your scores, list the order you would *expect* your spouse's/friend's gifts to manifest, where "1" is most likely, and "9" is least likely.

	Gift	Rank Order
1.	Administration	
2.	Teaching	
3.	Exhortation	
4.	Faith	
5.	Giving	
6.	Leadership	
7.	Mercy	
8.	Prophecy	
9.	Serving/Helps	

Disclaimer: This survey was adapted from a variety of unknown sources.

Spiritual Gifts Assessment Scoring

Administration		
Question	Yours	Other
8		
12		
26		
30		
43		
51		
55		
66		
78		
10		
Totals:		

Teaching		
Question	Yours	Other
5		
15		
20		
33		
44		
47		
60		
70		
81		
83		
Totals:		

Exhortation		
Question	Yours	Other
6		
10		
23		
29		
41		
53		
57		
68		
76		
85		
Totals:		

Faith		
Question	Yours	Other
3		
18		
19		
31		
42		
49		
62		
64		
74		
90		
Totals:		

Giving		
Question	Yours	Other
1		
11		
24		
35		
38		
46		
59		
69		
80		
84		
Totals:		

Leadership		
Question	Yours	Other
7		
16		
21		
36		
37		
54		
58		
72		
73		
86		
Totals:		

Mercy		
Question	Yours	Other
2		
14		
27		
28		
39		
50		
63		
65		
75		
87		
Totals:		

Prophecy		
Question	Yours	Other
4		
13		
25		
34		
45		
48		
61		
71		
77		
88		
Totals:		

Serving/Helps		
Question	Yours	Other
9		
17		
22		
32		
40		
52		
56		
67		
79		
89		
Totals:		

Place your scores and the scores from the "Spouse's/Other" survey in the appropriate columns. Next, determine the mathematical difference between the scores. Where did you disagree the most? This can make for some interesting discussion. Also, rank the order of your scores from the lowest number (1st), to the highest number (9th). The lower numbers help you identify your spiritual gift(s).

COMPARATIVE SCORING ON SPIRITUAL GIFTS					
Spiritual Gift	Your Score	Others Score	Difference	Your Rank	Others Rank
Administration					
Teaching					
Exhortation					
Faith					
Giving					
Leadership					
Mercy					
Prophecy					
Serving/Helps					

Regarding Spiritual Gifts

When we became Christians, we received the gift of the indwelling Holy Spirit. We also received some type of gifting to enable us to serve our Savior and His church. A truly satisfied Christian is one who knows his gifts and fully exercises them. Spiritual gifts are different from talents, which we can have whether we are a Christian or not. Spiritual gifts come to us as part of our salvation and indwelling Holy Spirit.

As believers, we are commanded to be aware of spiritual gifts. We are to keep them in our minds and hearts on a constant basis as we seek to be more effective for the Lord Jesus Christ. The Apostle Paul makes this clear to the church in Corinth that was having trouble understanding and properly using their gifts.

DEFINING SPIRITUAL GIFTS

While we see spiritual gifting evidenced throughout the Bible, we will focus on Scripture that most directly addresses the subject.

> *"Now about the gifts of the Spirit, brothers and sisters, I do not want you to be uninformed. You know that when you were pagans, somehow or other you were influenced and led astray to mute idols. Therefore I want you to know that no one who is speaking by the Spirit of God says, 'Jesus be cursed,' and no one can say, 'Jesus is Lord,' except by the Holy Spirit.*
>
> *There are different kinds of gifts, but the same Spirit distributes them. There are different kinds of service, but the same Lord. There are different kinds of working, but in all of them and in everyone it is the same God at work.*
>
> *Now to each one the manifestation of the Spirit is given for the common good. To one there is given through the Spirit a message of wisdom, to another a message of knowledge by means of the same Spirit, to another faith by the same Spirit, to another gifts of healing by that one Spirit, to another miraculous powers, to another prophecy, to another distinguishing between spirits, to another speaking in different kinds of tongues, and to still another the interpretation of tongues. All these are the work of one and the same Spirit, and he distributes them to each one, just as he determines.*
>
> *Just as a body, though one, has many parts, but all its many parts form one body, so it is with Christ. For we were all baptized by one Spirit so as to form one body – whether Jews or Gentiles, slave or free – and we were all given the one Spirit to drink. Even so the body is not made up of one part but of many.*
>
> *Now if the foot should say, 'Because I am not a hand, I do not belong to the body,' it would not for that reason stop being part of the body. And if the ear should say, 'Because I am not an eye, I do not belong to the body,' it would not*

for that reason stop being part of the body. If the whole body were an eye, where would the sense of hearing be? If the whole body were an ear, where would the sense of smell be? But in fact God has placed the parts in the body, every one of them, just as he wanted them to be. If they were all one part, where would the body be? As it is, there are many parts, but one body.

The eye cannot say to the hand, 'I don't need you!' And the head cannot say to the feet, 'I don't need you!' On the contrary, those parts of the body that seem to be weaker are indispensable, and the parts that we think are less honorable we treat with special honor. And the parts that are unpresentable are treated with special modesty, while our presentable parts need no special treatment. But God has put the body together, giving greater honor to the parts that lacked it, so that there should be no division in the body, but that its parts should have equal concern for each other. If one part suffers, every part suffers with it; if one part is honored, every part rejoices with it.

Now you are the body of Christ, and each one of you is a part of it. And God has placed in the church first of all apostles, second prophets, third teachers, then miracles, then gifts of healing, of helping, of guidance, and of different kinds of tongues. Are all apostles? Are all prophets? Are all teachers? Do all work miracles? Do all have gifts of healing? Do all speak in tongues? Do all interpret? Now eagerly desire the greater gifts" (1 Corinthians 12:1-31, NIV).

THER PURPOSE—Why are there spiritual gifts?

God has set in place a plan for the orderly functioning of the Church: The Body of Christ. Part of this plan is that believers are supernaturally endowed with spiritual enablement (i.e., abilities, gifts) for the purpose of building up the Body of Christ, so it can be an effective witness of the gospel of the Lord Jesus Christ. We bring our gifts together to build the unity of the body.

"…until we all reach unity in the faith and in the knowledge of the Son of God and become mature, attaining to the whole measure of the fullness of Christ. Then we will no longer be infants, tossed back and forth by the waves, and blown here and there by every wind of teaching and by the cunning and craftiness of people in their deceitful scheming. Instead, speaking the truth in love, we will grow to become in every respect the mature body of him who is the head, that is, Christ. From him the whole body, joined and held together by every supporting ligament, grows and builds itself up in love, as each part does its work"
(Ephesians 4:13-16, NIV).

THEIR SOURCE—Where did they come from?

The source of these spiritual abilities/gifts is none other than God, the Holy Spirit. Spiritual gifts are not for a select few, but for every believer. Gifts are given to us; not chosen by us. You can wish all you want for a particular gift, but they are distributed only under the sovereign will of

God Almighty. The gifts we receive have nothing to do with our spiritual maturity. A new believer is as gifted as a mature believer, although the mature believer is more experienced in its exercise. Even a carnal believer is still as gifted as a spiritual believer, although the carnal believer certainly can't use his gift effectively.

THEIR NATURE—What are they?

Spiritual gifts differ from natural talents, which all humans are capable of having (e.g., musical talent or athletic ability). Spiritual gifts are given exclusively to Christians as empowered by the Holy Spirit. They are spiritually derived and are clearly seen as gifts. They are manifestations of the Holy Spirit working in a person's life. They did not exist before one's conversion. They may allow us to use our talent in a new and exciting way, but they are not the talent itself. Though they may be extraordinarily talented, no unbeliever has a spiritual gift.

THEIR DURATION—When do we receive them?

We receive spiritual gifting when we become Christians (1 Corinthians 12:11-13). Some argue we can receive new types of gifting throughout our lives. It is hard to say for sure. Others argue that 2 Timothy 1:6 ("For this reason I remind you to fan into flame the gift of God, which is in you through the laying on of my hands.") indicates some ability to continue to acquire gifting. This could be speaking of the apostolic commissioning of Timothy and is merely descriptive and not prescriptive. That is, it describes what happened to *him*, but it is not necessarily true for *every* believer.

Once given, spiritual gifts last a lifetime. While some argue they can be lost, this seems unlikely, though it is possible for us, through sin, to stifle the spiritual gift within us. In 1 Timothy 4:14, Paul encourages Timothy: "Do not neglect the spiritual gift within you...." We certainly can have a spiritual gift and not use it. We can even have a spiritual gift and use it incorrectly. This becomes clear in 1 Corinthians 14, where the Corinthian Christians were misusing their gifts.

THEIR FRUIT—What do they produce?

Their purpose is to enable us to better serve the Body of Christ by fulfilling our role within the greater Body. When properly used by each member of the Body of Christ, the result is tremendous! The effective working of the gifts of the Body results in:

- Maturity in individual believers
- Doctrinal stability and effective service in the Church
- Effective witness in the community

Hebrews 2:4 tells us God bears witness to the world by the gifts of the Holy Spirit operating in the lives of individual believers: "God also testified to it by signs, wonders and various miracles, and by gifts of the Holy Spirit distributed according to His will."

THEIR NUMBER—How many gifts are there?

To some this is an especially important question. To others it is not so critical. Our survey includes nine gifts. That does not mean we believe this represents all the potential gifts. 1 Corinthians 12:4 tells us there are "varieties" of gifts, so it is a mistake to suggest the work of the Holy Spirit in gifting can be constrained to a particular list. This really comes down to whether you believe the lists of gifts in Scripture are complete, or if they overlap. In Romans Chapter 12, Paul indicates that 1 Corinthians 12 does not present an exclusive list.

> *"For just as each of us has one body with many members, and these members do not all have the same function, so in Christ we, though many, form one body, and each member belongs to all the others. We have different gifts, according to the grace given to each of us. If your gift is prophesying, then prophesy in accordance with your faith; if it is serving, then serve; if it is teaching, then teach; if it is to encourage, then give encouragement; if it is giving, then give generously; if it is to lead, do it diligently; if it is to show mercy, do it cheerfully"* (Romans 12:4-8, NIV).

So, what is the complete list? Some add Ephesians 4:11-12, or 1 Peter 4:10-11:

> *"So Christ himself gave the apostles, the prophets, the evangelists, the pastors and teachers, to equip his people for works of service, so that the body of Christ may be built up"* (Ephesians 4:11-12, NIV).

> *"Each of you should use whatever gift you have received to serve others, as faithful stewards of God's grace in its various forms. If anyone speaks, they should do so as one who speaks the very words of God. If anyone serves, they should do so with the strength God provides, so that in all things God may be praised through Jesus Christ. To him be the glory and the power forever and ever. Amen"* (1 Peter 4:10-11, NIV).

There are various lists of spiritual gifts. The Holy Spirit has gifted the Body of Christ in all the ways necessary to conduct His work in the service of God, wherever that work appears.

THEIR RANKING—Which gifts are most important?

There is no hierarchy of gifts, where those more favored by God get the better gifts. In fact, as we see in 1 Corinthians, it was that type of wrong-headed thinking the Apostle Paul was addressing in Chapter 12 and following. The goal is to learn our gifting, and to respect the gifting of others. They are all necessary, and is why God gives them to the church. (We recognize there is ongoing debate about some of the gifts, as to whether they have ceased or are no longer needed.)

NO EXCUSES, SERVE WHENEVER AND WHEREVER NEEDED

Just because we do not have a particular spiritual gift, is not an excuse for failing to serve in an area of need. While each Christian should focus on utilizing their spiritual gifts in the service of Christ and to the benefit of the Body, that does not give them a pass on performing duties in areas where they are not gifted. Just because giving is not your gift does not mean you do not have to give, any more than if you could say you no longer have to serve or have faith. We want the gifted people encouraging and leading the rest of us in those areas, not carrying the entire load.

HOW MANY GIFTS DOES EACH INDIVIDUAL BELIEVER HAVE?

While certainly capable of doing whatever He needed to do at any time, there is no evidence Jesus had all the gifts outlined above. At least, He did not manifest them all during his lifetime on earth. The same is true of the Apostle Paul and the rest of the Apostles. They were clearly gifted but were not *universally* gifted.

Some believe every believer gets one gift ("manifestation of the Spirit"). Others believe you may have multiple gifts throughout your lifetime. A third view is that you have a dominant gift and have subordinate gifts that work together to serve the Lord. At the end of the day, it is important to find your gifts and utilize them for the service of God. The most satisfied Christians are those who are actively using their gifts for the Glory of God and His kingdom purposes.

Spiritual Gifts Exercise

[In-class exercise]

Imagine one of our men has been admitted to the hospital for emergency surgery. The surgery is serious enough that he will be in the hospital for at least five days. After that, he will be at home recuperating for at least four weeks. He has a wife and three children (2-year-old girl, 7-year-old girl, and a 14-year-old boy).

DISCUSSION IN GROUPS OF LIKE-GIFTEDNESS

Divide the class into groups of men who are alike in spiritual gifts (i.e., your primary or secondary gift). Once together, spend ten minutes discussing how people with your spiritual gift would minister to this man and his family.

REPORTS TO THE WHOLE CLASS

Once you have collected your ideas, select one member of your group to report your conclusions to the whole class.

CLASS DISCUSSION

1. In what ways did the individual efforts complement each other?
2. Which groups took the most different approaches to this situation?
3. Which groups came up with issues to address that never occurred to your group?
4. Are there any additional issues none of the groups addressed?
5. What does this tell us about how various spiritual gifts work within the church body?
6. Besides direct ministry to this person, what is the role of each gift in encouraging, equipping, and building up the whole church?

NOTES

SESSION 10
Leadership in the Local Church and Introduction to the Case Study

To succeed in getting things done through others is the highest type of leadership.

SESSION 10
Leadership in the Local Church and Introduction to the Case Study

Class discussion

The content below will be discussed during class. If you miss class this week, you are required to read them on your own time, prior to next week's class.

Application from the last session

Pick one thing you learned from the last session you can apply in your life as either an action item or a truth you should embrace.

_____

_____

Before class

____ Continued your Solo Initiative
____ Read the Bible at least four times this week
____ My Life Focus: Final review and turn in
____ Reviewed and rated the Case Studies (See session materials)
____ Attended church (Sermon topic: _____)
____ Met with my Accountability Partner

Bible reading

Date	Book/Chapters	At least one thought from what you read

Accountability checklist

___ Asked accountability questions	___ Discussed Solo Initiative
___ Discussed what you are learning in class	___ Prayed

My prayer request:
Accountability partner's prayer request:
Time/Place of next meeting:

(Have you attended a men's event or done a service project yet?)

At the beginning of class

- Put on your name tag (Right side)
- Pick-up your envelope if you turned in forms last week (Re-file forms in your manual)
- Drop off envelope if you are turning in any new forms
- Join a prayer group (3-4 men), praying with different men each week

Class schedule

- 20 minutes: Small group prayer
- 10 minutes: Attendance and announcements (e.g., missing chair, service projects)
- 20 minutes: Share testimonies
- 35 minutes: Teach and discuss "Leaders in the Local Church"
  Add optional: "Worker Dead for Five Days"
- 15 minutes: Small Group Discussion
- 10 minutes: Break
- 15 minutes: Teach and discuss "Preparing and Presenting Your Case Study"
  Add optional: "Peel the Orange" exercise
- 10 minutes: Review and assign "Church Leadership Case Studies"
- 10 minutes: Review "Case Study Worksheet"
- 5 minutes: Review next week's assignments

Weekly prayer requests

Name	Request
Yours	

Calling a missing chair
"…You will be missed because your seat will be empty" (1 Samuel 20:18)

Missing chair:	
Phone number:	Email:
Contacted:	Status:

Testimonies

Name	Application

Teaching goal
That men would understand God's requirements for leadership in the Church and how the standards are a measuring tool for all that seek to serve in any capacity.

Leaders in the Local Church

EVERY CHURCH LEADER NEEDS TO UNDERSTAND:

Doctrine	Direction	Development	Determination
What do we believe God wants?	Where are we going?	What is the specific plan to get us there?	What are we willing to do to make this happen?

WHAT IS AN ELDER?

The starting point for a discussion about elders is to understand what an elder is, as presented in the New Testament. The Apostle Paul uses a number of terms for the structure by which the church is to operate. Three interchangeable terms refer to the same basic job description:

> "...Paul sent to Ephesus for the elders of the church....Keep watch over yourselves and all the flock of which the Holy Spirit has made you overseers. Be shepherds of the church of God, which he bought with his own blood" (Acts 20:17, 28; NIV).

When taken together, the terms begin to form a job description of an elder. The term "elder" (Greek: *presbuteros*) clearly denotes spiritual as opposed to chronological maturity. The term "overseer" (Greek: *episcopos*) applies to one who has administrative oversight duties. The term "shepherd" (Greek: *poimen*) conveys the idea of leadership and protection for the flock.

HOW MANY ELDERS ARE THERE IN EACH LOCAL CHURCH?

While there is no specified number, elders are always referred to in the plural:

> "Paul...appointed elders for them in each church..." (Acts 14:23, NIV).

(cf. Acts 11:30; 15:2; 16:4; 20:17; Philippians 1:1; 1 Thessalonians 5:12-13; Titus 1:5; Hebrews 13:17; James 5:14; and 1 Peter 5:1, 5.)

Some advance the idea of a single ruling elder. It is important we look at the overall thrust of Scripture, as opposed to relying on a single verse. The weight of biblical evidence is for a group of elders. This allows men of various giftings to come together and better serve the church. It also provides a mechanism where the entire group can hold each other accountable.

If a church finds themselves with only one qualified elder that might be a default result because we certainly do not want to place unqualified men in this important position. At the same time, if this were to happen, that solo elder's primary job would be to seek out and mentor additional men so the situation is remedied as soon as possible. A plurality of elders in a local church is the rule, not the exception.

WHAT ARE THE QUALIFICATIONS FOR THE OFFICE OF ELDER?

The following sections of Scripture lay out the basic requirements for an elder.

> *"It is a trustworthy statement: if any man aspires to the office of overseer, it is a fine work he desires to do. An overseer, then, must be above reproach, the husband of one wife, temperate, prudent, respectable, hospitable, able to teach, not addicted to wine or pugnacious, but gentle, peaceable, free from the love of money. He must be one who manages his own household well, keeping his children under control with all dignity (but if a man does not know how to manage his own household, how will he take care of the church of God?), and not a new convert, so that he will not become conceited and fall into the condemnation incurred by the devil. And he must have a good reputation with those outside the church, so that he will not fall into reproach and the snare of the devil." (1 Timothy 3:1-7, NASB).*

> *"…set in order what remains and appoint elders in every city as I directed you, namely, if any man is above reproach, the husband of one wife, having children who believe, not accused of dissipation or rebellion. For the overseer must be above reproach as God's steward, not self-willed, not quick-tempered, not addicted to wine, not pugnacious, not fond of sordid gain, but hospitable, loving what is good, sensible, just, devout, self-controlled, holding fast the faithful word which is in accordance with the teaching, so that he will be able both to exhort in sound doctrine and to refute those who contradict" (Titus 1:5-9, NASB).*

He must be:	He must *not* be:
• A man	• A new convert
• Desirous of serving in the role	• Addicted to wine
• Above reproach	• Pugnacious (quick tempered)
• The husband of one wife (loyal and faithful)	• Contentious
• Temperate (not given to excess)	• Lover of money
• Prudent (sensible)	• Fond of sordid gain
• Respectable	• Accused of dissipation
• Good manager of his household (with children who are under control)	• Accused of rebellion
• Hospitable	• Self-willed
• Able to teach, and faithful to the Word	• Conceited
• Able to exhort and refute from Scripture	
• Gentle, humble and peaceable	
• Good reputation outside the church	
• Lover of what is good, sensible, just	
• Self-controlled	

An elder need not be an older man, but must possess the wisdom, gravity, balance, and soberness of many years (cf. Psalm 119:100).

HOW ARE THE ELDERS CHOSEN IN THE LOCAL CHURCH?

This is not a process to be taken lightly. Men should not be chosen hastily, but only after close observation, followed by prayer and contemplation. Obviously, the men must meet the standards explained above. This does not mean they are without flaws. If that were the case, we would never find anyone qualified to serve. However, they should not be failing in any category, and they should seek to constantly improve in areas where they are not as strong.

The men should be vetted and affirmed by the congregation (1 Thessalonians 5:12-13; cf. Acts 6). Those chosen must be willing and must desire to serve the body as an elder.

WHAT IS THE PRIMARY RESPONSIBILITY OF THE ELDERS IN THE LOCAL CHURCH?

The role of elders is multi-faceted, and they should be prepared to handle a variety of functions. They primarily serve sacrificially as shepherds of the local flock, leading, feeding, and protecting the church at all times. They set the highest examples as men of the Word and prayer.

> *"Be shepherds of God's flock that is under your care, watching over them—not because you must, but because you are willing, as God wants you to be; not pursuing dishonest gain, but eager to serve; not lording it over those entrusted to you, but being examples to the flock" (1 Peter 5:2-3, NIV).*

(cf. Acts 6:4, 20:28-31; Hebrews 13:7, 17, 24: 1 Thessalonians 5:12; 1 Peter 5:3; 1 Timothy 4:13, 5:17; 2 Timothy 2:15; Ephesian 4:11-13; Romans 12:8; Matthew 20:26-28; Mark 10:42-43; Luke 22:24-27; James 5:14-16.)

WHAT AUTHORITY DO ELDERS HAVE IN THE LOCAL CHURCH?

Christ is the only Head of His Body, the Church:

> *"...and God placed all things under his [Christ's] feet and appointed him to be head over everything for the church" (Ephesians 1:22, NIV).*

> *"Then Jesus...said, "All authority in heaven and on earth has been given to me. Therefore go and make disciples of all nations, baptizing them in the name of the Father and of the Son and of the Holy Spirit" (Matthew 28:18-19, NIV).*

Christ has not surrendered His authority to any man or institution. He is still present and active in His local church. Elder's shepherd the flock in His presence, not in His absence. As the actual head of the church, Christ communicates His will for His church through the Word.

Elders are not Christ's representatives on earth, nor are they a select few of mediators (priests) between the congregation and God. Christ is our only mediator and there is a priesthood of all believers.

"For there is one God and one mediator between God and mankind, the man Christ Jesus" (1 Timothy 2:5, NIV).

"…you also, like living stones, are being built into a spiritual house to be a holy priesthood, offering spiritual sacrifices acceptable to God through Jesus Christ…But you are a chosen people, a royal priesthood, a holy nation, God's special possession, that you may declare the praises of him who called you out of darkness into his wonderful light" (1 Peter 2:5, 9, NIV).

Elders are ultimately leaders among equals. Any authority elders have lies primarily in their conformity to the Word. In areas where the Word is silent, the elders as a group pray for God's leading for His church. Elders are not to be a dictatorial body whose objective is to bring the flock to a position of blind servitude. They are to be a group of mature men of God who guide Christ's local church by teaching the Word and stimulating its application in every member.

WHAT IS THE LOCAL CHURCH'S RESPONSIBILITY TO THEIR ELDERS?

Christ has His part, the elders have their part, and the congregation has their part in making the church function the way God intended. When each fills their proper role, the church can function appropriately. The following instructions exist for the congregation in relationship to their elders:

1. Submit to their Biblical guidance and instruction (Hebrews 13:17; 1 Corinthians 6:15-16; 1 Peter 5:5)
2. Live in peace with them (1 Thessalonians 5:13b)
3. Pray for them (James 5:16)
4. Appreciate them (1 Thessalonians 5:12-13a)
5. Honor them (1 Timothy 5:17-18)
6. Imitate them (Hebrews 13:7; 1 Peter 5:3b; 1 Corinthians 11:1; 1 Thessalonians 1:6; Luke 6:40)

WHAT ATTITUDE SHOULD AN ELDER BRING TO HIS SERVICE?

One of the most important attributes of an elder is humility. Do not think of the position as one of great power, but rather one of great responsibility. It is never the elder's will or way that prevails, but rather Christ's will. It is a role of submission to Christ and sacrifice for the congregation. It is a privilege to serve, not an ego trip to exploit. An elder who would lord his position over others is immediately disqualified from serving.

Elders carry a weighty responsibility. They must use restraint and discretion in exercising authority. While they are to seek God's will in all things, no one appointed them as "junior holy spirits" for those in the congregation. When correction is needed, it should always be performed in a loving, Christ-like manner. Even when discipline is called for, it is done out of love and concern for the one disciplined. Elders are first and foremost accountable to God. Beyond that, they are accountable to each other and ultimately to the congregation.

WHAT IS THE DIFFERENCE BETWEEN AN ELDER AND A DEACON/DEACONESS?

The Bible describes a variety of positions of responsibility within the church. Prominent among these are elder and deacon. While both are important, the functions and qualifications are slightly different. Elders oversee every area of the local church (spiritual and temporal), while deacons *assist* the elders in the affairs of the local church. Deacons are assigned *specific* areas of responsibilities, while elders serve in a more *general* administrative and oversight position, as well as being shepherds. Just like elders, there are multiple deacons. Early in the church the need for deacons was identified to enable elders to focus on their responsibilities:

> "In those days when the number of disciples was increasing, the Hellenistic Jews among them complained against the Hebraic Jews because their widows were being overlooked in the daily distribution of food. So the Twelve gathered all the disciples together and said, 'It would not be right for us to neglect the ministry of the word of God in order to wait on tables. Brothers and sisters, choose seven men from among you who are known to be full of the Spirit and wisdom. We will turn this responsibility over to them and will give our attention to prayer and the ministry of the word.' This proposal pleased the whole group. They chose Stephen, a man full of faith and of the Holy Spirit; also Philip, Procorus, Nicanor, Timon, Parmenas, and Nicolas from Antioch, a convert to Judaism. They presented these men to the apostles, who prayed and laid their hands on them" (Acts 6:1-6, NIV).

There is a list of qualifications for deacons as well as elders. If you compare them, you will find them similar, but deacons are not required to be able to teach or refute false doctrine. However, matters of moral character are identical.

> "In the same way, deacons are to be worthy of respect, sincere, not indulging in much wine, and not pursuing dishonest gain. They must keep hold of the deep truths of the faith with a clear conscience. They must first be tested; and then if there is nothing against them, let them serve as deacons. In the same way, the women are to be worthy of respect, not malicious talkers but temperate and trustworthy in everything. A deacon must be faithful to his wife and must manage his children and his household well. Those who have served well gain an excellent standing and great assurance in their faith in Christ Jesus" (1 Timothy 3:8-13, NIV).

WHAT ABOUT FEMALE ELDERS?

Although there is much debate today, we hold to a "complementarian" position that the Bible does not provide for a female equivalent to elders. However, there is a female equivalent when it comes to the role of deacon and deaconess. They, like the deacons, perform specific functions within the church. In several of his books, the Apostle Paul references female deacons (cf. Romans 16:1). We are committed to build Christ's Church on the backs of strong men who serve alongside Godly women as they fulfill their God-given roles.

ARE ALL ELDERS EQUAL IN POSITION?

We believe there are no Biblical categories or hierarchy of elders. Although some are more gifted than others, all elders are to rule and teach. Some may have more spiritual influence, but all are equal. We do recognize the unique position of the Pastor-Teacher. The Pastor-Teacher is one of the elders but serves in a special capacity as primarily responsible for equipping the saints and teaching doctrine. Beyond that special responsibility he is simply one among equals.

HOW LONG DO ELDERS SERVE IN THE LOCAL CHURCH?

First, we need to recognize that a church may have many men who are elders, with a select few serving in an official "corporate" capacity at any one time. So, a man will be an elder if he meets the qualifications of an elder, whether he is on a board or not.

From this pool of men, individuals are selected to fill roles within the governance structure of the church. Scripture is silent on issues relating to length of terms for official service. Most churches find it best to limit service to some specific number of years, with opportunities to serve multiple terms after brief times away from the board. This gives more men the chance to serve. To say it simply, we believe the local church is to be:

Elder-guided → Staff-managed → People-implemented

Small Group Discussion

1. Get into groups of no more than five men.
2. Pick a leader to facilitate discussion and make sure everyone participates.
3. You have 15 minutes.
4. Topic: The role and responsibility of elders.
5. Discussion questions:
   a. Look over the list of criteria for being an elder in the local church. Which items on the list would you find the most challenging and why?
   b. Discuss the attitude an elder should have while in service—and after his time of service.
   c. Share about how you can best support an elder board.

(For further study, read "Questions for the Man Who Would Serve as an Elder," in Appendix C.)

Worker Dead for Five Days

[Optional in-class discussion]

The following story is an urban legend. Whether true or not, it provides an opportunity to discuss the importance for leaders to be keen observers of the people they serve. Read the story and then answer the questions below.

Bosses of a publishing firm are trying to work out why no one noticed that one of their employees had been sitting dead at his desk for five days before anyone asked if he was feeling okay. George Turklebaum, 51, who had been employed as a proof-reader at a New York firm for 30 years, had a heart attack in the open-plan office he shared with 23 other workers.

He quietly passed away on Monday, but nobody noticed until Saturday morning when an office cleaner asked why he was working during the weekend.

His boss, Elliot Wachiaski, said: "George was always the first guy in each morning and the last to leave at night, so no one found it unusual that he was in the same position all that time and didn't say anything. He was always absorbed in his work and kept much to himself."

A post-mortem examination revealed that he had been dead for five days after suffering a coronary. George was proofreading manuscripts of medical textbooks when he died.

You may want to give your co-workers a nudge occasionally. The moral of the story: Don't work too hard. Nobody notices anyway. –Author unknown

Discussion questions:

Try to identify why such a work environment existed:

1. What was the role of the man who died?   _____
2. The role of the co-workers?   _____
3. The role of the manager?   _____
4. The role of the man's family?   _____
5. The role of others?   _____

What does this article suggest about the role of leaders in the home, the church, and the community?

Preparing and Presenting Your Case Study

The Case Study assignment allows us to grapple with some real-life issues that church boards face. We will experience what it is like to face a problem requiring immediate attention and resolution. We will come to realize that every set of choices and decisions has positives and negatives associated with it. There is rarely a decision that will make everyone happy, but nonetheless the decision has to be made after a careful exploration of the issue.

INSTRUCTIONS TO COMPLETE YOUR CASE STUDY

Please note: You must complete the case study assignment in order to graduate.

1. **Familiarize yourself with the scenarios**
   a. Read all of the scenarios carefully.
   b. Score each of the scenarios according to how hard you personally would find dealing with the issue.

2. **Preparing your case study**
   a. You will be assigned a case study in class.
   b. Using the case study worksheet, prepare your assigned case study well in advance of your presentation. This will take several hours.
   c. You may get help from anyone or any source you choose (e.g., church constitution, other leaders/elders/staff from this or other churches, class notes, books, etc.).
   d. Draw upon what you have learned from class lectures, homework, readings, testimonies, etc.
   e. If applicable, speak from your own experience.

3. **Presenting your case study (Session 12)**
   a. Imagine you are an elder serving on the Elder Board at Men in Action Bible Church (i.e., our fictitious local church).
   b. On the Case Study night, you will break into groups of no less than three.
   c. Your group will assign a chairman. The chairman will make sure each member keeps to his time restraints and stays on task.
   d. Your board has 25 minutes to handle each issue.
      i. You have ten minutes to present your case study.
      ii. Use the remaining 15 minutes for your fellow board members to ask you questions, make comments, and come up with a recommendation from the entire board.

4. **Submit your case study**
   a. After you have completed your homework, presented your case study, and received input from your fellow elders, hand in the Case Study Worksheet with your findings, your board notes, and final recommendations.

5. **In case of excused absence**
    a. Contact the class leader immediately if you determine you will miss Session 12 so other arrangements can be made to complete the assignment.
    b. Submit the final assignment either at the end of Session 12 or at the soonest time possible.

PEEL THE ORANGE EXERCISE

The following exercise may be used to help reinforce the value of Biblical prudence (Hebrew = *orma* = The ability to strip away the obvious to get to the heart of a matter); that is, digging deeper into matters that may seem simple.

1. Break into groups of four.
2. Give each group one orange.
3. Team member #1: Act as the timer. When they say "Go!" the time starts.
4. Team member #2: Peel the orange completely, then hand to Team member #3.
5. Team member #3: Separate the pieces of the orange as neatly as possible, then places them on a plate. Pass the plate to Team member #4.
6. Team member #4: Distribute the pieces to all the team members, including himself.
7. Once the last piece is handed out, the timer stops the time.
8. Team member writes down their time.
9. Each group reports their time.
10. The team with the best time wins.

Church Leadership Case Studies

The following scenarios are real-life situations taken from churches. Carefully read each scenario and evaluate it on a scale from 1 to 10, with 1 being easy to solve, and 10 being very complex (difficult to solve). Pick three of the scenarios that you give a score of at least an eight or higher that you would like to tackle as your case study. One of them will be assigned to you.

1. A group of 20 people from another church have started visiting our church. Among them are some of their elders. It is obvious this is a "splinter group" leaving their church and coming to our church.

   1   2   3   4   5   6   7   8   9   10

2. A very influential and well-known person has decided to leave our church. He/She has been telling others they are dissatisfied with the church.

   1   2   3   4   5   6   7   8   9   10

3. The constitution requires we have seven elders, but only six have come forward for nomination.

   1   2   3   4   5   6   7   8   9   10

4. The board has been informed giving only reached 75% of what is expected by that time in the fiscal year. You recognize you must either increase giving or decrease expenses. How would you propose doing both?

   1   2   3   4   5   6   7   8   9   10

5. Your staff decides to allow some "gray area" activity (e.g., *add your own*) on church property. A group of people react and threaten to leave if it is held.

   1   2   3   4   5   6   7   8   9   10

6. You are given the task of determining the range of church music for Sunday Worship services. You know most of the older people favor traditional music whereas the young people favor contemporary music.

   1   2   3   4   5   6   7   8   9   10

7. You have a group of people who believe the church should never borrow money (even for building). Another group accepts responsible debt as long as it is managed properly.

   1   2   3   4   5   6   7   8   9   10

8. The staff member over whom you have direct oversight shares with you he/she feels their department is being ignored and treated as "second-rate".

    1   2   3   4   5   6   7   8   9   10

9. You are on the board with an elder who sees his role as representing a group of people, and is not necessarily as concerned about the whole church.

    1   2   3   4   5   6   7   8   9   10

10. One of the elders confesses in the board room he feels unqualified to be an elder. This feeling continues for months.

    1   2   3   4   5   6   7   8   9   10

11. The former pastor held a different view than the present pastor regarding some debatable matters (e.g., divorce/debt/music style/staffing/theology/etc.).

    1   2   3   4   5   6   7   8   9   10

12. You get word that a church member or his/her family have threatened to sue the church if the church publicly disciplines him/her for his/her unrepentant sin.

    1   2   3   4   5   6   7   8   9   10

13. You see an elder candidate's name presented and you know something that would disqualify him that no one else knows.

    1   2   3   4   5   6   7   8   9   10

14. You are aware a beloved widow who is a member of your church has donated a very large sum of money and has asked that the new building be named in honor of her deceased husband. He was not a member of the church and there is no clear evidence he was a believer.

    1   2   3   4   5   6   7   8   9   10

15. You have a choice in selecting as the chairman of a new building committee a person who has attended the church for twenty years, but has never become a member, or person who has been a member for 18 months. Both are well-reputed people and well-recognized for their leadership and capability to handle the job.

    1   2   3   4   5   6   7   8   9   10

16. You are the only member of the elder board who voted no on a motion. It turns out the board decision was wrong and there are substantial consequences. Someone comes to you and expresses their displeasure in the board decision.

    1   2   3   4   5   6   7   8   9   10

17. The Senior Pastor (the Lead Pastor) of our multi-staff church believes a particular staff member is not the right person for the position and should be asked to leave the staff in a few months. You disagree.

    1   2   3   4   5   6   7   8   9   10

18. You are working with a married couple who have a very dysfunctional relationship. The wife accuses the husband of improper touching their ten-year-old daughter. The husband vehemently denies it, and all the wife has is very circumstantial evidence.

    1   2   3   4   5   6   7   8   9   10

19. Your best friend and his family do not like the youth pastor. They share with you that if the church does not do something about it immediately they will leave the church. You happen to know (confidentially) the Senior Pastor is working with the youth pastor and has placed him on probation.

    1   2   3   4   5   6   7   8   9   10

20. An unmarried daughter of one of the elders is pregnant. She still lives at home.

    1   2   3   4   5   6   7   8   9   10

21. Someone comes to you and shares something that could dramatically affect the whole church, but tells you to keep the matter confidential.

    1   2   3   4   5   6   7   8   9   10

22. You have a different interpretation of a controversial passage your Pastor preached. People come to you and ask you what your view is. Even though you did not share your specific view, as you listen to these people you find you agree with their position.

    1   2   3   4   5   6   7   8   9   10

23. One of our church members wants to immediately donate a portion of his lottery winnings. Your pastor has just preached a message on his concerns about gambling. The amount this person wants to donate is more than the church's entire yearly budget.

1   2   3   4   5   6   7   8   9   10

24. Two Christians are having a conflict over a business deal involving tens of thousands of dollars. One of them is a member of our church; the other a member of a like-minded sister church. They are considering suing each other, but both have sought counsel from their respective churches.

1   2   3   4   5   6   7   8   9   10

25. A woman who is a church member comes to you announcing that she just discovered the minister who performed her wedding 25 years ago was not legally licensed to perform the ceremony. To make matters even more complicated, the couple has been separated for years and the husband was now living with another woman. She now wants a divorce and comes to you for counsel, asking what to do. She is especially concerned about her children and whether their marriage was "legitimate."

1   2   3   4   5   6   7   8   9   10

26. The chairman of your Elder Board sends out a letter to the members of the congregation accusing the senior pastor of improper conduct. He did this on his own, without Board knowledge or consent.

1   2   3   4   5   6   7   8   9   10

27. The son of a key church leader announces he is gay. He is a senior in high school and is an active part of the youth group. He swears he is in no way sexually active but is convinced of his sexual orientation.

1   2   3   4   5   6   7   8   9   10

28. A married couple who are church members are having significant marital and family issues. Several church members come to you as an elder and say they have observed the husband being verbally abusive to his wife and children. They have no knowledge or reports of physical abuse, but expressed that the family is concerned it may come to this.

1   2   3   4   5   6   7   8   9   10

29. After a six-month absence, a church member you formerly knew as Bob returns as Bernadette, having gone through gender reassignment surgery. Bernadette wants to rejoin the choir however that deep bass is now a lovely alto. The choir director says over his dead body.

    1   2   3   4   5   6   7   8   9   10

30. A prominent church member feels that the preaching direction of the church is not focused or strong enough regarding [choose your topic]. He has solicited support from various other church members.

    1   2   3   4   5   6   7   8   9   10

Your class leader may add other case studies:

31. Description:

    1   2   3   4   5   6   7   8   9   10

32. Description:

    1   2   3   4   5   6   7   8   9   10

33. Description:

    1   2   3   4   5   6   7   8   9   10

Case Study Worksheet

[Make a copy and turn this in]

Your name: _____ Date of presentation: _____

The purpose of the Case Study is to give you a taste of what it means to be an elder in a local church. Issues come before the leaders of churches all the time. To be resolved these problems often must be tackled on multiple levels. Rarely is there a simple answer to the problem. Every option for a solution has its own set of consequences, some of which can be worse than the initial problem. It will take some real concerted effort on your part to successfully complete this project.

While you may organize your case study into any format you want, the following elements need to be included:

1. **State the situation.** While you have been assigned a specific church issue, in its current form it is a short summary of the problem. You will need to add facts and circumstances. Make the situation more compelling by telling about the people involved and providing additional background facts. Remember, you are dealing with people, so add some interesting personalities into the mix. Have fun with this, but keep it grounded in reality.

2. **Lay out the real issues.** In any real-life church situation, you will be dealing with *scriptural issues*, but often the *people issues* can be just as important. You need to lay out both types of issues to have a realistic discussion. Do not overlook the fact many situations can involve "church politics" and you ignore those at your peril.

3. **Collect the information needed to accurately assess the problem.** Often, the most important part of the work is figuring out what questions need to be asked in order to get accurate information, leading to a meaningful discussion and an informed decision. What scriptural input do we need? What facts need to be investigated and confirmed? What further questions need to be asked and answered? Who are our trustworthy sources? Is there any expertise we need to obtain? Who will we seek out for their expertise?

4. **Describe any third party input you received, or other resources you reviewed.** You are encouraged to seek input from any pastors, leaders or mature Christians to help guide you in the process. You are also encouraged to do some independent study.

5. **Explain your initial opinion and strategy.** You have spent more time on this issue than the men in your group. Come to the meeting with an opinion as to what should be done, and a strategy for implementing that solution. Include how to deal with any fallout from your decision.

6. **State why the action is necessary.** It is important to create some sense of immediacy in addressing the issue. Discuss the problems that will result from not addressing the situation. Describe what can happen if you do not act.

In 10 minutes, lay out items 1-6 for your fellow elders. Be quick and concise. Make good notes for your presentation. After you present, spend the remaining 15 minutes answering questions, discussing your proposed solution, and developing a final collective recommendation.

State the situation: Men, I have the following issue to present to you for your input...

_____

_____

What are the real issues?

_____

_____

What information do we need to make an accurate assessment, and to present a plan?

_____

_____

What third party input have you received that has helped you formulate your position (e.g., name sources, people, etc.)?

_____

_____

What specifically should be said or done? State your initial opinion and a preliminary strategy. Discuss both the potential positive and negative results from your recommendation.

_____

_____

What are the implications/potential consequences if this matter is not resolved?

_____

_____

Fellow elder input

Once you have explained everything, it is time for a discussion of the situation with your fellow MIA "elders." The discussion should address the following:

1. They should ask any additional questions they have about the situation or the issues.
2. They should share any additional expertise any of them have on the subject matter.
3. Discuss the Scriptural issues.
4. Discuss the people issues.
5. Discuss any potential political issues that might arise in the church.

6. Discuss options.
7. Discuss consequences, both positive and negative, that flow from the options.
8. Make a decision.
9. Develop a strategy for implementing the decision.

Notes on your discussion with your fellow elders (Do not list names):

_____
_____
_____
_____

REPORT ON DECISIONS MADE

Do not complete this section until you have received input from your fellow elders. Turn this in at the end of class (or within the next few days, if for some reason it cannot be completed by the end of class).

As a Board we recommend the following action(s) be taken:

_____
_____

We recommend the following implementation of our decision:

_____
_____

State the main basis for your recommendations:

_____
_____

What do you believe the positive and negative results of your recommendations will be?

_____
_____

Each of your MIA Elders need to sign off on the decision you have reached:

Name: _____ Initials: _____

Name: _____ Initials: _____

Name: _____ Initials: _____

Comments from class leader on your case study:

NOTES

SESSION 11
Christ's Plan for His Church

A leader is a developer of people.

SESSION 11
Christ's Plan for His Church

Class discussion
The content below will be discussed during class. If you miss class this week, you are required to read them on your own time, prior to next week's class.

Application from the last session
Pick one thing you learned from the last session you can apply in your life as either an action item or a truth you should embrace.

_____

_____

Before class
____   Continued your Solo Initiative
____   Read the Bible at least four times this week
____   Worked on Case Study (end of last week's materials)
____   Answer the questions on "Forming a MIA Bible Church" (class materials below)
____   Attended church (Sermon topic: _____)
____   Met with my Accountability Partner

Bible reading

Date	Book/Chapters	At least one thought from what you read

Accountability checklist

____ Asked accountability questions ____ Discussed what you are learning in class	____ Discussed Solo Initiative ____ Prayed
My prayer request:	
Accountability partner's prayer request:	
Time/Place of next meeting:	

(Have you attended a men's event or done a service project yet?)

At the beginning of class

- Put on your name tag (Right side)
- Pick up your envelope if you turned in forms last week (Re-file forms in your manual)
- Drop off envelope if you are turning in any new forms
- Join a prayer group (3-4 men), praying with different men each week

Class schedule

- 20 minutes: Small group prayer
- 10 minutes: Attendance and announcements (e.g., missing chair, service projects)
- 20 minutes: Share testimonies
- 25 minutes: Teach and discuss "The Master's Plan for the Church"
- 15 minutes: Small Group Discussion
- 10 minutes: Break
- 20 minutes: Discuss "What is a Local Church To Do?"
- 25 minutes: Teach and discuss "Forming Men in Action Bible Church"
- 5 minutes: Discuss schedule for Case Study night

Weekly prayer requests

Name	Request
Yours	

Calling a missing chair

"…You will be missed because your seat will be empty" (1 Samuel 20:18).

Missing chair:	
Phone number:	Email:
Contacted:	Status:

Testimonies

Name	Application

Teaching goal

That men would understand what is involved in developing a local church that honors God and serves His purpose.

The Master's Plan for His Local Churches

There are many ways to describe the purpose of the local church, but it comes down to three main responsibilities:

1. To present the Gospel to the lost so they might be saved by its power.
2. To mature the saved so they can have a witness to the lost world.
3. To honor and glorify God in all that we do.

These three principles can be stated in different ways. Regardless of how they are phrased, the principles must remain. For example, at Campus Bible Church our focus is as follows:

OUR MISSION
Linking together to make a difference for Christ in our world.

OUR PURPOSE
The purpose of this church is to glorify God in carrying out the Great Commission and to build up believers in the Christian faith.

WHY WE EXIST
We exist to equip men, women and children to be mature, healthy, reproducing disciples of Jesus Christ, who are expanding their influence globally.

We summarize it all in three key words:
Come, Grow and Go!

Just like the individual, the local church that has no clear sense of its purpose will go nowhere. In fact, it is impossible to stand still when God has called us to action (Daniel 11:32). For additional insight on what Scripture says about the importance of corporate vision for the people of God, read Isaiah 55:8-9, Proverbs 16:2-3, and James 4:13-17. Especially keep in mind:

> *"Where there is no vision (i.e., revelation from God), the people are unrestrained, but happy is he who keeps the law" (Proverbs 29:18, NASB; my addition).*

The church should be sure it is carrying out this purpose in everything it does. If there is not alignment with the above purpose, the activity should not proceed. It is a vital means of staying focused on why we are here.

THE MASTER'S UNIVERSAL PLAN, DEMONSTRATED THROUGH THE LOCAL CHURCH

God has a plan for His church, which has multiple elements (standards). These are not optional, allowing a church to pick and choose. To be effective, the church needs to build itself around these standards. These standards apply universally, to all Bible-believing churches.

The church Universal is made up of many local bodies. As a local church, we must be certain we are working within the Master's Universal Plan for His Church. We must also be clear how our local church will carry out our role in the Master's Universal Plan. The Master Plan in *our* local church is to be the unique outworking of the Master's Plan for *every* local church.

To avoid the appearance they are ranked by importance, the following list of standards is presented alphabetically. Each standard should be considered on its own merit.

1. God is calling us to be a **Bible-believing church** that stands, without compromise, on the truths of the Word of God as our only true source of faith and practice (Acts 2:41-42; 2 Timothy 3:16-17; 1 Thessalonians 2:13; Colossians 1:25; 2 Timothy 2:15; 2 Timothy 4:1-4).

2. God is calling us to be a **Christ-centered church** made up of born-again people who have trusted in Jesus Christ alone for their salvation, and who choose to submit to Him as the ultimate authority in this church (Colossians 1:18; Ephesians 1:22-23; Ephesians 5:25; Hebrews 12:2; Matthew 16:16, 18).

3. God is calling us to be a **discipling church** where the people are actively involved in the process of helping each other become more like Jesus Christ (Matthew 28:19; 2 Corinthians 3:18).

4. God is calling us to be a **disciplining church** that lovingly and humbly confronts sin in our midst and in the community (Ephesians 5:11; 1 Peter 4:17; Galatians 6:1; James 19; Matthew 18:15-17).

5. God is calling us to be a **diverse church** where there truly exists a Spirit-led unity amidst a wonderful diversity of people, ethnicity, culture, giftedness, worship-style and ministry focus (cf. Acts 2; James 2:1, 8-9; Galatians 3:28).

6. God is calling us to be an **efficient church** where faithful stewards are making the best use of the time, talent and treasure He gives us (1 Corinthians 4:2; 1 Corinthians 14:40; Colossians 4:5; 1 Timothy 3:5).

7. God is calling us to be an **enthusiastic church** where the people of God have a genuine excitement about what God has done, is doing, and will continue to do in our midst (Acts 2:43; Philippians 4:4-5; Ephesians 5:29).

8. God is calling us to be an **equipping church** where His people can come and be trained to serve the Lord of Glory locally and globally (Ephesians 4:11-13; 1 Corinthians 14:12).

9. God is calling us to be a **faithful church** that believes Almighty God wants to do great things in us and through us (Hebrews 11:1, 6; 2 Corinthians 5:7; Jeremiah 33:3).

10. God is calling us to be a **family church** where every member of the family of God experiences the warmth of fellowship and the stimulation of growing with their brothers and sisters in Christ (Ephesians 3:14-19).

11. God is calling us to be a **fasting church** that temporarily foregoes some of the necessities or pleasures of life in order to focus our attention on the Lord (2 Chronicles 20:3; Daniel 9:3 Acts 13:2; Joel 1:14).

12. God is calling us be a **fellowshipping church** where believers are developing significant relationships with other Christians outside of the corporate worship services (1 John 1:7; Acts 2:42; cf. "one another" verses in the New Testament).

13. God is calling us to be a **fruitful church** where there are visible and measurable results of our faithfulness and service to the Lord (John 15:7-8, 16).

14. God is calling us to be a **gathered church** where people meet regularly for study and worship (Hebrews 10:24-25).

15. God is calling us to be a **giving church** where people give generously, cheerfully and sacrificially of their finances (2 Corinthians 8:1-5; Malachi 3:10-12).

16. God is calling us to be a **grace-oriented church** where we strive to live by following the leading of the indwelling Holy Spirit and not by the external rules of man (Galatians 2:20-21; 5:1, 16,18, 25).

17. God is calling us to be a **healing church** where those who are hurting can come and find a place to be nurtured, fed, loved and restored (Matthew 11:28-30; 1 John 3:17-18).

18. God is calling us to be a **healthy church** where we labor diligently to encourage and teach people how to grow and become mature in Christ (Colossians 1:28-29; Ephesians 4:14-15).

19. God is calling us to be a **heaven-bound church** whose attitudes and actions are impacted by the truth that this earth is not our home (Hebrews 12:23; Philippians 3:20; 1 Peter 2:11; Colossians 3:1-4).

20. God is calling us to be an **historic church** that appreciates and learns from the past as it moves into the future (1 Corinthians 10:6; Hebrews 12:1).

21. God is calling us to be a **hospitable church** that extends the love of Christ to friends and strangers alike (Romans 12:13; Hebrews 13:2).

22. God is calling us to be an **imitable church** that strives to have the qualities that serve as an example to other churches (1 Corinthians 11:1; 1 Thessalonians 1:6).

23. God is calling us to be an **imitating church** that emulates the passions of other Spirit-led churches and ministries (1 Thessalonians 1:6-7; 2:14).

24. God is calling us to be an **innovative church** where the leaders and the people are constantly looking for new ways to communicate the old gospel message (Colossians 4:5).

25. God is calling us to be a **loving church** that places His value and worth on even the most unlovable with whom we come in contact (John 13:35; 1 Thessalonians 4:9-10; Matthew 5:44-48).

26. God is calling us to be a **multi-generational church** where young and old learn from each other and demonstrate mutual respect and appreciation (Psalm 71:18; 78:4,6; 145:4; Titus 2:1-6).

27. God is calling us to be an **obedient church** where we acknowledge the lordship and authority of Jesus Christ and God's Word in every area of our lives (Colossians 1:18; John 14:15).

28. God is calling us to be an **outreaching church** with a passion to be involved in presenting the truth of the Gospel of Jesus Christ in a wide variety of ways (Matthew 28:19-20; Colossians 4:5; 1 Thessalonians 1:8).

29. God is calling us to be a **partnering church** that is willing to share its resources to build up the universal, world-wide Church (2 Corinthians 8:1-4; 1 Corinthians 16:1; 1 Thessalonians 2:8; 2 Corinthians 11:28; Acts 15:41; 16:5).

30. God is calling us to be a **people-implemented church** where every member is a minister and missionary using his or her spiritual gifts and talents to build up the Body of Christ and spread the gospel around the world (Ephesians 4:11-16; 1 Thessalonians 1:3).

31. God is calling us to be a **praying church** that is actively engaged in prayer as privileged and intimate communication between our Heavenly Father and His children (Isaiah 56:7; Matthew 6:5-13).

32. God is calling us to be a **repentant church** that humbly confesses and repents of our corporate and individual sin (James 5:16a; Nehemiah 1:5-7).

33. God is calling us to be a **respectful church** that obeys and appreciates its God-given leaders (Hebrews 13:17; 1 Thessalonians 5:12-13).

34. God is calling us to be a **resting church** that encourages those times and seasons for waiting on the Lord (Psalm 37:7a).

35. God is calling us to be a **role-defined church** where the people understand and function in their clearly stated roles in God's economy (Romans 12:8).

36. God is calling us to be a **second-coming church** that allows the truth of Christ's soon return to motivate a godly life of love, obedience and service for the Lord (Titus 2:13-14; 1 John 3:2-3; Colossians 3:1-4).

37. God is calling us to be a **sending church** that willingly sends its best to serve the Lord around the world (Acts 1:8; 15:22; Luke 10:2).

38. God is calling us to be a **shepherd-guided** church that is led by a group of godly and mature "under-shepherds" who love, feed, protect and equip the flock that ultimately belongs to the Chief Shepherd (Acts 20:28; 1 Peter 5:1-4; Hebrews 13:17).

39. God is calling us to be a **Spirit-led church** that moves out in God's power and not our own (Acts 1:8; 2 Timothy 1:7; Romans 1:13; Acts 16:7; 1 Thessalonians 1:5).

40. God is calling us to be a **steadfast church** that endures life's tribulations and trials with our eyes fixed on Jesus (Hebrews 12:1-2; 2 Timothy 2:3; Romans 12:12).

41. God is calling us to be a **suffering church** that understands that serving the Lord in the world often results in persecution (John 15:18-19; 2 Timothy 3:12; 1 Peter 3:13-15).

42. God is calling us to be a **testifying church** that is unashamed of our faith and openly shares our excitement about serving Christ (Romans 1:16; Matthew 10:32; 1 John 4:14; Acts 20:24; 14:27; 15:3).

43. God is calling us to be a **transformed church** that is continually turning to God from the idolatry in our lives (1 Thessalonians 1:9-10; Colossians 3:5-10).

44. God is calling us to be a **unified church** that seeks to demonstrate to the world our unity of purpose in the midst of our diversity of opinions (Psalm 133:1; John 17:23; Ephesians 4:3, 13; Colossians 3:14; Acts 2:46-47).

45. God is calling us to be a **visionary church** that looks to the Lord of Glory for its direction and not man (Proverbs 29:18; Ephesians 5:15-17).

46. God is calling us to be a **worshiping church** that responds in adoration and celebration to the infinite majesty of God (John 4:23-24; Colossians 3:16).

CONCLUDING CHALLENGE

"For this reason also, since the day we heard of it, we have not ceased to pray for you and to ask that you may be filled with the knowledge of His will in all spiritual wisdom and understanding, so that you may walk in a manner worthy of the Lord, to please Him in all respects, bearing fruit in every good work and increasing in the knowledge of God; strengthened with all power, according to His glorious might, for the attaining of all steadfastness and patience; joyously giving thanks to the Father, who has qualified us to share in the inheritance of the saints in light" (Colossians 1:9-12, NASB).

"…to Him be the glory in the church and in Christ Jesus to all generations forever and ever. Amen" (Ephesians 3:21, NASB).

Come, Grow and Go!

Small Group Discussion

1. Get into groups of no more than five men.
2. Pick a leader to facilitate discussion and make sure everyone participates.
3. You have 15 minutes.
4. Topic: You are a small committee charged with getting a new church up on its feet. What is on your "To Do" list, and what are the priorities on that list?
5. Discussion questions:
   a. Review the list "God calls us to be a _____ church… Which two are the ones that draw you in the most? Why?
   b. On the same list, where do you see your church as strong or weak?

"What is a Local Church to Do?"

WHY DO WE EXIST AS A LOCAL CHURCH?

> *"So then, those who had received his word were baptized; and that day there were added about three thousand souls. They were continually devoting themselves to the apostles' teaching and to fellowship, to the breaking of bread and to prayer. Everyone kept feeling a sense of awe; and many wonders and signs were taking place through the apostles. And all those who had believed were together and had all things in common; and they began selling their property and possessions and were sharing them with all, as anyone might have need. Day by day continuing with one mind in the temple, and breaking bread from house to house, they were taking their meals together with gladness and sincerity of heart, praising God and having favor with all the people. And the Lord was adding to their number day by day those who were being saved"* (Acts 2:41-47, NASB).

The local church "gathers" for discipleship and "scatters" for evangelism. This can be expressed as three forces: COME! GROW! GO!

1. COME = Centripetal Force = Becoming an Invitational Local Church

> *"…let us consider how to stimulate one another to love and good deeds, not forsaking our own assembling together (Greek: episunagoge), as is the habit of some, but encouraging (Greek: parakaleo) one another; and all the more as you see the day drawing near"* (Hebrews 10:24-25, NASB).

> *"And He (Jesus) began to teach and say to them, "Is it not written, 'My house shall be called a house of prayer for all the nations'?'"* (Mark 11:17, NASB).

2. GROW (Healthy) = Internal Force = Becoming a Disciple-Making Local Church

> *"…grow in the grace and knowledge of our Lord and Savior Jesus Christ"* (2 Peter 3:18, NASB).

> *"O, restore me to health…"* (Isaiah 38:16, NASB).

> *"Go therefore and make disciples of all the nations…"* (Matthew 28:19, NASB).

3. GO = Centrifugal Force = Becoming an Evangelistic Local Church

> *"…you shall be My witnesses both in Jerusalem, and in all Judea and Samaria, and even to the remotest part of the earth"* (Acts 1:8, NASB).

HOW DO WE GROW HEALTHY AS A LOCAL CHURCH? GUIDELINES FROM THE BOOK OF TITUS

1. **We must strive to have leaders who are constantly developing as:**
   a. Bondslaves with a purpose (Titus 1:1).
   b. Faith-builders who point people to God (Titus 1:2).
   c. Knowledge-builders (Greek: *epignosis*) who equip people to be godly (Titus 1:1).
   d. Hope-builders who hold on to the promises of God (Titus 1:2).
   e. Change-makers who are willing to do what is lacking and necessary (Titus 1:5).
   f. Team-builders who gather a group of qualified leaders to oversee the church (Titus 1:5-9).
   g. Truth-champions who know and defend the truth of the gospel (Titus 1:10-16).

2. **We must strive to have spiritually healthy people who are constantly growing (Titus 2:1):**
   a. Closer through fellowship (i.e., significant contact with other believers beyond the corporate worship assembly).
   b. Stronger through doctrine (i.e., understanding our beliefs and doctrinal positions).
   c. More passionate through worship (i.e., the adoring response to the majesty of God).
   d. Broader through service (i.e., using gifts and talents to serve others).
   e. Larger through evangelism (i.e., locating and picking spiritual fruit ripened by the Holy Spirit).
   f. Deeper through discipleship (i.e., becoming more like Jesus).
   g. More effective through prayer (i.e., praising, repenting, asking, yielding, entreating, rejoicing).

3. **We must develop a generation that trains the next generation (Titus 2:2-8):**
   a. Older men teaching younger men (Titus 2:2, 6).
   b. Older women teaching younger women (Titus 2:3).
   c. Maturing young people who are an example to all (Titus 2:6-9).

4. **We must strive to be a healthy local church that expands its outreach to:**
   a. Family
   b. Neighborhood
   c. Workplace or school
   d. City
   e. State/Region
   f. Nation
   g. World

"For the grace of God has appeared that offers salvation to all people. It teaches us to say "No" to ungodliness and worldly passions, and to live self-controlled, upright and godly lives in this present age, while we wait for the blessed hope—

the appearing of the glory of our great God and Savior, Jesus Christ, who gave himself for us to redeem us from all wickedness and to purify for himself a people that are his very own, eager to do what is good" (Titus 2:11-14).

"Devote yourselves to prayer, keeping alert in it with an attitude of thanksgiving; praying at the same time for us as well, that God will open up to us a door for the word, so that we may speak forth the mystery of Christ…" (Colossians 4:2-3).

Consider the many wonderful outreach opportunities as a healthy local church develops a strategy and strategic partnerships to spread the gospel to a needy world. Using the graphic below you have scores of different ministry opportunities (e.g., developing fellowship in the family, encouraging service in neighborhoods, and promoting prayer for the world, etc.).

"Go therefore and make (spiritually healthy) disciples of all the nations…"
(Matthew 28:19, NASB).

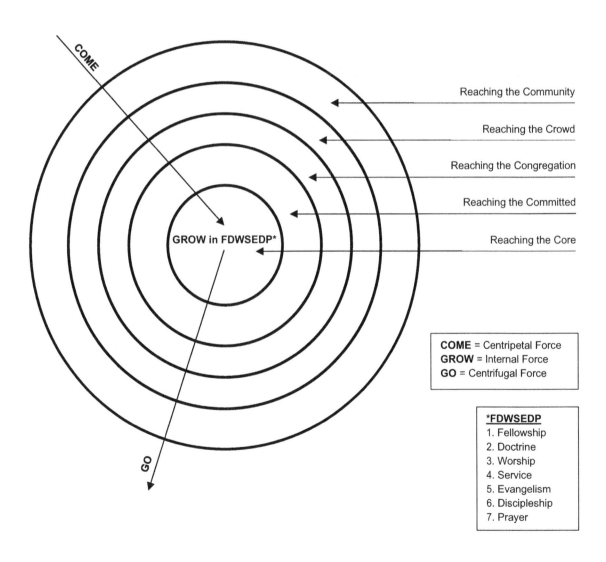

Healthy Christian Worksheet

[Complete before this week's session]

State what you are currently doing to become a healthy Christian by growing in:

1. Fellowship: _____
2. Doctrine: _____
3. Worship: _____
4. Service: _____
5. Evangelism: _____
6. Discipleship: _____
7. Prayer: _____

State what you are currently doing to become a healthy Christian by reaching out to:

1. Family: _____
2. Neighborhood: _____
3. Work/School: _____
4. City: _____
5. Region: _____
6. Nation: _____
7. World: _____

Forming Men In Action Bible Church

SELECTING LEADERS OF THE LOCAL CHURCH

Imagine we have decided to start a new church. Each of us represents one family unit, with an average of about 3-4 people in each family. We have chosen a temporary name ("Men in Action Bible Church") and have a space to meet. We will meet Sunday afternoons in one combined gathering of about 100 people. We are not yet affiliated with any other church or denomination, and we do not yet have paid staff. We need a committee to guide us in the process of selecting a formal leadership team that will take us through the necessary steps.

Referencing the notes from "Leaders in the Local Church" (Session 10), and what we have learned in this class, discuss the following:

1. What kind of leadership structure do we want in this new church? Leaders? Elders? Deacons? Pastors?
2. Who will be in charge of what?
3. What will be the leaders' responsibilities?
4. How will we pick them?
5. How long will they serve?
6. What role will the congregation have in selecting leaders?
7. How do we determine who in the congregation plays a role?
8. Will we have deacons? Elders? Both?
9. If multiple kinds of leadership roles, are all leaders equal in their roles?
10. What other issues do we need to discuss?

SETTING PRIORITIES

1. What do we do first, second, third, etc.?
2. What is important to decide right away, and what can wait?
3. What practical things must we deal with?
4. How do we decide who does what?
5. What form of organization will we employ?

List the first ten essentials that need to be decided in order to move forward.

1. _____
2. _____
3. _____
4. _____
5. _____
6. _____
7. _____
8. _____
9. _____
10. _____

NOTES

SESSION 12
Case Study Presentations

Discernment is God's call to intercession,
never to fault-finding.

SESSION 12
Case Study Presentations

If you will miss this session, let us know as soon as possible. Arrangements will be made to complete your Case Study. Completion is a prerequisite to graduating.

Application from the last session
Pick one thing you learned from the last session you can apply in your life as either an action item or a truth you should embrace.

_____

_____

Before class
____ Continued your Solo Initiative
____ Completed your Case Study and be prepared to present it (End of Session 10 materials)
____ Read the Bible at least four times this week
____ Attended church (Sermon topic: _____)
____ Met with my Accountability Partner
____ Completed the "Healthy Christian Worksheet"
____ Have testimony prepared to turn in (Optional; Appendix B)

Bible reading

Date	Book/Chapters	At least one thought from what you read

Accountability checklist

___ Asked accountability questions	___ Discussed Solo Initiative
___ Discussed what you are learning in class	___ Prayed

My prayer request:

Accountability partner's prayer request:

Time/Place of next meeting:

At the beginning of class

- Put on name tag (Right side)
- Pick up your envelope if you turned in any forms last week (Re-file forms in your manual)
- Turn in any late paperwork (Use envelope in manual)

Class schedule

- 75 minutes: Get into groups of three men and present your Case Studies
  - Each man will have 25 minutes
  - Present the issues
  - Present your thoughts and solution
  - Obtain input from the other men
  - Discuss options
  - Make a decision
- 10 minutes: Break
- 10 minutes: Complete and turn in Case Study Final Report
- 10 minutes: Attendance and Announcements, next week's Graduation
- 15 minutes: Class debrief of Case Studies
- 10 minutes: Complete and turn in Class Evaluation and Questionnaire (Appendix B)
- 5 minutes: Complete and turn in Class Check-Out sheet (Appendix B)
- 5 minutes: Complete and turn in any other paperwork

Calling a missing chair

"…You will be missed because your seat will be empty" (1 Samuel 20:18).

Missing chair:	
Phone number:	Email:
Contacted:	Status:

Teaching goal

That men would understand and appreciate the challenges that come with being a leader in the Body of Christ.

IMPORTANT: If for any reason you are not able to turn in your Case Study or Class Evaluation at the end of this class session, then you need to provide both documents to one of the class leaders within the next few days.

Case Study Debrief

After completing the small group discussions on the case studies, we will come together as a class for a general debriefing and discussion.

1. What input did you find the most beneficial in reaching your conclusion?
2. Did any group end up in disagreement on how to handle the matter at the end of the discussion?
3. Did anyone end up with a different recommendation than they expected when they began the project?
4. If you had been given more time, what would you have liked to have done before having to make your final recommendation?
5. Even after you made your recommendations, what sort of negative consequences are you anticipating from your decision? How do you plan to deal with them?
6. What was the hardest part of the assignment?
7. How did this assignment prepare you to be an encouragement to your present church leaders?
8. What did this exercise do to help you understand your own potential as a church leader?

NOTES

SESSION 13
Celebrating Our Victories

"But of all God's miracles large and small, the most miraculous one of all, is that out of a worthless lump of clay, God has made a man today."
("Miracle of Miracles," by Jerry Bock; from the musical "Fiddler on the Roof")

SESSION 13
Celebrating Our Victories

Before class

____ Continued your Solo Initiative
____ Read the Bible at least four times this week
____ Attended church (Sermon topic: _____)
____ Met with my Accountability Partner
____ Invite guests to the Graduation

Bible reading

Date	Book/Chapters	At least one thought from what you read

Accountability checklist

____ Asked accountability questions	____ Discussed Solo Initiative
____ Discussed what you are learning in class	____ Prayed

My prayer request:

Accountability partner's prayer request:

Time/Place of next meeting:

Documents to be sure you have turned in

- Class Evaluation
- End of the Class Testimony (optional)
- Testimony of Wife (optional)
- Testimony of Accountability Partner (optional)
- Two Service Projects
- Attend a Men's Event report

Schedule for graduation

1. 1-1 ½ hours: [Prior to graduation] Set-up crew (tables, chairs, nametags, etc.)
2. 15 minutes: Name tags for attendees/Mix and mingle
3. 5 minutes: Welcome and prayer
4. 30 minutes: Serve and eat dinner/dessert
5. 15 minutes: Explanation of Men in Action
6. 40 minutes: Awards and graduation
7. 10 minutes: Personal reflections from the audience
8. 10 minutes: Prayer of dedication
9. 5 minutes: Continuing the Journey – Other men's ministries
10. 15 minutes: Dessert
11. Dismiss after any final paperwork is turned in; clean up

Teaching goal

That men and their guests will celebrate and appreciate what they have accomplished over the last 12 weeks. They will leave with a challenge to apply what they have learned as they move forward with a lifelong commitment to grow as Men in Action.

What's Next?

Congratulations! You have graduated from Men in Action. You have worked through a program that challenged you to look at the man you are, and the man God wants you to become. The class challenged you to accomplish a series of first steps towards your goals. But they are only first steps.

The real question is, what are you going to do tomorrow, next week, next month, next year? This is where the rubber meets the road. You can take what you have learned and turn it into something of permanent value beyond anything this world offers. It is up to you. How will this class change you for the better? That work really starts now.

Below are some suggestions of things you can do to turn temporary experiences into lifelong habits:

1. Keep a regular accountability relationship with another Christian man.
2. Make it a practice to attend church weekly.
3. Become a generous giver of your time, talent and treasure to your local church.
4. Become active in one or more ministries.
5. Read the Bible regularly (set a specific time to do this).
6. Pray and then pray some more (let those in your family see you praying/pray with them).
7. Spend meaningful time with your spouse.
8. Spend meaningful time with your children.
9. Review your "My Life Focus" at least one time each year, to both update it and to remind yourself of the commitments you made.

God, Make us Men

Dear God,

- Make us men…
    - ribbed with the steel of Your Spirit…
    - who will not flinch when the battle is fierce,
    - who won't acquiesce at the bargaining table or compromise principle.

- Make us men…
    - who won't retreat on the battlefield…
    - who won't sell out for lucre or convenience.

- Make us men…
    - who won't be bought, bartered, or badgered by the enemy…
    - who will go the distance, pay the price, suffer the loss...
    - who will make the sacrifice, stand the ground, and hold high the torch of conviction in the face of pressure.

- Make us men…
    - obsessed with principle instead of pleasure…
    - committed to Your Word, stripped of self-seeking and a yen for security,
    - who will pay the high price of freedom and go any lengths for truth.

- Make us men…
    - delivered from mediocrity…
    - with vision high, pride low, faith wide, love deep, and patience long...
    - who will dare to march to the drumbeat of a different drummer,
    - who will not surrender right for a mess of pottage,
    - or run from trials and evade conflict.

- Make us men…
    - more interested in scars instead of medals, work instead of leisure, challenge instead of easy projects, and in winning instead of just a tie.

- Make us men…
    - who will give their lives for a moment in time...
    - who are fearless in the face of danger…
    - calm in the midst of criticism.

- Make us men…
    - who will pray earnestly, work long, preach clearly, fight bravely, love ridiculously, and wait patiently.

- Make us men…
  - whose walk is by faith, whose behavior is by principle, whose dreams are God's and whose direction is forward.

- Make us men…
  - whose strength is equal to the task...
  - who won't fade under the searchlight of the enemy,
  - who won't fear at the shouting of the opposition,
  - who won't bend under the heavy load of responsibility.

- Make us men…
  - willing to be a minority, to stand for an unpopular cause…
  - who can perform without approval and applause…
  - who can stay in the battle without being stroked, thanked, awarded or promoted.

- Make us men…
  - willing to forfeit personal preference for the higher cause, personal rights for deeper responsibilities and convenience comfort for consecrated convictions.

God, make us men.

(Author unknown, adapted)

APPENDIX A
Alternative Sessions

So that the senior pastor can focus on what he thinks will best serve the needs of this particular group of men, the middle four weeks of the class are designed to provide the senior pastor with options in what to teach. The first four sessions are foundational, and the last four sessions focus on the larger role of men in the Body of Christ. The middle four sessions represent a bridge as you move from the foundation to that larger role. Do not consider yourself constrained to teach Sessions 5-8 as set forth in the current materials. Review the current Sessions 5-8 and the Alternative Sessions in this appendix and pick the four you believe are most relevant. If you use any of the alternate sessions, you will need to identify which tasks are to be completed each week.

If you have a topic or study you want to use instead of one of the four optional lesson plans, please feel free. One consistent item through these middle weeks will be working on My Life Focus.

1. Evangelism
2. Personal Finances
3. Fundamentals of the Faith
4. A Man's Physical, Mental and Emotional Health

NOTES

Alternative Session 1: Evangelism

Class discussion
The content below will be discussed during class. If you miss class this week you are required to read them on your own time, prior to next week's class.

Application from the last session
Pick one thing you learned from the last session of the class which struck you as something to apply in your life as either an action item or a truth you should embrace.

_____

_____

Before class
____ Continued your Solo Initiative
____ Read the Bible at least four times this week
____ Prepared My Life Focus
____ Reviewed and Rated the Case Studies (see class materials below)
____ Attended church (Sermon topic: _____)
____ Met with my Accountability Partner

Bible reading

Date	Book/Chapters	At least one thought from what you read

Accountability checklist

___ Asked accountability questions	___ Discussed Solo Initiative
___ Discussed what you are learning in class	___ Prayed

My prayer request:

Accountability partner's prayer request:

Time/Place of next meeting:

(Have you attended a men's event or done a service project yet?)

At the beginning of class
- Put on your nametag (Right side)
- Pick up your envelope if you turned in forms last week (Re-file forms in your manual)
- Drop off envelope if you are turning in any new forms
- Join a prayer group (3-4 men), praying with different men each week

Class schedule
- 20 minutes: Small group prayer
- 10 minutes: Attendance and announcements (e.g., missing chair, service projects)
- 20 minutes: Share testimonies
- 35 minutes: Discuss "How to Share Your Faith: Evangelism 101"
- 15 minutes: Small Group Discussion
- 10 minutes: Break
- 35 minutes: Discuss "A Strategy for Evangelism"
- 5 minutes: Review next week's assignments

Weekly prayer requests

Name	Request
Yours	

Calling a missing chair

"…You will be missed because your seat will be empty" (1 Samuel 20:18).

Missing Chair:	
Phone Number:	Email:
Contacted:	Status:

Testimonies

Name	Application

Teaching goal

That men will understand there is a lost world they have been called to reach and they can acquire the tools that will help eliminate the fear of evangelizing.

How to Share Your Faith: Evangelism 101

A Study by Pastor George Posthumus

Have you ever thought of what your job description is as a Christian? One of the fundamental questions of philosophy is "Why am I here?" As Christians, we have the answer to that question: it is to share our faith, the Gospel message with the lost, to mature and encourage the saved so they are equipped to share their faith, and to do all to the honor and glory of the Lord. So, evangelism is a key element of our core duties as a Christian. Given that truth, it is surprising how many Christians feel a lack of competence when it comes to this responsibility.

What keeps you from evangelizing and avoiding this duty? We tell ourselves we are not gifted in this area and so we should get a pass when it comes to sharing our faith. We convince ourselves we should leave the task to those especially "gifted" to reach the lost. The problem is that Christ does not leave that as an option. Here is Christ's last instruction, known as The Great Commission, to us as He ascends after His resurrection:

> *"Then Jesus came to them and said, 'All authority in heaven and on earth has been given to me. Therefore go and make disciples of all nations, baptizing them in the name of the Father and of the Son and of the Holy Spirit, and teaching them to obey everything I have commanded you. And surely I am with you always, to the very end of the age'" (Matthew 28:18-20, NIV).*

You might argue Christ was only talking to a select group in giving this direction (a weak argument at best). However, Peter is writing to the general church body when he says:

> *"But in your hearts revere Christ as Lord. Always be prepared to give an answer to everyone who asks you to give the reason for the hope that you have. But do this with gentleness and respect…" (1 Peter 3:15, NIV).*

KEY CONCEPTS

1. Be ready to share the gospel…*to make a defense to everyone who asks.*
2. Do it with tact…*with gentleness and reverence.*

We should be motivated by what the Bible tells us to do. However, further motivation should be found in the fact that every person born is headed to one of two places: heaven or hell. There is no third option. While we understand this *intellectually*, we often do not let it impact us the way it should *emotionally*. Look at those around you as people you should deeply care about. Many are headed for hell and are completely ignorant of this reality. So, for each person there is no bigger issue to face between their birth and death. What excuse can you give for why you are not committed to develop the tools necessary to be as effective as possible in sharing the Gospel message with others?

In this lesson you will understand the key elements of the Gospel. This knowledge will equip you to present the Gospel. You will learn how to move the conversation toward a point of conclusion and decision. It may be a decision for Christ or a willingness to think about the Gospel and opportunity for further talks. Always remember, you are not saving anyone, that is the role of the Holy Spirit. You are the means; the Holy Spirit delivers the Gospel Message.

Remember, true Men in Action KNOW THE GOSPEL AND ARE ABLE TO LEAD SOMEONE TO CHRIST! Only God can penetrate the heart of a sinner. We are God's agents with the message He uses to accomplish this. It is not an argument you are trying to win. If you are dominating the conversation with a person that is lost, you are probably not accomplishing much. You want to ask questions and allow them to open up and respond, to engage them in a real give-and-take communication.

Here are a couple of questions to memorize because they can trigger some deep conversation:

1. Have you come to a place in your spiritual life where you can say with certainty that if you were to die today you would go to heaven?
2. Suppose you were to die today, and you were to stand before God, and God were to say to you, "WHY SHOULD I LET YOU INTO MY HEAVEN?" What would you say?

Many times, a person will reply that they do not know and will ask how anyone can know. Alternatively, they may answer that they are sure they would go to heaven but cannot articulate any basis for their belief. Finally, they may say they know but are simply basing the belief off completely illegitimate grounds (i.e., their good deeds). It is at this point you can introduce them to the source of knowledge that clears up all the uncertainty by citing the following verse:

> "I write these things to you who believe in the name of the Son of God so that you may know that you have eternal life" (1 John 5:13, NIV).

Again, the goal is to get them thinking and to move them toward Scripture and its Gospel message. You want to spark their curiosity and have them invite you to continue. Ask a question like, *"Would you mind if I shared with you what I have learned about eternal life?"*

You want to stay close to the Bible, but you *also* want to personalize your presentation because in the end it is not a creed they are signing on to, but rather a relationship they are entering. That is why being open to discuss your own relationship with the Lord is an important part of this exchange.

FIVE POINTS OF THE GOSPEL

(Borrowed from Evangelism Explosion/Discipleship Evangelism)

It is helpful to have some tools to assist you in addressing the key points of the Gospel. Using your fingers, label them according to these helpful tips:

1. Thumb: Think of "thumbing" for a free ride.
   a. Key thought – **Grace:** Heaven is a free gift. It is neither earned nor deserved.
2. Index/Pointer finger: Think of shaking it accusingly.
   a. Key thought – **Sin:** Man is a sinner and cannot save himself.

3. Middle finger: In the middle of it all, the most powerful.
    a. Key thought – **God:** God is loving and merciful and does not want to punish us. But God is also just and must punish sin.
4. Ring finger: The wedding band represents your marriage to Christ.
    a. Key thought – **Jesus:** God sent His Son as the only means to pay for our sins.
5. Pinky finger: Little like mustard seed faith.
    a. Key thought – **Faith:** Our part is the faith. We must accept and believe what the other fingers are telling you.

PRACTICE

Turn to the person next to you and recite the two questions from the previous section. After that, practice using your hand to cover the five points of the Gospel message. Do this at least twice.

MAKING IT PERSONAL

Remember, this is not a lecture you are *delivering*, but an invitation you are *presenting*. The above presentation can be dry if it comes out as something you have simply committed to memory. You should personalize the presentation. You can do this by including facts and stories about your own journey to Christ and what it has meant to you. Your own humility in presenting God's Gospel should be clearly felt and communicated.

BRINGING THE CONVERSATION TO A DECISION-POINT

The purpose of all the information being presented is to bring the person to a point where they see there is a decision to be made. If the decision is not to accept, then the decision is to reject. To not accept is to continue down the road they are on, and it leads to destruction. There is only one way on this road, to accept the free gift of God offered in Jesus Christ.

When you get to this point, ask a very simple question: *"Does this make sense?"* Give them a chance to answer this question. This may mean you have a period of silence when no one is speaking. This can be uncomfortable but is okay because you want a thoughtful response. Try to avoid getting simple "yes" or "no" answers. Probe further with follow-up questions to draw the person out.

THE INVITATION

Remind the person that they have just heard:

1. The greatest *story* ever told,
2. About the greatest *offer* ever made,
3. By the greatest *person* who ever lived.

This raises the greatest question they will ever have to answer: "Would you like to receive the gift of eternal life right now?" They can say yes, no, or that they would like more time to think.

1. **"Yes."** If this is the answer, then pray with the person right then. Follow-up is key at this point. There will be a lot of "What is next?", but that goes beyond this lesson. The journey of sanctification follows salvation, and none of us can do this on our own. Remember, the more fully and clearly one understands their salvation, the more they are prepared to start the process of sanctification.

2. **"No."** This is not necessarily the end of the conversation. While you need to be respectful of the answer, try to find an opportunity to talk again in the future. Gently ask what is holding them back. If you get a second "No," accept it respectfully. Hopefully, you have planted the seed. They may come back to you, or the Lord may place another opportunity squarely in your lap or possibly the lap of another.

3. **"I need more time."** This is an encouraging answer and allows you to continue the dialogue. Find out what additional information they are interested in (what questions are most concerning to them). Set a specific time for further discussion. If they are not able or willing to commit to a specific date, contact them in the future to follow up.

KEY BIBLE VERSES

While you want to personalize your presentation, there is nothing that calls a person to Christ better than the words of Scripture. Below are helpful verses to have at your disposal when witnessing. When someone challenges you with "What makes you right and so many others wrong?" Your answer is: "Nothing about *me* makes me right. What is right is the Word of God, which I and millions of others have relied on as the source of Truth from God."

1. **Grace**
   a. Heaven is a free gift. It is neither earned nor deserved.

   > *"For the wages of sin is death, but the free gift of God is eternal life in Christ Jesus our Lord" (Romans 6:23, NIV).*

   > *"For by grace you have been saved through faith; and that not of yourselves, it is the gift of God; not as a result of works, so that no one may boast" (Ephesians 2:8-9, NASB).*

   > *"...he saved us, not on the basis of deeds which we have done in righteousness, but according to His mercy, by the washing of regeneration and renewing by the Holy Spirit..." (Titus 3:5, NASB).*

   b. While man's natural inclination is to try to earn whatever he can, this is truly a gift and you cannot pay for it through anything you do.
   c. Here is a helpful illustration called "Buying superpowers": Your greatest desire in life is to be able to fly on your own. How much would you have to pay to gain this power? The fact is, no matter how much wealth you accumulate, you could never purchase this ability. God is offering something you do not have the power to earn, no matter how hard you try.

2. **Sin**

    a. Man is a sinner. This is the universal condition for all humans. Worse yet is that there is nothing we can do to save ourselves.

    b. So, while salvation is a free gift based solely on the grace of God, we have a problem. We are all sinners, and by that sin we are separated from God and cannot merit the free gift, no matter how good we think we are or try to be. No one can be perfect. No matter how good you try to be, you are still a sinner.

> *"…for all have sinned and fall short of the glory of God…"*
> *(Romans 3:23, NASB).*
>
> *"Indeed, there is not a righteous man on earth who continually does good and who never sins" (Ecclesiastes 7:20, NASB).*
>
> *"There is a way which seems right to a man, but its end is the way of death" (Proverbs 14:12, NASB).*
>
> *"Therefore you are to be perfect, as your heavenly Father is perfect" (Matthew 5:48, NASB).*

    b. Here is another illustration, using the Grand Canyon: Imagine we are at the top of the Grand Canyon running from danger. We near the edge of the canyon. The only way to escape would be to jump across the canyon. Some may jump five feet, some 10 feet, some 20 feet. No one has ever jumped 30 feet. So, no matter how hard we try on our own we will all fall short of the other side.

3. **God**

    a. God is the loving and merciful father of us all and does not want to punish us. But He's also just, and due to His unalterable nature, He must punish sin. This creates a conflict that man cannot resolve, only God can.

> *"… I have loved you with an everlasting love …"*
> *(Jeremiah 31:3, NASB).*
>
> *"…He will by no means leave the guilty unpunished …"*
> *(Exodus 34:7, NASB).*
>
> *"It is a terrifying thing to fall into the hands of the living God"*
> *(Hebrews 10:31, NASB).*

    b. Good judge/Bad judge illustration: If someone kidnapped and murdered a loved one and they were brought before a judge, what would you expect? Let's say they told the judge they had once helped an old lady cross the street, so they should be forgiven. Would a good judge let them off the hook, or require justice and punishment? That is our same situation. We have done sinful things against God and should not think our moments of good conduct will make up for it.

4. **Jesus**

    a. God alone can solve our sin problem, which He did by sending His Son, the Lord Jesus Christ. Jesus is the infinite God-Man: Fully God and fully man. No man was ever like Him or will ever be like Him.

> *"In the beginning was the Word, and the Word was with God, and the Word was God" (John 1:1, NASB).*

> *"And the Word became flesh, and dwelt among us, and we saw His glory, glory as of the only begotten from the Father, full of grace and truth" (John 1:14, NASB).*

> *"I have come that they may have life, and have it to the full" (John 10:10, NIV).*

> *"All of us like sheep have gone astray, each of us has turned to his own way; but the LORD has caused the iniquity of us all to fall on Him" (Isaiah 53:6, NASB).*

> *"...and He said to them, 'Thus it is written, that the Christ would suffer and rise again from the dead the third day, and that repentance for forgiveness of sins would be proclaimed in His name to all nations, beginning from Jerusalem'" (Luke 24:46-47, NASB).*

> *"And there is salvation in no one else; for there is no other name under heaven that has been given among men, by which we must be saved" (Acts 4:12, NASB).*

> *"And the witness is this, that God has given us eternal life, and this life is in His Son. He who has the Son has the life; he who does not have the Son of God does not have the life" (1 John 5:11-12, NASB).*

    b. The sacrificial switchman illustration: A switchman (someone who works in a railyard that controls trains) notices a train loaded with passengers is traveling too fast and is headed towards another train (also loaded with passengers). He knows if they crash many will die on both trains. He knows he can switch the moving train to a side rail and save everyone. When he looks down at the rail, he sees his only child playing on it and he has only a second to decide what to do. He pulls the switch, sacrificing his son but saving hundreds on both trains.

5. Faith

    a. God has done it all. The only requirement for men and women is to put their faith in what God has done through Jesus Christ. All that God has done calls for a response. What will your response be? Faith is not simply intellectual agreement with facts. It is real and active and influences your actions and reactions. Faith is trusting Jesus Christ alone for forgiveness and salvation.

> *"Now faith is the assurance of things hoped for, the conviction of things not seen" (Hebrews 11:1, NASB).*

> *"...that if you confess with your mouth Jesus as Lord, and believe in your heart that God raised Him from the dead, you will be saved" (Romans 10:9, NASB).*

> *"… Whoever will call on the name of the Lord will be saved" (Romans 10:13, NASB).*

> *"He who believes in the Son has eternal life; but he who does not obey the Son will not see life, but the wrath of God abides on him" (John 3:36, NASB).*

    b. High blood pressure illustration: Imagine you have very high blood pressure that can only be controlled by diet, exercise and medication. Without these three things in your life, you are not expected to live more than a few months. You firmly *believe* the doctor's diagnosis and the prescribed remedy. Does your *belief* do you any good? Does your belief *alone* cure you of your high blood pressure? No. So what do you need to do? You need to *act* on it through diet, exercise, *and* medication. It is not simply *belief*, but rather *action* on that belief.

Small Group Discussion

1. Get into groups of no more than five men.
2. Pick a leader to facilitate discussion and make sure everyone participates.
3. You have 15 minutes.
4. Topic: Learning to evangelize
5. Question: What are your biggest fears that make you hesitant to tell others about Christ? What steps can you take to overcome them?

A Strategy for Evangelism

The earlier material we looked at provides a set of tools for sharing the Gospel with others. The most powerful tool is the Word of God. You should commit to memory—or at least be able to accurately paraphrase—key verses relating to the need for salvation and the steps to being saved. You need to be prepared to help a person see their need and then be prepared to help them fulfill the need.

We also need to understand our role. No man has ever saved anyone, and they never will. It is solely the work of the Holy Spirit that calls and convicts that person. Our job is to be a conduit through which the Holy Spirit delivers the message. This should take some pressure off. As a conduit I should strive to be the best conduit possible.

LIFESTYLE/FRIENDSHIP EVANGELISM

There is no one "secret" formula for evangelism. There are many ways people come to Christ, and there is not a Biblically preferable method. With that said, it is a good idea to have some tools on hand that give you confidence when the opportunity comes to present the Gospel.

> *"But in your hearts revere Christ as Lord. Always be prepared to give an answer to everyone who asks you to give the reason for the hope that you have. But do this with gentleness and respect…" (1 Peter 3:15, NIV).*

This is the foundation of apologetics. Note that the instruction is not "do it like this" but rather "be prepared." You are to know the Gospel and to be prepared to explain it. Scripture also tells us people will ask us to explain "our hope". This implies that people should *see* something different in us that causes them to ask. Next, it tells us our story, in the context of our relationship to Christ, is part of the message. Finally, it stresses that our attitude when presenting the Gospel is to be one of gentleness and respect. Calling a person an ignorant fool (even if they are one) is not a method recommended by Peter, who led the first great revival.

You should be prepared to witness to complete strangers. Sometimes the Lord will put them in your path in the most interesting ways. However, of even more immediacy and importance is being able to evangelize those closest to you. You have friends, neighbors, relatives, and co-workers you know need Christ. While you may not be called to a far-away country to be a missionary, where you live is your mission field.

> *"Then he said to his disciples, 'The harvest is plentiful but the workers are few'"* (Matthew 9:37, NIV).

This is a zero-sum game. Peoples' souls are going to heaven or hell. There is no third option. Look around you, to the people you care about. Where are they headed? Do you care? A true friend cares more about their friend's spiritual condition than their social relationship. Are you willing to put a relationship at risk by having a discussion about spiritual matters? The true opposite of love is not hate, but indifference. To whose fate are you indifferent? You cannot say you genuinely love that person and not care about where they will spend eternity.

Do you see yourself surrounded by opportunities to be a worker for Christ in his Great Commission, or are you a bench warmer hoping not to be called up to bat? Ask yourself:

Who are the people closest to me who I doubt are Christians?

_____

_____

Do these people know I am a born-again Christian? If so, how?

_____

_____

Do I display the Fruit of the Spirit to those closest to me? _____

Do I ever engage in spiritual discussions with non-Christians who are close to me? How and when?

_____

_____

What can I do to help those with whom I am closest find their way to Christ?

_____

_____

THE FIRST THREE BEATITUDES

Evangelism is not a cookie-cutter process where one size fits all. Everyone is unique, and they come to a discussion about spiritual matters from different perspectives. To have a meaningful discussion you need to understand where they are coming from and start from that point. One way to start a conversation and assess where a person is spiritually is to find where they appear to be on a scale created by looking at the first three Beatitudes.

> _"Blessed are the poor in spirit, for theirs is the kingdom of heaven. Blessed are those who mourn, for they will be comforted. Blessed are the meek, for they will inherit the earth" (Matthew 5:3-5, NIV)._

For many of the people you communicate with, all three of these Beatitudes are counter-intuitive to their natural way of thinking. They do not see the world as spiritual. To them, what you can experience through the five senses is all there is. Until you can deal with that issue, talking about sin and the need for a savior will not be productive. Some see the spiritual world as real but believe they can earn "spiritual merit badges" by doing good works.

The Beatitudes trace a course from not believing there is a spiritual world, to missing the point on how we approach God in seeking salvation. You cannot have a meaningful discussion if you start at a level higher than where that person currently is. Let them tell you about their views, and from that point, you can figure out where to focus your conversation.

Level 1	They do not believe (or at least question) whether there is a spiritual world.
Level 2	They question whether man is part of that spiritual world.
Level 3	They see themselves in control by being a good person (works).
Level 4	They do not see themselves as a sinner, or at least do not see their conduct as really bad.
Level 5	They do not see their sin as against God and something to be grieved over due to its consequences.
Level 6	They believe they can approach God on their own terms rather than in total humility.

Put each of the levels into your own words by giving an example of the kind of thinking involved.

Level 1	
Level 2	
Level 3	
Level 4	
Level 5	
Level 6	

LISTEN MORE, TALK LESS

Remember to listen more than you talk. Be interested and respond to what the other person has to say. Remember, this is not an argument but a conversation. People like to be heard. Real communication involves active listening. Never get too focused on what *you* have to say. If you want to have a meaningful dialogue, be responsive to where the other person is coming from.

Building a Life Focus Statement

[Insert any materials (talking points, updates, etc.) for the My Life Focus from the regular class materials for whatever session you swap this lesson for.]

NOTES

Alternative Session 2: Personal Finances

Class discussion

The content below will be discussed during class. If you miss class this week you are required to read them on your own time, prior to next week's class.

Application from the last session

Pick one thing you learned from the last session you can apply in your life as either an action item or a truth you should embrace.

_____

_____

Before class

___	Continued your Solo Initiative
___	Read the Bible at least four times this week (See "Bible Reading" below; "Daily Bible Reading Chart," in Appendix C)
___	Prepared My Life Focus
___	Reviewed and rated the Case Studies (see class materials below)
___	Attended church (Sermon topic: _____)
___	Met with my Accountability Partner

Bible reading

Date	Book/Chapters	At least one thought from what you read

Accountability Check list

___ Asked accountability questions	___ Discussed Solo Initiative
___ Discussed what you are learning in class	___ Prayed

My prayer request:
Accountability partner's prayer request:
Time/Place of next meeting:

(Have you attended a men's event or done a service project yet?)

At the beginning of class

- Put on your nametag (Right side)
- Pick up your envelope if you turned in forms last week (Re-file forms in your manual)
- Drop off envelope if you are turning in any new forms
- Join a prayer group (3-4 men), praying with different men each week

Class Schedule

- 20 minutes: Small group prayer
- 10 minutes: Attendance and announcements (e.g., missing chair, service projects)
- 20 minutes: Share testimonies
- 15 minutes: Discuss "The Stuff of This World: God's Part/Your Part"
- 15 minutes: Discuss "The Debt Trap"
- 15 minutes: Small Group Discussion
- 10 minutes: Break
- 20 minutes: Discuss "A Financial Plan: Budgeting"
- 20 minutes: Review "Biblical Giving"
- 5 minutes: Review next week's assignments

Weekly prayer requests

Name	Request
Yours	

Calling a missing chair

"…You will be missed because your seat will be empty" (1 Samuel 20:18).

Missing Chair:	
Phone number:	Email:
Contacted:	Status:

Testimonies

Name	Application

Teaching goal

That men understand how to manage (steward) their finances and the resources God has given them as evidence of where they are spiritually.

The Stuff of This World: God's Part/Your Part

For many people, life is about acquiring "things." God tells us life is about relationships, first with Him, and then with others. So many of us use *people* to obtain *things*. God wants us to use *things* to build relationships with *people*. How you focus on this foundational issue makes all the difference.

When it comes to issues of finances and the "stuff" in our lives, we need to recognize God has His clear role, and we have ours. Ultimately, God is the author, owner, and provider of everything. The reality is that you are a steward of all that is God's. The question is, what kind of steward are you? Until we come to this understanding and align our thoughts and actions with God's will, we will never be able to fully address financial matters in a Biblical way.

There are no absolute truths outside of God. My natural thinking alone will not take me in God's direction on any issue. No matter how smart I may be, my ways simply cannot hope to measure up to God's ways. To know God's will I must study His Word. It is an absolute requirement. The world is full of very smart people who create all sorts of brilliant ways of thinking. They are the philosophers of today and years gone by. You could spend the rest of your life studying their philosophies, but unless they are Bible-centered, they are of no more use in arriving at the truth than if you obtain your philosophy from fortune cookies. Again, we must remember God's truth is above man's thinking. If we stick with man's thinking, we will always miss the target.

> *"For my thoughts are not your thoughts, neither are your ways my ways,'*
> *declares the LORD. As the heavens are higher than the earth, so are my ways*
> *higher than your ways and my thoughts than your thoughts'" (Isaiah 55:8-9, NIV).*

If you are not willing to seek what His word says on the subject, then you will never find the heart of God and truth in this area of your life. The only way you can operate under God's system is if you study His Word diligently and incorporate His truths into your life. The major distinction between God system and man systems is whether they are anchored in God's truth. His will exists in His system and not in any other. You will not make right decisions about this subject without study of His Word. Natural man will not come to correct conclusions.

Information on the handling of finances and possessions is well-documented in Scripture. The Bible has more than 2,350 verses on the subject of money and possessions. God knew possessions and money would be one of the biggest competitors for His claim on your time and attention. Will God, or "stuff" control your life? Jesus taught that trying to serve both God and money is not just impractical or inadvisable; it is impossible.

> *"No one can serve two masters; for either he will hate the one and love the other,*
> *or he will be devoted to the one and despise the other. You cannot serve both*
> *God and wealth" (Matthew 6:24, NASB).*

Other Scriptures agree:

"Yours, O LORD, is the greatness and the power and the glory and the victory and the majesty, indeed everything that is in the heavens and the earth; Yours is the dominion, O LORD, and You exalt Yourself as head over all. Both riches and honor come from You, and You rule over all, and in Your hand is power and might; and it lies in Your hand to make great and to strengthen everyone"
(1 Chronicles 29:11-12, NASB).

"The land, moreover, shall not be sold permanently, for the land is Mine; for you are but aliens and sojourners with Me" (Leviticus 25:23, NASB).

"...for every animal of the forest is mine, and the cattle on a thousand hills. I know every bird in the mountains, and the creatures of the field are mine. If I were hungry I would not tell you, for the world is mine, and all that is in it" (Psalm 50:10-12, NIV).

"The silver is mine and the gold is mine declares the Lord Almighty"
(Haggai 2:8, NIV).

If you think any of your stuff is ultimately yours, you are fooling yourself. He is not only the creator of all things, He is the owner. Whatever we think we own is only in our possession because God allows it.

So, if it all belongs to God, what is *your* role?

_____

_____

We are simply stewards for God of "God's stuff". Once I accept this, it places a significant duty on me. He is watching to see how I handle what He has given to me.

So, what is a steward? A steward manages another's property and interests for the owner's benefit. The steward is to manage with the best interest of the owner at heart. He has what is called "fiduciary duty." He is held to the highest duty regarding his stewardship management.

This truth makes every spending decision a spiritual decision. This is one of the most powerful concepts from God. Every penny I have is God's, so when I buy something, I am making a stewardship decision on how to allocate His resources.

There is another powerful truth here, and it relates to how I care for my possessions. Understanding that God ultimately owns everything I have, and I am only a steward of those possessions, my desire should be to take good care of anything in my possession.

> *"Therefore if you have not been faithful in the use of unrighteous wealth, who will entrust the true riches to you?" (Luke 16:11, NASB)*

"Now, it is required that those who have been given a trust must prove faithful"
(1 Corinthians 4:2, NIV).

So, what does this mean for how we handle the things God has given us?

_____

_____

How you handle your finances says a tremendous amount about your relationship with God and your spiritual maturity. It is not just the idea of giving God a small percentage and then you do what you want with the rest. One hundred percent of what you have and how you use it falls under your stewardship responsibility. You should always be asking yourself, "What does God want me to do *not* just with my giving but with my *spending*?"

Before moving on to a discussion about debt, we want to be sure one thing is clear: Having wealth, or the lack of it, is *not* a sign of God's pleasure or displeasure with you. God gives to meet our needs, and then for His purposes. He may have purposes for you that require a greater amount of wealth, or His purpose for you may require only a minimal amount of wealth. The important thing is to figure out how to best use the resources God has given you. When you have more than you need, you should ask yourself, "What does God want me to do with the excess?" The answer may not always align with your personal desires.

The Debt Trap

Debt is a trap that ensnares the unwary. When you go into debt, you are giving control of part of your future to some third party, and in most cases not a very benevolent third party. This is taught repeatedly in the Bible, but is summed up well in Proverbs:

> *"The rich rule over the poor, and the borrower is slave to the lender"*
> *(Proverbs 22:7, NIV).*

Debt is likened to *slavery*. Why is that? Years ago, you and your family could be sold to pay for debt. Today that is not allowed but that doesn't mean you can't be enslaved by debt. One of the biggest pressure points in marriages is finances. People feel trapped and hopeless. They have debt beyond their ability to pay. Most families spend much more a year than they have available. Left unaddressed, this compounds over the years.

If God called you to some sacrificial ministry today, would you be prevented from going because of your financial condition? Many of our options in life are limited by debt. It is one of the main issues preventing people from entering the mission field.

The problem of debt is not a matter of lack of *income* as much as it is a lack of *self-control*. There are plenty of wealthy people with six-figure incomes that find themselves in bankruptcy. As people make more money, they should focus on reducing and eliminating the debt side of their financial picture. Instead, so often they view the additional income as an opportunity to simply consume more. More income often just means more debt.

Paul has advice on the only type of debt one should owe:

> *"Let no debt remain outstanding, except the continuing debt to love one another, for whoever loves others has fulfilled the law" (Romans 13:8, NIV).*

The only debt Paul supports is relational in nature. He says we owe each other love, but to avoid financial entanglements.

Credit card companies fully support charging purchases to their credit cards. This means more money for them as a result of the interest rates they charge (sometimes as high as 20%). Debt is a trap. It is seductive. You can have whatever you want today for no money out of pocket. You simply have to agree to pay for it in the future with interest. The Bible warns against presuming on tomorrow as we live today.

> *"Now listen, you who say, 'Today or tomorrow we will go to this or that city, spend a year there, carry on business and make money.' Why, you do not even know what will happen tomorrow. What is your life? You are a mist that appears for a little while and then vanishes. Instead, you ought to say, 'If it is the Lord's will, we will live and do this or that'" (James 4:13-15, NIV).*

If you are in debt today, develop a plan to eliminate it. This may take time, but with discipline, it can be done. It may require you to change aspects of your lifestyle and spending habits. Be aware that the world will encourage you to plunge back into debt. Everyone wants to give you credit all the time. It is all so tempting, especially when we think of all the "stuff" we can buy.

We do not want to leave the impression all debt is bad and should never be used. It is just that it should only be used when it is necessary, and where it can be paid off as quickly as possible. You buy a house as an investment. If you do not over-extend yourself, it is a justifiable reason for most people to go into debt. Unless you have a complete market collapse you have an asset worth more than the debt. Homes normally increase in value and provide you with a place to live. Even loans for college can be justified since you are investing in yourself. However, you must count the cost and strive to borrow only when it is *absolutely* necessary. It is all the better if you can find a way to work your way through school. Many students find themselves with student loans equal to a house payment and a job that barely covers the necessities.

A Financial Plan: Budgeting

You are alone, in unfamiliar territory with your family and you need to get to a city 30 miles away before nightfall, but you have no idea which direction to go. You also have no knowledge of what lies between you and the city, so there is no way to determine whether you are headed in the right direction. At that point, what do you need more than anything else? A map. The map not only tells you where your destination is but gives you markers along the way so you know how you are doing on your journey.

The above situation is analogous to our financial lives. We are stranded in a world where spending seems to outpace income. We know where we need to get for our family – financial security. However, we have no real idea of where it is located, and even if we did, we have no idea of how to get there. This is when a map becomes a necessity. In this case, that map is a *budget*. Given that money is the number one stress in marriages, it is surprising how few couples make any effort at budgeting. They treat the matter as if things will simply magically work out.

Below are a set of principles to use in getting your financial house in order:

1. Include your spouse in developing your budget (both of you should contribute to the process).
2. Track your actual expenses for several months to determine where your money is going so your budget is practical and realistic.
3. Order your expenses from the most basic necessities to the most frivolous expenditures. Then eliminate items on the list until you have a budget that allows you to do all the things in #4 below. If you start to cut into necessities, you need to figure out how to supply necessities at a smaller cost (hint: cable TV is not a necessity).
4. Eliminate expenses until your budget allows you to regularly do the following:
    a. Give cheerfully, generously and sacrificially.
    b. Pay your bills.
    c. Save for major expenses (car, college, Christmas, vacation, etc.).
    d. Save for a rainy day.
    e. Save for retirement.
5. Raises and bonuses should not be used to expand your lifestyle. They should be used to help eliminate your debt faster.
6. Spend less than you bring in each month.
7. Plan for both the known and the unknown. Often the unknown events in life take precedence over the known.
8. If you have built up debt, develop a schedule to pay it off. Start with the most pressing debt first.
9. Never use debt to obtain any non-essential items (hint: with few exceptions, most stuff is non-essential).
10. Credit cards are okay only if they are paid off monthly.
11. Teach your children to budget (this is a habit that should be encouraged from an early age).

12. All that you have is God's and you are but caretakers of it. What type of steward are you?

Which of the above rules do you have the most trouble following?

_____

_____

Try following one of these principles this month, and then add a new principal each month for the next five or six months. You might be surprised how much better your financial situation becomes. These are not overnight solutions. Usually it takes a long time and a lack of discipline to get into financial crisis, so it will take discipline and time to get out of it.

You certainly can add items to the above list of principles. The point is that this is not a process that should be put off until a "better time". Find a budgeting book, take a Christian finance course, or reach out to a trusted friend who is good with finances to help you.

Not every financial crisis is a result of bad planning and undisciplined spending. Sometimes despite good planning, an extraordinary event occurs for which no real preparations can overcome. Loss of a job, or unexpected medical expenses can throw a well-oiled financial plan into disarray. Even in those situations the above principles will be a help to you as you begin to sort things out.

Small Group Discussion

1. Get into groups of no more than five men.
2. Pick a leader to facilitate discussion and make sure everyone participates.
3. You have ten minutes.
4. Topic: Biblical stewardship
5. Discussion question
   a. If you _truly_ accepted the fact that everything you have belongs to God, how would it impact how you handle your finances and assets?

Biblical Giving

INTRODUCTION

"Do not store up for yourselves treasures on earth, where moth and rust destroy, and where thieves break in and steal. But store up for yourselves treasures in heaven, where neither moth nor rust destroys, and where thieves do not break in or steal; for where your treasure is, there your heart will be also"
(Matthew 6:19-21, NASB).

GOD'S PERSPECTIVE

1. **Money is a Highly Spiritual Issue**
   a. O.T. Reminder #1: All riches belong to God (cf. 1 Chronicles 29:12; Haggai 2:8)
   b. O.T. Reminder #2: God gives to us as He pleases (cf. Deuteronomy 8:18)
   c. O.T. Reminder #3: There is great danger in focusing on money (cf. Exodus 20:23; Proverbs 11:28; Psalm 39:6)
   d. N.T. Reminder #1: Earthly riches are temporary (cf. Luke 12:33)
   e. N.T. Reminder #2: You cannot worship and serve God and money (cf. Luke 16:13-15)
   f. N.T. Reminder #3: The love of money can destroy us (cf. Hebrews 13:5; 1 Timothy 6:6-10)
   g. N.T. Reminder #4: Heavenly treasures are of greater value than earthly riches (cf. Matthew 19:21-24; Matthew 6:19-33; 1 Timothy 6:17-19)
   h. You will never get victory in the area of finances until you get victory in the area of giving!

   "We make a living by what we get; we make a life by what we give."
   -Duane Hulse

2. **Giving is a Heavenly-mandated activity**
   a. "Giving is not God's way of raising money. It is God's way of raising children."
   b. The Nine Commandments for Giving Biblically
      i. Commandment #1: Thou shalt give worshipfully
         1. "Thus all the tithe of the land, of the seed of the land or of the fruit of the tree, is the LORD'S; it is holy to the LORD" (Leviticus 27:30, NASB).
         2. "Thanks be to God for His indescribable gift" (2 Corinthians 9:15, NASB)!
         3. "...freely you received, freely give" (Matthew 10:8, NASB).
         4. "You shall bring the choice first fruits of your soil into the house of the Lord your God!" (Exodus 23:19, NASB).
         5. "Honor the LORD from your wealth, and from the first of all your produce; so your barns will be filled with plenty, and your vats will overflow with new wine" (Proverbs 3:9-10, NASB).

  ii. Commandment #2: Thou shalt give willingly

    1. "Tell the sons of Israel to raise a contribution for Me; from every man whose heart moves him you shall raise My contribution" (Exodus 25:2).

    2. "Each one must do just as he has purposed in his heart, not grudgingly or under compulsion; for God loves a cheerful giver" (2 Corinthians 9:7, NASB).

  iii. Commandment #3: Thou shalt give generously

    1. "Now, brethren, we wish to make known to you the grace of God which has been given in the churches of Macedonia, that in a great ordeal of affliction their abundance of joy and their deep poverty overflowed in the wealth of their liberality" (1 Corinthians 8:1-2, NASB).

    2. "Now this I say, he who sows sparingly shall also reap sparingly; and he who sows bountifully shall also reap bountifully" (2 Corinthians 9:6, NASB).

    3. "Give, and it will be given to you; good measure, pressed down, shaken together, running over, they will pour into your lap. For by your standard of measure it will be measured to you in return" (Luke 6:38, NASB).

    4. "Instruct those who are rich in this present world...to do good, to be rich in good works, to be generous and ready to share, storing up for themselves the treasure of a good foundation for the future, so that they may take hold of that which is life indeed" (1 Timothy 6:17-19, NASB).

  iv. Commandment #4: Thou shalt give cheerfully

    1. "Let each one do just as he has purposed in his heart; not grudgingly or under compulsion; for God loves a cheerful giver" (2 Corinthians 9:7, NASB).

  v. Commandment #5: Thou shalt give sacrificially

    1. "...I will not offer burnt offerings to the Lord my God which cost me nothing" (2 Samuel 24:24, NASB).

    2. "Now, brethren, we wish to make known to you the grace of God which has been given in the churches of Macedonia, that in a great ordeal of affliction their abundance of joy and their deep poverty overflowed in the wealth of their liberality. For I testify that according to their ability, and beyond their ability they gave of their own accord, begging us with much entreaty for the favor of participation in the support of the saints, and this, not as we had expected, but they first gave themselves to the Lord and to us by the will of God" (2 Corinthians 8:1-5, NASB).

  vi. Commandment #6: Thou shalt give regularly

    1. "Now concerning the collection for the saints, as I directed the churches of Galatia, so do you also. On the first day of every week

let each one of you put aside and save, as he may prosper, that no collections be made when I come" (1 Corinthians 16:1-2, NASB).

     vii. Commandment #7: Thou shalt give wisely

        1. "Now concerning the collection for the saints, as I directed the churches of Galatia, so do you also" (1 Corinthians 16:1, NASB).

     viii. Commandment #8: Thou shalt give carefully

        1. "On the first day of every week let each one of you put aside and save, as he may prosper, that no collections be made when I come. And when I arrive, whomever you may approve, I shall send them with letters to carry your gift to Jerusalem..." (1 Corinthians 16:2-3).

     ix. Commandment #9: Thou shalt give immediately

        1. Luke 16:10-11 "He who is faithful in a very little thing is faithful also in much; and he who is unrighteous in a very little thing is unrighteous also in much. If therefore you have not been faithful in the use of unrighteous mammon, who will entrust the true riches to you" (Luke 16:10-11, NASB; cf. Matthew 25:14-30).

        2. "Will a man rob God? Yet you are robbing Me! But you say, 'How have we robbed You?' In tithes and offerings" (Malachi 3:8, NASB).

        3. "You are those who justify yourselves in the sight of men, but God knows your hearts; for that which is highly esteemed among men is detestable in the sight of God" (Luke 16:15, NASB).

        4. "I have been young, and now I am old; Yet I have not seen the righteous forsaken, or his descendants begging bread" (Psalm 37:25, NASB).

3. Our choices

    a. "Instruct those who are rich in this present world not to be conceited or to fix their hope on the uncertainty of riches, but on God, who richly supplies us with all things to enjoy. Instruct them to do good, to be rich in good works, to be generous and ready to share, storing up for themselves the treasure of a good foundation for the future, so that they may take hold of that which is life indeed" (1 Timothy 6:17-19, NASB).

    b. "Not that I seek the gift itself, but I seek for the profit which increases to your account" (Philippians 4:17, NASB).

NOTES

Alternative Session 3:
Fundamentals of the Faith

Class discussion

The content below will be discussed during class. If you miss class this week you are required to read them on your own time, prior to next week's class.

Application from the last session

Pick one thing you learned from the last session you can apply in your life as either an action item or a truth you should embrace.

_____

_____

Before class

____ Continued your Solo Initiative

____ Read the Bible at least four times this week

____ Prepared My Life Focus

____ Attended church (Sermon topic: _____)

____ Met with my Accountability Partner

Bible reading

Date	Book/Chapters	At least one thought from what you read

Accountability Check list

___ Asked accountability questions	___ Discussed Solo Initiative
___ Discussed what you are learning in class	___ Prayed

My prayer request:
Accountability partner's prayer request:
Time/Place of next meeting:

(Have you attended a men's event or done a service project yet?)

At the beginning of class

- Put on your nametag (Right side)
- Pick up your envelope if you turned in forms last week (Re-file forms in your manual)
- Drop off envelope if you are turning in any new forms
- Join a prayer group (3-4 men), praying with different men each week

Class schedule

- 20 minutes: Small group prayer
- 20 minutes: Share testimonies
- 10 minutes: Attendance and announcements (e.g., missing chair, service projects)
- 20 minutes: Discuss "The Five Solas"
- 10 minutes: Break
- 20 minutes: Discuss "The Trinity"
- 15 minutes: Small Group Discussion
- 30 minutes: Discuss "Justification, Sanctification and Glorification"
- 5 minutes: Review next week's assignments

Weekly prayer requests

Name	Request
Yours	

Calling a missing chair

"…You will be missed because your seat will be empty" (1 Samuel 20:18).

Missing Chair:	
Phone number:	Email:
Contacted:	Status:

Testimonies

Name	Application

Teaching goal

That men would understand their faith as a reasonable and practical faith, which serves as a guide for daily living.

The Five Solas

The foundation of the Protestant Reformation is anchored in what is known in Latin as the Five Solas. The word "sola" means it "stands alone"; that this is all you need and nothing more. Each of these Solas were developed to stand in direct contrast to church teaching that existed at the time of the Reformation (1517 AD and following).

The Solas represent a firm place to anchor your faith. Theologies that drift away from these foundational doctrines will at some level become heresy. No matter how reasonable some philosophy might sound at first blush, it is in fact a trap if it ignores these five solas.

1. **Sola Scriptura**
   a. Translation: "The Scripture alone."
   b. It is the final word on what is true. Apart from God's word, man is only guessing as to what is true. They may be very well-reasoned and intelligent, but outside of God, guessing is all that man has to sort out truth from falsehood.
   c. All doctrine of the church must be anchored in Scripture. Scripture is self-validating and all Scripture must be interpreted in light of other Scripture from Genesis through Revelation.

2. **Sola Fide**
   a. Translation: "By faith alone."
   b. In the salvation equation, our only charge is to have faith (and God supplies our ability to believe). Works have nothing to do with our salvation. As the Beatitudes say, "Blessed are the poor in spirit," which implies that we have no resources on our own that can provide our salvation.

3. **Sola Gratia**
   a. Translation: "By grace alone."
   b. God's grace is sufficient. In fact, it is beyond sufficient because there is no substitute for it. All the grace you will ever need is granted to you at the point of salvation.

4. **Sola Christus**
   a. Translation: "Christ alone."
   b. Christ is the only mediator between man and God. He is the only source of our salvation. No human being on earth holds the keys to the kingdom. They belong to Christ alone and His work on the cross.

5. **Soli Deo Gloria**
   a. Translation: "All glory to God alone."
   b. All Christians are equal in the sight of God and we do not glory in ourselves, nor do we place others in a position of glory. While we can respect the work of the clergy and the great men and women of the faith that have preceded us to heaven, we do not worship them. God is worthy of all the glory!

The Trinity

God is one. We are monotheists, which means a single God. Unlike the Greeks and Romans, we do not believe in a pantheon of gods that created and rule the universe. However, within the Godhead (another term for the Trinity) are three distinct persons working together in perfection and harmony. We can explain different roles played by each, but it is still God the Father, God the Son, God the Holy Spirit at the end of the day. Co-equal and serving each other.

It is basic truth that the Father is not the Son, the Son is not the Holy Spirit, the Holy Spirit is not the Father, and yet they are all one. We refer to this truth as the Trinity, and yet the term is found nowhere in the Bible.

While the truth of the Trinity is fundamental to our faith, it is a doctrine often challenged, rejected and ridiculed. We base our salvation on the belief that Christ is God, the Son of the Father. It was the fully divine Son of God on the Cross, who in His love and perfection not only died for us but atoned for us. Islam not only rejects any thought of the trinity, it is offended by the very assertion that Christ is more than a man (albeit a great prophet), let alone the Son of God. Many cults have trouble reconciling the concept of the Trinity, and reject it outright.

Let's look at verses in the New Testament that speak both to the unity of and the roles within the Godhead. In reading these verses, what conclusions do you reach about the existence of our God being Triune (made of three yet one)? It should be noted that even the greatest theologians have not been able to fully explain and reconcile the Trinity. Sometimes God's truth is so deep and unfathomable for our finite minds, we in faith simply need to believe the truth, even if we cannot fully comprehend it.

> *"Therefore go and make disciples of all nations, baptizing them in the name of the Father and of the Son and of the Holy Spirit…" (Matthew 28:19, NIV).*

> *"…yet for us there is but one God, the Father, from whom all things came and for whom we live; and there is but one Lord, Jesus Christ, through whom all things came and through whom we live" (1 Corinthians 8:6, NIV).*

> *"…who have been chosen according to the foreknowledge of God the Father, through the sanctifying work of the Spirit, to be obedient to Jesus Christ and sprinkled with his blood: Grace and peace be yours in abundance" (1 Peter 1:2, NIV).*

> *"I and the Father are one" (John 10:30, NIV).*

> *"In your relationships with one another, have the same mindset as Christ Jesus: Who, being in very nature God, did not consider equality with God something to be used to his own advantage; rather, he made himself nothing by taking the very nature of a servant, being made in human likeness. And being found in*

appearance as a man, he humbled himself by becoming obedient to death—
even death on a cross" (Philippians 2:5-8, NIV).

"For in Christ all the fullness of the deity lives in bodily form…"
(Colossians 2:9, NIV).

"Very truly I tell you," Jesus answered, "before Abraham was born, I am!"
(John 8:58, NIV)

"The Son is the image of the invisible God, the firstborn over all creation. For in
him all things were created: things in heaven and on earth, visible and invisible,
whether thrones or powers or rulers or authorities; all things have been created
through him and for him. He is before all things, and in him all things hold
together. And he is the head of the body, the church; he is the beginning and the
firstborn from among the dead, so that in everything he might have the
supremacy. For God was pleased to have all his fullness dwell in him, and
through him to reconcile to himself all things, whether things on earth or things in
heaven, by making peace through his blood, shed on the cross"
(Colossians 1:15-20, NIV).

The following is adapted from Article III, Section B, of the Constitution and By-Laws of Campus Bible Church, Fresno CA:

Of the Godhead: We believe that there is only one true and living God, infinite in every excellence, and that in the unity of the Godhead there are three divine persons—the Father, and the Son and the Holy Spirit—who are one in essence and equal in every divine attribute (Isaiah 48:16; Matthew 28:19-20). We believe in the absolute deity of the Son (John 1:1), and that as a man He was miraculously begotten of God the Holy Spirit and born of the virgin Mary. Jesus Christ is fully God and fully man (Matthew 1:20; Luke 1:26-38; John 1:1-18).

Small Group Discussion

1. Get into groups of no more than five men.
2. Pick a leader to facilitate discussion and make sure everyone participates.
3. You have 15 minutes.
4. Topic: The Five Solas and the Trinity.
5. Questions
   a. What is the value of teaching the "Five Solas" today?
   b. How would you handle attempting to explain the doctrine of the Trinity?

Justification, Sanctification and Glorification

Our salvation has three aspects we need to understand. The Bibles words regarding our salvation are often misinterpreted, or proclaiming to have contradictions, when the reality is that the reader often simply misunderstands what aspect of salvation the author is referring to. Historically, out of these disputes sprang the Protestant Reformation.

A proper understanding of justification, sanctification and glorification are key to our Christian walk, and while interrelated in some respects, in the end they are distinct.

JUSTIFICATION

> *"This righteousness is given through faith in Jesus Christ to all who believe. There is no difference between Jew and Gentile, for all have sinned and fall short of the glory of God, and all are justified freely by his grace through the redemption that came by Christ Jesus. God presented Christ as a sacrifice of atonement, through the shedding of his blood—to be received by faith. He did this to demonstrate his righteousness, because in his forbearance he had left the sins committed beforehand unpunished—he did it to demonstrate his righteousness at the present time, so as to be just and the one who justifies those who have faith in Jesus" (Romans 3:22-26, NIV).*

Justification is a "point in time" event. It is a result of faith alone in the work of Christ alone through His death and resurrection to atone for all of man's sin. There is no work on our part, all work was Christ's. All we do is believe in that work, and accept it for our salvation. By this we are justified. We are at the point of justification given and clothed in Christ's righteousness because our own righteousness is and remains as filthy rags.

We have nothing to offer God that can earn or justify our salvation. It is why the Beatitudes start with the expression, "Blessed are the poor in spirit." Our true spiritual journey begins when we come to understand that in the spiritual realm we are completely impoverished, lacking even the most basic means to save ourselves. As we said earlier, this is where Sola Gratia/Sola Christus comes into play. We play no active role. We simply accept Christ's all surpassing gift. It is foolish and, in fact, offensive to God to suggest that somehow Christ's work is not sufficient and our works must be added to it.

There are many who call themselves Christian who claim it requires more than Christ's work to achieve salvation, and that it is a lifelong process that only *starts* with Christ, but requires *our* works to retain our salvation. This is confusing the work of *justification* with the work of *sanctification*. Some teach that we work to perfect our justification over time. However, our justification is perfect in Christ and nothing can be added to it. Nor once received can it be lost.

It is clear from Scripture that we are saved by faith and not by works: "For it is by grace you have been saved, through faith—and this not of yourselves, it is the gift of God—not by works, so that no one can boast" (Ephesians 2:8). The real question is not whether we need to, or can do anything to earn our salvation. It is clear that we cannot; it is an unmerited gift:

"For all have sinned and fall short of the glory of God" (Romans 3:23).

As a man, acting outside of God, there is nothing I can do to reach Him or reconcile myself to Him. He acted by sending His Son to die on the cross to be the final atonement for my sin. "For while we were yet sinners Christ died for us" (Romans 5:8). He then offers salvation to all who accept Him. "But as many as received him, to them he gave the right to become children of God, even to those who believe in his name" (John 1:12).

When did Christ justify you? In other words, when did you receive Christ's free gift of salvation?

_____

_____

SANCTIFICATION

So, are our works of no importance and just a waste of time? This is where sanctification comes into play. If I have accepted Jesus Christ, do I have any obligations? The Gospels provide ample evidence that accepting Christ means having obligations and responsibility. They were not optional. If you accept Christ, you will change.

In John, Christ, near his crucifixion, says:

> "…the hour has come for the Son of Man to be glorified. I tell you the truth,
> unless a kernel of wheat falls to the ground and dies, it remains only a single
> seed. But if it dies, it produces many seeds. The man who loves his life will lose it,
> while the man who hates his life in this world will keep it for eternal life. Whoever
> serves me must follow me; where I am, my servant also will be. My Father will
> honor the one who serves me" (John 12:23-26, NASB).

Christ is clearly talking about salvation here since the kernel dying (Christ) produces many seeds (those to be saved). He says two key things. First, that you should hate your life in this world; and second, that those who serve Him follow Him. In Luke, Christ makes this point again in the form of the parable of the wise and foolish builders:

> "Why do you call me 'Lord, Lord,' and do not do what I say? As for everyone who
> comes to me and hears my words and puts them into practice, I will show you
> what they are like. They are like a man building a house, who dug down deep
> and laid the foundation on rock. When a flood came, the torrent struck that house
> but could not shake it, because it was well built. But the one who hears my words
> and does not put them into practice is like a man who built a house on the ground
> without a foundation. The moment the torrent struck that house, it collapsed and
> its destruction was complete" (Luke 6:46-49, NIV).

Here again, Jesus is talking in terms of what it truly means to call on the Lord. You must put His words into practice. The person who calls Jesus "Lord" but does not put His words into practice will have his life end in a destruction that is complete. This in no way creates your salvation or enhances it. What it really does is serve as evidence you belong to Christ.

The faith that saves is the same faith that creates obedience. Our calling is for something more than just our salvation. We have been saved and now belong to Christ, not the world. I, as a Christian, am obligated to do the good works He planned for me before the beginning of time.

> *"For we are God's handiwork, created in Christ Jesus to do good works, which God prepared in advance for us to do" (Ephesians 2:10, NIV).*

Why would God save ones that would refuse to do the good works that he is saving them for? Paul, writing to the church in Philippi, says the relationship of works to salvation is an ongoing process. Not only does God save us for good works, He also gives us the will and strength to complete them. The good works are God working through me.

> *"Therefore, my dear friends, as you have always obeyed—not only in my presence, but now much more in my absence—continue to work out your salvation with fear and trembling, for it is God who works in you to will and to act according to his good purpose. Do everything without complaining or arguing, so that you may become blameless and pure, children of God without fault in a crooked and depraved generation in which you shine like stars in the universe"*
> *(Philippians 2:12-15, NIV).*

What evidence of your salvation do you see of Christ working in you for His good pleasure?

_____

_____

> *"Examine yourselves to see whether you are in the faith; test yourselves. Do you not realize that Christ Jesus is in you unless, of course, you fail the test?" (2 Corinthians 13:5, NIV)*

The purpose of our sanctification is to allow Christ to work through us to mature us, and to make us more Christ-like through this effort. At the point of *justification* we are all babes in Christ. It is then that the process of our *sanctification* grows and matures us. We are saved *for* good works, not *by* good works.

GLORIFICATION

Glorification is the end-product of the processes of justification and sanctification. We are headed towards a perfection that can never be achieved this side of heaven. At our death our spirit will be glorified, and we will receive a new resurrection body.

> *"And we know that in all things God works for the good of those who love him, who have been called according to his purpose. For those God foreknew he also*

predestined to be conformed to the image of his Son, that he might be the firstborn among many brothers and sisters. And those he predestined, he also called; those he called, he also justified; those he justified, he also glorified" (Romans 8:28-30, NIV).

It is a process that starts with His justification, and ends in His glorification of those that are His. If you are His and are not dead yet, then you are in the process of sanctification. How willing a participant are you in this process? It is the Holy Spirit's work to produce sanctification in you.

How yielded and submitted are you to the Holy Spirit in this effort?

_____

_____

The more we understand and embrace our salvation and what comes with it, the easier it is for our sanctification to proceed. All truths of our salvation are key to living in our new reality. We receive the Holy Spirit to lead and guide our lives. He is there to mature us and enable us to have a witness. We are not working to earn our salvation, we are living to serve God, out of thankfulness and obedience, and for His pleasure.

Building a Life Focus Statement

Your teacher will provide any materials for the My Life Focus exercise.

Alternative Session 4: A Man's Physical, Mental and Emotional Health

Class discussion
The content below will be discussed during class. If you miss class this week, you are required to read them on your own time, prior to next week's class.

Application from the last session
Pick one thing you learned from the last session you can apply in your life as either an action item or a truth you should embrace.

_____

_____

Before class
____ Reviewed the names of your fellow MIAs
____ Continued your Solo Initiative
____ Read the Bible at least four times this week
____ My Life Focus: Completed tasks 6-7 (Appendix D)
____ Completed "Taking My Physical Pulse"
____ Attended church (Sermon topic: _____)
____ Met with my Accountability Partner

Bible reading

Date	Book/Chapters	At least one thought from what you read

Accountability checklist

___ Asked accountability questions ___ Discussed what you are learning in class	___ Discussed Solo Initiative ___ Prayed
My prayer request:	
Accountability partner's prayer request:	
Time/Place of next meeting:	

(Have you attended a men's event or done a service project yet?)

At the beginning of class

- Put on your name tag (Right side)
- Pick up your envelope if you turned in forms last week (Re-file forms in your manual)
- Drop off envelope if you are turning in any new forms
- Join a prayer group (3-4 men), praying with different men each week

Class schedule

- 20 minutes: Small group prayer
- 10 minutes: Attendance and announcements (e.g., missing chair, service projects)
- 20 minutes: Share testimonies
- 15 minutes: Teach and discuss "Our Physical Health" and "Taking My Physical Pulse"
- 15 minutes: Small Group Discussion
- 10 minutes: Break
- 30 minutes: Teach and discuss "Our Mental Health"
- 25 minutes: Teach and discuss "Our Emotional Health"
- 5 minutes: Review next week's assignments

Weekly prayer requests

Name	Request
Yours	

Calling a missing chair

"…You will be missed because your seat will be empty" (1 Samuel 20:18).

Missing chair:	
Phone number:	Email:
Contacted:	Status:

Testimonies

Name	Application

Teaching goal

That men would understand caring for their physical, mental and emotional health is a key part of a balanced life, affecting our witness.

Our Physical Health

Spiritual health is the key goal of Men in Action. However, we need to take some time to evaluate our *physical* health. A poor physical condition may get a person to heaven faster, but the time spent on earth is a lot less pleasant, and poor physical shape will impact all aspects of our lives.

It is unlikely we are unaware of our general physical condition. We know we are overweight, out of shape, or have other physical ailments. We also know what we need to do to address the issue (in most cases centering around diet and exercise). The issue is not a matter of *knowledge*, it is a matter of *will*. It is easier to eat the chocolate cake than to go for a run or walk. As with so many things we want to accomplish in life, good physical health takes commitment and discipline.

As part of this week's session, we will evaluate our physical health. We also suggest you keep a diary of what you eat for a week. Pay attention to *how much* you eat (the volume), and the *number of calories* you consume. Use "My Physical Body: Pulse, Diet and Exercise Tracking" in Appendix C to track your sleep, diet, and exercise.

WHEN IS THE LAST TIME YOU HAD A PHYSICAL?

Part of monitoring your health includes having a regular physical. This is especially true for men who are 40 years of age or older. Many men have left the area of dealing with disease to chance. With cancer, heart disease and diabetes easier to diagnose and to treat, ignorance is *not* bliss. These maladies aren't referred to as "silent killers" for nothing. Left untreated, they affect every aspect of one's life, and will eventually end it prematurely. We encourage you to contact your doctor for a complete physical. You cannot treat what you do not know about.

Taking My Physical Pulse

While we all recognize the importance of taking good physical care of ourselves, we often experience more failure than success. While we are working on the *spiritual* man, we should not ignore the *physical* man.

> *"…the Lord is for the body" (1 Corinthians 6:13, NASB).*

> *"Or do you now know that your body is a temple of the Holy Spirit who is in you, whom you have from God, and that you are not your own? For you have been bought with a price: therefore glorify God in your body" (1 Corinthians 6:19-20, NASB).*

Take a few minutes to assess your physical health by completing the questions below. If you are not happy with the outcome of the survey, do something about it! Use these next few minutes as the catalyst for change in your life.

1. **I am getting plenty of rest:**   Yes   No   I don't know
   Goal to improve:

   _____

   _____

2. **I am getting sufficient exercise:**   Yes   No   I don't know
   Goal to improve:

   _____

   _____

3. **I have had a recent physical examination:**   Yes   No   I don't know
   Goal to improve:

   _____

   _____

4. **I am taking a regular day off:**   Yes   No   I don't know
   Goal to improve:

   _____

   _____

5. **I am in need of a few days off soon:**   Yes   No   I don't know
   Goal to improve:

   _____

   _____

6. **I am in need of a longer vacation soon:**   Yes   No   I don't know
    Goal to improve:

    _____

    _____

7. **I am pleased with my present body weight:**   Yes   No   I don't know
    Goal to improve:

    _____

    _____

8. **I am pleased with my present eating habits:**   Yes   No   I don't know
    Goal to improve:

    _____

    _____

9. **Overall, my health is:**   Excellent   Good   Fair   Poor
    Goal to improve:

    _____

    _____

10. **My last blood pressure reading was:**   High   Normal   Low

    Date of reading: _____

11. **In general, my health problems are:**

    _____

    _____

12. **To improve my present health condition, I promise to:**
    a. _____
    b. _____
    c. _____

AS YOU FEEL COMFORTABLE, SHARE THESE COMMITMENTS WITH YOUR ACCOUNTABILITY PARTNER.

(For further study, complete "My Physical Body: Blood Pressure, Diet and Exercise Tracking," in Appendix C.)

Small Group Discussion

1. Get into groups of no more than five men.
2. Pick a leader to facilitate discussion and make sure everyone participates.
3. You have 15 minutes.
4. Topic: How is your physical health? If it is not where you want it to be, what are you willing to do?
5. Discussion questions:
    a. Review "Taking My Physical Pulse."
    b. What changes should you make and why?
    c. How can the other men encourage you?

Our Mental Health: In Pursuit of Wisdom and Knowledge

"The fear of the LORD is the beginning of wisdom. A good understanding have all those who do His commandments; His praise endures forever"
(Psalm 111:10, NASB).

"The fear of the LORD is the beginning of wisdom, and the knowledge of the Holy One is understanding" (Proverbs 9:10, NASB).

We all struggle with knowing the right thing to do in everyday situations. We also struggle to *do* the right thing even *after* we know what it is. Issues come up at home, at work, and in our personal relationships where our response is not very edifying to those around us, nor honoring to the Lord. What is right and wrong and how we should respond is made known within the Bible.
There is one book, in particular, that is full of practical advice on everyday life—the Book of Proverbs.

The Book of Proverbs starts with the reason the proverbs were given:

"The proverbs of Solomon son of David, king of Israel:
for gaining wisdom and instruction;
  for understanding words of insight;
for receiving instruction in prudent behavior,
  doing what is right and just and fair;
for giving prudence to those who are simple,
  knowledge and discretion to the young—
let the wise listen and add to their learning,
  and let the discerning get guidance—
for understanding proverbs and parables,
  the sayings and riddles of the wise.
The fear of the LORD is the beginning of knowledge,
  but fools despise wisdom and instruction" (Proverbs 1:1-7, NIV).

The study of Proverbs helps us attain wisdom and understand words of insight. Development of wisdom, insight and knowledge requires the self-discipline of study and application. God's Word is truth. Whether we correctly *understand* and *apply* it is the challenge before us.

List some of the attributes one would obtain by studying the Proverbs as indicated in chapter 1, verses 1-7 above.

1._____ 2._____ 3. _____

4._____ 5._____ 6. _____

The purpose of Proverbs is to give us the tools to interact with the truth God has given us. When we strive for these attributes in our lives, we can live in ways that please the Lord.

SEEKING A HEART OF WISDOM: THE BRILLIANT FACETS OF WISDOM (HEBREW: CHOKMAH)

> *"But if any of you lacks wisdom, let him ask of God, who gives to all generously and without reproach, and it will be given to him. But he must ask in faith without any doubting, for the one who doubts is like the surf of the sea, driven and tossed by the wind. For that man ought not to expect that he will receive anything from the Lord, being a double-minded man, unstable in all his ways"*
> *(James 1:5-8, NASB).*

We must look for wisdom as for a hidden treasure, more valuable than silver or gold (Proverbs 2:4; 3:13-15; 8:11).

Facet #1: Discerning Wisdom (Hebrew: Binah)

Discerning wisdom is the ability to divide and separate truth from error, fact from fantasy, good from bad, right from wrong, and facts from feelings.

> James 1:5 "If any of you lacks discerning wisdom, let him ask of God..."

Facet #2: Skillful Wisdom (Hebrew: Tebunah)

Skillful wisdom is the specific ability to reason and think through complicated matters, come up with an effective action plan, and make it happen.

> James 1:5 "If any of you lacks skillful wisdom, let him ask of God..."

Facet #3: Prudent Wisdom (Hebrew: Ormah)

Prudent wisdom is the quality of laying bare a situation, stripping away the façade, peeling the surface layers off, getting to the core issues.

> James 1:5 "If any of you lacks prudent wisdom, let him ask of God..."

Facet #4: Experiential Wisdom (Hebrew: Sakal)

Experiential wisdom refers to practical insight into everyday situations.

> James 1:5 "If any of you lacks experiential wisdom (and we do), let him ask of God..."

Facet #5: Discrete Wisdom (Hebrew: Mezimmah)

Discrete wisdom is the ability to concentrate on a matter and formulate a carefully laid out plan of action without being swayed.

James 1:5 "If any of you lacks discrete wisdom, let him ask of God..."

Facet #6: Sound Wisdom (Hebrew: Tushiyyah)

Sound wisdom is a stabilizing wisdom that remains efficient and calm, without wavering.

James 1:5 "If any of you lacks sound wisdom, let him ask of God..."

Concluding Challenge: "Happy is the man that findeth wisdom."

"...we have this treasure in earthen vessels, so that the surpassing greatness of the power will be of God and not from ourselves; we are afflicted in every way, but not crushed; perplexed, but not despairing; persecuted, but not forsaken; struck down, but not destroyed; always carrying about in the body the dying of Jesus, so that the life of Jesus also may be manifested in our body. . . .Therefore we do not lose heart, but though our outer man is decaying, yet our inner man is being renewed day by day. For momentary, light affliction is producing for us an eternal weight of glory far beyond all comparison, while we look not at the things which are seen, but at the things which are not seen; for the things which are seen are temporal, but the things which are not seen are eternal"
(2 Corinthians 4:7-10, 16-18, NASB).

"Lord, give us a heart of genuine wisdom
so that we might reflect your eternal power to a foolish world."

GROWING IN THE FEAR OF THE LORD

"The fear of the LORD is the beginning of knowledge; Fools despise wisdom and instruction" (Proverbs 1:7, NASB).

What does Proverbs 1:7 say is the starting point of knowledge and wisdom? Write the entire verse:

_____

Some other reminders:

"...The fear of the Lord—that is wisdom..." (Job 28:28, NIV).

"The fear of the Lord is the beginning of wisdom" (Psalm 111:10, NIV).

"The fear of the Lord is the beginning of wisdom…" (Proverbs 9:10, NIV).

"Wisdom's instruction is the fear of the Lord" (Proverbs 15:33, NIV).

"He will be the sure foundation for your times, a rich store of salvation and wisdom and knowledge; the fear of the Lord is the key to this treasure" (Isaiah 33:6, NIV).

Scripture is clear, true wisdom is impossible unless we fear the Lord. Remember, we can approach God boldly because we are his. As the Apostle John says:

"This is how love is made complete among us so that we will have confidence on the day of judgment: In this world we are like Jesus. There is no fear in love. But perfect love drives out fear, because fear has to do with punishment. The one who fears is not made perfect in love" (1 John 4:17-18, NIV).

Our position in Christ is sure and we should have no fear. It is our *condition,* not *position,* that should be of concern. A true and properly understood fear of the Lord includes the following:

1. The fear of failing to please Him;
2. The fear of harming His reputation through our words or actions

Did you ever stop to think why we sin—why we fail to do that which the Lord desires us to do? Our sin is motivated by one of two things, fear or hedonism. Hedonism simply means the pursuit of personal pleasure (selfishness). We sin because we serve ourselves and pursue immediate gratification.

Because we are focusing on the other driver of sin (fear), we will not delve into a deeper discussion of hedonism at this point. It is here that "fearing the Lord as the beginning of wisdom" starts to become clear. Why do we not do what the Lord wants us to do, or do what He does not want us to do? It's because we fear something else more than we fear the Lord.

What are some things men fear that can cause them to stray from God's will?

_____

_____

Fear is a big motivation in our lives. Why don't we witness to our neighbor? Why don't we speak up when the Lord is defamed at work? Why do we laugh when we hear a dirty joke at a family gathering? Isn't it fear of one of the things mentioned above? However, fear is not always negative. It can be a positive motivation if it is a holy and righteous fear.

How does the fear of the Lord work in this context? Our fear should be that we will fail to please the Lord in our day-to-day living, or that we will harm His reputation by our conduct. When this type of fear motivates us and becomes a driving force in our lives, we begin to make godly decisions.

This kind of fear is the key to right decision-making and is the beginning of wisdom. When fear of the Lord (disappointing Him or harming His reputation) becomes the number one fear in our life, all other fears are trumped. We do not need to fear anything but God and seeking His approval. Our only fear should be letting our conduct act outside of God's love and protection.

We must place our faith fully in God. Our fear of God must be greater than our fear of other people or giving up control of our lives. A true and proper fear of the Lord cannot exist outside of complete trust in who God is and what He can do.

Ungodly fear stands at the door to block our way. Satan uses fear of judgement or punishment to paralyze his victims. Satan uses these fears to weaken our service to the Lord. He gets us so preoccupied with the concerns of today we never get around to doing the desires of the Lord. This is Satan at his best, blunting our effectiveness by having us joust with the beast of a future that may never come.

How can we tell if we have a proper fear of the Lord? It is the only fear that brings peace. Once our only fear is God, what else do we need to fear? The fear of the Lord comes with an abundance of God's promises we can fully trust and will bring about the inner peace and joy we all crave.

Next time we are tempted to sin ask, "What do I fear more in this temptation than God?" This is a key question for the man who truly desires to mature in the Lord. When we find an answer in these moments, we will begin to see why this concept is so important to success in our daily lives. Any fear greater than the fear of the Lord will create sin in our lives. We overcome sin by overcoming fear. We are not to fear man or this world. The Bible is clear on this point.

> *"The Lord is my light and my salvation—whom shall I fear? The Lord is the stronghold of my life—of whom shall I be afraid" (Psalm 27:1, NIV)?*

> *"Fear of man will prove to be a snare, but whoever trusts in the Lord is kept safe" (Proverbs 29:25, NIV).*

> *"I tell you friends, do not be afraid of those who kill the body and after that can do no more. But I will show you whom you should fear: Fear him who, after the killing of the body, has the power to throw you into hell. Yes, I tell you, fear him" (Luke 12:4-5, NIV).*

In Matthew and Luke, Christ assures us God will meet all our real needs. He is as concerned for us as we are for ourselves. Our trust in the Lord is inversely proportional to our fear of worldly matters. There is nothing wrong with a proper fear of the Lord:

> *"Serve the Lord with fear and celebrate His rule with trembling" (Psalm 2:11, NIV).*

"My flesh trembles in fear of you; I stand in awe of your laws"
(Psalm 119:120, NIV).

"Teach me your way, LORD, that I may rely on your faithfulness; give me an undivided heart, that I may fear your name" (Psalm 86:11, NIV).

"The fear of the Lord is pure, enduring forever" (Psalm 19:9, NIV).

"His mercy extends to those who fear him, from generation to generation"
(Luke 1:50, NIV).

"…I now realize how true it is that God does not show favoritism but accepts from every nation the one who fears him and does what is right" (Acts 10:34-35, NIV).

As a church body we should corporately fear the Lord. The problem with much of the church today is it fears man and man's opinions more than God's. It isn't that they don't love the Lord, it's that their concerns don't have Him as their primary focus. They are afraid of not being relevant. They reject the Word when it might give offense, and in becoming man-pleasers they destroy their purpose for being a church of Christ. In the early church, the fear of the Lord was a key to church growth. Notice their greatest fear in Acts:

"Then the church throughout Judea, Galilee and Samaria enjoyed a time of peace was strengthened. Living in the fear of the Lord and encouraged by the Holy Spirit, it increased in numbers" (Acts 9:31, NIV).

A failure to properly fear the Lord explains why so many people can read and study God's word, and yet never accept Jesus Christ as their personal Savior. There are people that *know* the Word, but never truly *understand* it. They know the *facts* but miss the *purpose*. It is because they don't approach the text with a righteous and holy fear of the Lord. This keeps them from ever understanding what true fear of the Lord is.

In Ecclesiastes, Solomon also declared the primacy of the fear of the Lord. After 11 chapters of exploring every type of human effort and achievement and finding each to be vanity, he concludes his book by saying:

"Now all has been heard; here is the conclusion of the matter: Fear God and keep his commandments, for this is the duty of all mankind" (Ecclesiastes 12:14, NIV).

Godly wisdom is not hidden from us. The Lord wants us to seek His wisdom in all that we do. But don't treat it as unimportant, turn your back on it, or ignore it. The consequences are rather dire. Wisdom requires diligent effort. We can't just summon it whenever we get into a sticky situation. It takes hard work to develop a heart and mind of wisdom, one that fears the Lord.

God's wisdom is a precious gift and it takes a man of faith to properly receive and apply it. As stated in James:

> *"If any of you lacks wisdom, you should ask God, who gives generously to all without finding fault, and it will be given to you. But when you ask, you must believe and not doubt, because the one who doubts is like a wave of the sea, blown and tossed by the wind. That person should not expect to receive anything from the Lord. Such a person is double-minded and unstable in all they do" (James 1:5-8, NIV).*

Knowing the right thing to do is not the same as doing it. Knowledge is not wisdom. In fact, knowledge to those who are faithless and without wisdom becomes a dangerous thing. Again, back to James:

> *"If anyone, then, knows the good they ought to do and doesn't do it, it is sin for them" (James 4:17, NIV).*

Our Emotional Health

INTRODUCTION TO THE EMOTIONS: GOD'S ENERGIZERS

Any study of the emotions must begin with a right understanding of who God is. A.W. Tozer, in his book *Knowledge of the Holy,* reminds us what comes into our minds when we think about God is the most important thing about us.

Why begin a discussion on the emotions with a challenge to think rightly about God? Because it was an all–wise, all–loving, all-powerful, all-knowing God who created us. Although He didn't have to, Genesis 1:27 tells us He created us "in His image." That means the God of the Universe and Creator of Heaven and Earth chose to impart to us humans a part of His own character. These are sometimes called communicable attributes.

When God created us, He gave us personality, in some ways like His personality. Like Him, we have intellect that enables us to reason and draw conclusions. Like Him, we have a will that enables us to choose to act or not to act on those conclusions. Like Him, we have emotion to drive us to action. Thus, the emotions are God's energizers. Let's consider a few pre-suppositions concerning the emotions. Let's call these:

THE ABC'S OF THE EMOTIONS

A. The emotions were created by God.
   1. We tend to treat the emotions as part of our human weakness. "After all," some suggest, "the emotional side of mankind is our worst feature!" However, when God created us humans with intellect, will and emotion He said, "It is good" and we have no right to say otherwise. A.W. Tozer was spot on when he described the essence of idolatry as the entertainment of thoughts about God that are unworthy of Him. Our goal is to say as a form of worship: "Thank you, God, for our emotions." We want to declare with King David: "I will give thanks to Thee for I am fearfully and wonderfully made (Psalm 139:14)." That includes our emotions.

B. The emotions were created for a purpose.
   1. Our Creator doesn't do anything without a divine and beneficent purpose. Why did He give us emotions? He did so to generate energy within us to do something. The English word "emotion" comes from the Latin word *emotio*, which means "to move out." That's what the emotions do. They move us out. They motivate us. They stimulate us. In science the symbol "e" in the formula $E = MC^2$ means "energy." Think of the emotions this way: "e" (energy) + motion = emotion. They truly are God's energizers when used as He designed them.

C. The emotions are neither right nor wrong, good nor bad.
   1. The rightness or the wrongness of an emotion depends on two things: the object of the emotion and how it is exercised. For example, for us to love our spouse is

right. The Bible says, "Husbands love your wives as Christ loves the Church." Right behavior (love)…right object (wife). But the Bible is also clear: "The love of money is the root of all sorts of evil." Right behavior (love)...wrong object (money).

2. Secondly, the rightness or wrongness of an emotion depends not only on the object of the emotion but how the emotion is exercised. Someone's anger at government stimulates him to blow up a government building. Right emotion (anger) but certainly exercised in the wrong way.

THE FIVE BASIC EMOTIONS

Emotion #1: Anger

Almighty God created us with ability to express the emotion of anger. Do we need to convince any of us of this? What is the God-intended purpose for anger? Very simply, anger generates energy to change things. We get angry at injustice; the emotion of anger motivates us to go out and change the laws. We get angry at our children's disobedience and the emotion generates energy to make appropriate changes in us and in our kids. It was this God-given emotion of anger the Apostle Paul talks about in Ephesians 4:26 when he wrote, "Be angry…yet do not sin." He is saying, "Get angry…at the right things…and express it in the right way." We thank God for the emotion of anger.

Unfortunately, as is often the case, we humans take that which God created for good and misuse, abuse and confuse it. So it is with the emotion of anger. Whereas God created anger to generate energy to change things, we turn it into an excuse for lashing out and hurting (i.e., hurting others, hurting ourselves, and even trying to hurt God). This is what is meant in James 1:20 when the brother of Our Lord writes, "The anger of man does not achieve the righteousness of God..." There is a vast difference between the anger of man (which is uncontrolled, lashing out to hurt and directed at the sinner) and the anger of God (which is controlled, exercised in love, and directed at the sin).

Emotion #2: Fear

Almighty God created us with the ability to express the emotion of fear. What is it's God-intended purpose? Fear generates energy to run. The Greek word *phobeo,* from which we get our word *phobia* literally means "to put to flight!" Fear motivates us to run toward God, run away from danger and to respond to power, especially the power of God. Thus, fear is the worship emotion!

We thank God for the emotion of fear in our lives. Yet, like anger, we humans also abuse this God-given emotion. What God created for good, man has allowed to cripple him, causing him to run away from God, to run in his own power and to sometimes run from things that are not real dangers. Some of us have been running so long we are consumed by fear and strangled in its relentless grip. We are addicted to unrighteous fear and worry.

Emotion #3: Loneliness

Almighty God also created us with the ability to express the emotion of loneliness. What is its God-intended purpose? Loneliness generates energy to find fulfillment. It is often the emotion of loneliness that stimulates us to find fulfillment in a right relationship to God. It is also the God-given emotion of loneliness that stimulates us to find fulfillment in a right relationship to a partner (e.g., a spouse). It is also loneliness that stimulates us to find fulfillment in a right relationship to a community of like-minded people (e.g., fellow Christians).

We thank God for the loneliness in our lives. But this emotion, too, is often misused and creates in us a drive toward two dangerous activities: self-pity and self-fulfillment.

Emotion #4: Jealousy

Almighty God created us with the ability to express the emotion of jealousy. What possibly could be its God-intended purpose? Jealousy generates energy to protect and sometimes to possess. This is one of the most misunderstood communicable attributes of God.

It was this God-given emotion of jealousy that stimulated Phineas in Numbers 25 to protect God's standards and execute God's judgment on two adulterers. It is this God-given emotion that generates energy within a wife to want to protect her husband when he is flirting dangerously with immorality (e.g., pornography). It is also the proper use of this God-given emotion of jealousy that can stimulate us to possess qualities we see in others and use them to serve God. Thus, in the Bible, it is often translated as the word zeal.

We thank God for the emotion of jealousy. However, we often abuse this emotion. It easily turns into hatred, bitterness, gossip, slander, fighting, and quarreling. Our righteous jealousy (i.e., zeal) morphs into sinful possessiveness and control. Thus, sinful jealousy is often linked in the Bible to selfish ambition.

Emotion #5: Love

Almighty God created us with the ability to express the emotion of love. What is the God-intended purpose of love? Most of us know the answer to this. Love generates energy to serve. It stimulates us to place worth on someone. It generates energy to self-sacrifice (e.g., Ephesians 5:25 "Husbands love your wives as Christ loved the Church and gave Himself up for Her"). Love also generates energy to obey God. Jesus said, "If you love me, keep my commandments..." That obedient love for God also stimulates us to love one another.

We thank the Lord for the God-given emotion of love. And yet, like anger, fear, loneliness and jealousy, we often misuse this God-given emotion of love. Instead of love generating energy to serve others, we have used it to serve ourselves and allowed selfishness to consume us.

God-given Emotion	God's Intended Purpose	Man's Abuses
Anger	• Make changes	• Lash out to hurt
Fear	• Respond to power • Run toward God • Run away from danger	• Run in our own power • Run away from God • Run from imagined danger
Loneliness	• Find fulfillment with God, a spouse and a community	• Self-pity • Self-fulfillment
Jealousy	• Exercise zeal to protect and possess righteous standards	• Hatred • Gossip • Possessiveness • Control
Love	• Serve and self-sacrifice	• Selfishness

Anger generates energy to change things. Fear generates energy to run. Loneliness generates energy to find fulfillment. Jealousy generates energy to protect. Love generates energy to serve. Of course, there are many more emotions to consider (e.g., grief, sadness, joy, etc.), but let these five basic emotions be the foundation for our consideration as emotional beings created in the image of God.

John Edrington writes: "Without the emotions we would be literally lifeless, having no desires or motivation. We would be just a blob with nothing but a few reflexes to identify us as alive." Does God want us to be emotional creatures? Absolutely. Imagine heaven's celebration without emotion. Imagine seeing Jesus without the ability to respond in adoration. God created us to be emotional, but He also created us to be emotionally healthy.

King Solomon said it well in Proverbs 25:28, "Like a city that is broken into and without walls is a man who has no control over his spirit." Like an unfortified city susceptible to all kinds of attacks, is someone emotionally out of control. God wants us healthy in every way, physically, spiritually, mentally, and emotionally. Take to heart the Apostle Paul's closing words:

> *"Now may the God of peace Himself sanctify you entirely; and may your spirit and soul and body be preserved complete, without blame at the coming of our Lord Jesus Christ" (1 Thessalonians 5:23, NASB).*

APPENDIX B
Additional Forms

1. Men in Action Service Project Report
2. End of Class Check Out Sheet
3. Attending a Men's Event
4. Class Evaluation & Questionnaire
5. Your End of Class Testimony
6. Testimony of Accountability Partner
7. Testimony from Your Wife

NOTES

Service Project #1 Report

[Make a copy and turn in]

Your name: _____

Describe the project:

_____

_____

_____

_____

Who was the Project Leader? _____

Date of project: _____   Length of project: _____

Who were your fellow MIA classmates involved in this service project?

_____

_____

What was your specific part or role?

_____

_____

What were your impressions of this experience?

_____

_____

What skills did you employ in doing this project?

_____

_____

Is there any follow-up work to be done?

_____

_____

Signature: _____   Date of report: _____

Service Project #2 Report

[Make a copy and turn in]

Your name: _____

Describe the project:

_____

_____

_____

_____

Who was the Project Leader? _____

Date of project: _____   Length of project: _____

Who were your fellow MIA classmates involved in this service project?

_____

_____

What was your specific part or role?

_____

_____

What were your impressions of this experience?

_____

_____

What skills did you employ in doing this project?

_____

_____

Is there any follow-up work to be done?

_____

_____

Signature: _____   Date of report: _____

End of Class Check-Out Sheet

[Complete, then make a copy and turn in before graduation]

You must answer the following questions and hand in at the end of Session 12.

1.	I personally attended at least nine classes.	Yes	No
2.	If I missed a class, I read the material on my own.	Yes	No
3.	I attended church regularly during MIA.	Yes	No
4.	I carried out my Solo Initiative.	Yes	No
5.	I memorized the Fruit of the Spirit.	Yes	No
7.	I met regularly with my accountability partner. Name of accountability partner: _____	Yes	No
8.	I completed the following number of service projects:		_____
9.	I attended a men's event.	Yes	No
10.	I prayed regularly during MIA.	Yes	No
11.	I read the Bible regularly during MIA.	Yes	No
12.	I gave my testimony during MIA.	Yes	No
13.	I completed my Spiritual Gifts Survey.	Yes	No
16.	I completed My Life Focus.	Yes	No
17.	I completed the Case Study.	Yes	No

If you did not answer "yes" to any of the above questions please explain:

_____

_____

Print name: _____

Signature: _____   Date: _____

NOTES

Attending a Men's Event

[Complete, then make a copy and turn in before graduation]

You are required to attend one men's event as part of the Men in Action program. This can be any event put on by the men's ministry at the church, or any other event cleared with your class leaders. Please turn in this form once the event has taken place.

Your name: _____

Event date: _____

Describe the event:

_____

_____

_____

Who put on the event: _____

Date of the event: _____

Length of the event: _____

Location of event: _____

Estimate the number of men in attendance: _____
How many other MIA's: _____

Describe your involvement at the event:

_____

_____

_____

Describe what you learned at the event:

_____

_____

_____

Signature: _____ Date: _____

NOTES

Class Evaluation and Questionnaire

[Complete, then make a copy and turn in before graduation]

Your name: _____ Date: _____

Please nominate *two* of your classmates for each of the following:

Most inspiring testimony: 1. _____   2. _____

Most likely to be an elder soon: 1. _____   2. _____

Best exemplifies what MIA is about: 1. _____   2. _____

Please evaluate the following areas of the class as to how important it was to the overall class experience (this helps us improve the course, so please be as candid as possible).

Rate each on a scale of 1 (Unnecessary) to 10 (Extremely Important), and write any comments:

1.   **The use of name tags:**   1 2 3 4 5 6 7 8 9 10
     _____
     _____

2.   **Prayer time:**   1 2 3 4 5 6 7 8 9 10
     _____
     _____

3.   **Share testimonies:**   1 2 3 4 5 6 7 8 9 10
     _____
     _____

4.   **Having an accountability partner:**   1 2 3 4 5 6 7 8 9 10
     _____
     _____

5.   **Teaching time:**   1 2 3 4 5 6 7 8 9 10
     _____
     _____

6.   **The small group discussion in each class:**   1 2 3 4 5 6 7 8 9 10
     _____
     _____

7.   **Preparing My Life Focus:**   1 2 3 4 5 6 7 8 9 10
     _____
     _____

8. **Doing the Case Study:** 　 1　2　3　4　5　6　7　8　9　10

_____

_____

9. **Memorizing/Focusing on Fruit of the Spirit:** 1　2　3　4　5　6　7　8　9　10

_____

_____

10. **Doing service projects:** 　 1　2　3　4　5　6　7　8　9　10

_____

_____

11. **The manual and materials:** 　 1　2　3　4　5　6　7　8　9　10

_____

_____

12. **What was the _most_ beneficial aspect of the class for you?**

_____

_____

13. **What aspect of the class had the _least_ impact on you?**

_____

_____

14. **What is one thing we could do differently that would improve the class?**

_____

_____

15. **Other miscellaneous thoughts or comments:**

_____

_____

16. **Name any men in the church you believe would benefit from taking MIA:**

_____

_____

Your End of Class Testimony

[Complete, then make a copy and turn in before graduation]

As you reach the end of your MIA experience, it is always good to hear from you on a more personal level than can be obtained from a survey. While it is optional, it is always helpful and encouraging to hear from the men who have just completed the class.

1. **How would you evaluate your overall performance over the last 12 weeks?**

   _____

   _____

2. **What have you learned about yourself from this experience?**

   _____

   _____

3. **What personal changes do you feel you have made during the class?**

   _____

   _____

4. **What is your level of commitment to keep things going after class ends (accountability, prayer, Bible Reading, Life Focus)?**

   _____

   _____

5. **If you took the class again where would you put the biggest emphasis?**

   _____

   _____

Print name: _____

Signature: _____ Date: _____

NOTES

Accountability Partner Testimony

[Complete, then make a copy and turn in before graduation]

While this is optional, it is good to hear from Accountability Partners at the end of each Men in Action Class. One of the most important aspects of the class is to have a solid accountability relationship that encourages and holds each man accountable for the commitments he has made. Each Accountability Partner should fill out the form and then give it to the Men in Action class member to turn in.

Accountability Partner's name: _____ Date: _____

Name of Men in Action participant: _____

1. **My relationship and knowledge of my partner before starting this relationship:**
   _____
   _____

2. **My partner's biggest concerns when the relationship started were:**
   _____
   _____

3. **I saw our relationship grow in the following ways during this time:**
   _____
   _____

4. **I saw progress in my partner in the following areas:**
   _____
   _____

5. **I will continue to encourage my partner in the following ways and areas of his life:**
   _____
   _____

6. **Any other comments or suggestions:**
   _____
   _____

Thank you for encouraging your brother to be the leader God has called him to be!!!

NOTES

Testimony From Your Wife

[Complete, then make a copy and turn in before graduation]

While it is optional, it is good to get feedback from the wives after their husband has taken the class. One of the biggest uses of these testimonies is to convince other wives of the importance of letting their husband take the class. This class is not designed to create perfect husbands, but rather to help men come to grips with their leadership responsibilities in all aspects of their lives, including in the home.

Wife's name: _____ Date: _____

Husband's name: _____

How long we have been married: _____ Number of children: _____

1. **My expectations for my husband taking this class were:**

   _____
   _____

2. **During this class I observed my husband doing the following things related to the class:**

   _____
   _____

3. **I have seen the following changes/improvements in my husband as a result of this class:**

   _____
   _____

4. **This class has improved our communication in the following ways:**

   _____
   _____

5. **I will continue to encourage him to apply the things he has learned in the following ways:**

   _____
   _____

6. **Comments or suggestions for future Men in Action classes:**

   _____
   _____

Thank you for encouraging your husband to be the leader God has called him to be!!

NOTES

APPENDIX C
Supplemental Materials

1. Daily Bible Reading Chart
2. Roadblocks to an Effective Prayer-Life
3. The Value of Accountability
4. Leadership Principles
5. A Guide to Daily Devotions
6. The Bible on Trial: Evidence for it's Reliability
7. Safeguarding My Personal Purity
8. The Taste Test for Godly Speech
9. Questions for the Man Who Would Serve as an Elder
10. My Physical Body: Blood Pressure, Diet and Exercise Tracking
11. Men in Action Game

NOTES

Daily Bible Reading Chart

We are being challenged to commit to regular Bible reading. Pick several books you would like to read and mark your progress below.

Books	Chapters
Genesis	1 2 3 4 5 6 7 8 9 10 11 12 13 14 15 16 17 18 19 20 21 22 23 24 25 26 27 28 29 30 31 32 33 34 35 36 37 38 39 40 41 42 43 44 45 46 47 48 49 50
Exodus	1 2 3 4 5 6 7 8 9 10 11 12 13 14 15 16 17 18 19 20 21 22 23 24 25 26 27 28 29 30 31 32 33 34 35 36 37 38 39 40
Leviticus	1 2 3 4 5 6 7 8 9 10 11 12 13 14 15 16 17 18 19 20 21 22 23 24 25 26 27
Numbers	1 2 3 4 5 6 7 8 9 10 11 12 13 14 15 16 17 18 19 20 21 22 23 24 25 26 27 28 29 30 31 32 33 34 35 36
Deuteronomy	1 2 3 4 5 6 7 8 9 10 11 12 13 14 15 16 17 18 19 20 21 22 23 24 25 26 27 28 29 30 31 32 33 34
Joshua	1 2 3 4 5 6 7 8 9 10 11 12 13 14 15 16 17 18 19 20 21 22 23 24
Judges	1 2 3 4 5 6 7 8 9 10 11 12 13 14 15 16 17 18 19 20 21
Ruth	1 2 3 4
1 Samuel	1 2 3 4 5 6 7 8 9 10 11 12 13 14 15 16 17 18 19 20 21 22 23 24 25 26 27 28 29 30 31
2 Samuel	1 2 3 4 5 6 7 8 9 10 11 12 13 14 15 16 17 18 19 20 21 22 23 24
1 Kings	1 2 3 4 5 6 7 8 9 10 11 12 13 14 15 16 17 18 19 20 21 22
2 Kings	1 2 3 4 5 6 7 8 9 10 11 12 13 14 15 16 17 18 19 20 21 22 23 24 25
1 Chronicles	1 2 3 4 5 6 7 8 9 10 11 12 13 14 15 16 17 18 19 20 21 22 23 24 25 26 27 28 29
2 Chronicles	1 2 3 4 5 6 7 8 9 10 11 12 13 14 15 16 17 18 19 20 21 22 23 24 25 26 27 28 29 30 31 32 33 34 35 36
Ezra	1 2 3 4 5 6 7 8 9 10
Nehemiah	1 2 3 4 5 6 7 8 9 10 11 12 13
Esther	1 2 3 4 5 6 7 8 9 10
Job	1 2 3 4 5 6 7 8 9 10 11 12 13 14 15 16 17 18 19 20 21 22 23 24 25 26 27 28 29 30 31 32 33 34 35 36 37 38 39 40 41 42
Psalms	1 2 3 4 5 6 7 8 9 10 11 12 13 14 15 16 17 18 19 20 21 22 23 24 25 26 27 28 29 30 31 32 33 34 35 36 37 38 39 40 41 42 43 44 45 46 47 48 49 50 51 52 53 54 55 56 57 58 59 60 61 62 63 64 65 66 67 68 69 70 71 72 73 74 75 76 77 78 79 80 81 82 83 84 85 86 87 88 89 90 91 92 93 94 95 96 97 98 99 100 101 102 103 104 105 106 107 108 109 110 111 112 113 114 115 116 117 118 119 120 121 122 123 124 125 126 127 128 129 130 131 132 133 134 135 136 137 138 139 140 141 142 143 144 145 146 147 148 149 150
Proverbs	1 2 3 4 5 6 7 8 9 10 11 12 13 14 15 16 17 18 19 20 21 22 23 24 25 26 27 28 29 30 31
Ecclesiastes	1 2 3 4 5 6 7 8 9 10 11 12
Song of Solomon	1 2 3 4 5 6 7 8
Isaiah	1 2 3 4 5 6 7 8 9 10 11 12 13 14 15 16 17 18 19 20 21 22 23 24 25 26 27 28 29 30 31 32 33 34 35 36 37 38 39 40 41 42 43 44 45 46 47 48 49 50 51 52 53 54 55 56 57 58 59 60 61 62 63 64 65 66
Jeremiah	1 2 3 4 5 6 7 8 9 10 11 12 13 14 15 16 17 18 19 20 21 22 23 24 25 26 27 28 29 30 31 32 33 34 35 36 37 38 39 40 41 42 43 44 45 46 47 48 49 50 51 52
Lamentations	1 2 3 4 5
Ezekiel	1 2 3 4 5 6 7 8 9 10 11 12 13 14 15 16 17 18 19 20 21 22 23 24 25 26 27 28 29 30 31 32 33 34 35 36 37 38 39 40 41 42 43 44 45 46 47 48
Daniel	1 2 3 4 5 6 7 8 9 10 11 12
Hosea	1 2 3 4 5 6 7 8 9 10 11 12 13 14

Joel	1 2 3
Amos	1 2 3 4 5 6 7 8 9
Obadiah	1
Jonah	1 2 3 4
Micah	1 2 3 4 5 6 7
Nahum	1 2 3
Habakkuk	1 2 3
Zephaniah	1 2 3
Haggai	1 2
Zechariah	1 2 3 4 5 6 7 8 9 10 11 12 13 14
Malachi	1 2 3 4
Matthew	1 2 3 4 5 6 7 8 9 10 11 12 13 14 15 16 17 18 19 20 21 22 23 24 25 26 27 28
Mark	1 2 3 4 5 6 7 8 9 10 11 12 13 14 15 16
Luke	1 2 3 4 5 6 7 8 9 10 11 12 13 14 15 16 17 18 19 20 21 22 23 24
John	1 2 3 4 5 6 7 8 9 10 11 12 13 14 15 16 17 18 19 20 21
Acts	1 2 3 4 5 6 7 8 9 10 11 12 13 14 15 16 17 18 19 20 21 22 23 24 25 26 27 28
Romans	1 2 3 4 5 6 7 8 9 10 11 12 13 14 15 16
1 Corinthians	1 2 3 4 5 6 7 8 9 10 11 12 13 14 15 16
2 Corinthians	1 2 3 4 5 6 7 8 9 10 11 12 13
Galatians	1 2 3 4 5 6
Ephesians	1 2 3 4 5 6
Philippians	1 2 3 4
Colossians	1 2 3 4
1 Thessalonians	1 2 3 4 5
2 Thessalonians	1 2 3
1 Timothy	1 2 3 4 5 6
2 Timothy	1 2 3 4
Titus	1 2 3
Philemon	1
Hebrews	1 2 3 4 5 6 7 8 9 10 11 12 13
James	1 2 3 4 5
1 Peter	1 2 3 4 5
2 Peter	1 2 3
1 John	1 2 3 4 5
2 John	1
3 John	1
Jude	1
Revelation	1 2 3 4 5 6 7 8 9 10 11 12 13 14 15 16 17 18 19 20 21 22

Roadblocks to an Effective Prayer-Life

INTRODUCTION

"...let us also lay aside every encumbrance, and the sin which so easily entangles us, and let us run with endurance the race that is set before us, fixing our eyes on Jesus, the author and perfecter of faith..." (Hebrews 12:1-2, NASB).

"Encumbrance" = Greek word: *ogkos* (pronounced "onkos") = A heavy weight, a major hindrance—a roadblock.

"...Lord, teach us to pray..." (Luke 11:1, NASB).

A HELPFUL METHOD

P.R.A.Y.E.R. = **P**raising - **R**epenting - **A**sking - **Y**ielding - **E**ntreating - **R**ejoicing

"Devote yourselves to prayer, keeping alert in it with an attitude of thanksgiving" (Colossians 4:2).

ROADBLOCKS

1. **Roadblock 1: Unbelief hinders prayer**
    a. The principle: I must be a born-again child of God in order to be effective in prayer.
    b. Apart from the prayers that come from a truth-seeking heart open to salvation in Jesus Christ (cf. Jer. 29; Mt. 7), God does not necessarily hear the general prayers of an unbeliever.
    c. The Biblical proof
        i. "For what is the hope of the godless...will God hear his cry?" (Job 27:8-10, NASB)
            a) The implied answer is: "No!"
        ii. Will he (i.e., the unbeliever) call on God at all times?
            a) The implied answer: Most likely, but God will not answer the call!
        iii. "The sacrifice (i.e., meaningless worship) of the wicked is an abomination to the Lord but the prayer of the *upright* is His delight" (Proverbs 15:8b).
        iv. "The LORD is far from the wicked. But He hears the prayer of the righteous" (Proverbs 15:29, NASB).
        v. "The Lord is near to those who call upon Him, to all who call upon Him in truth" (Psalm 145:18-19, NASB).
        vi. Matthew 6 refers to God as *our Father* eight times! Yet no one can come to the Father except through Jesus Christ who is the way, the truth and the life (John 14:6).

2. **Roadblock 2: Sin hinders prayer**
    a. The principle: I must be dealing with sin in order to be effective in prayer.

b. The Biblical proof
  i. "The effective prayer of a righteous man can accomplish much" (James 5:16b, NASB).
  ii. The SIN of disobedience hinders my prayer-life.
      a) "He who turns away his ear from listening to the law, Even his prayer is an abomination" (Proverbs 28:9, NASB).
      b) "If I regard wickedness in my heart, the Lord will not hear" (Psalm 66:18, NASB).
      c) "…And let his prayer become sin" (Psalm 109:7, NASB).
  iii. The SIN of idolatry hinders my prayer-life.
      a) "Therefore consider the members of your earthly body as dead to immorality, impurity, passion, evil desire and greed, which amounts to idolatry. For it is on account of these things that the wrath of God will come" (Colossians 3:5-6, NASB).
  iv. The SIN of pride hinders my prayer-life.
      a) "There they cry out, but He does not answer, because of the pride of evil men. 'Surely, God will not listen to an empty cry. Nor will the Almighty regard it'" (Job 35:12-13, NASB; cf. 2 Chronicles 7:14).

3. **Roadblock 3: Hypocrisy hinders prayer**
  a. The principle: I must be dealing with the inconsistencies in my life in order to be effective in prayer.
  b. The Biblical proof
    i. Not being honest *with myself* hinders my prayer-life. Isaiah speaks of how much God hated all the offerings, sacrifices, and religious observances of hypocritical Israel (cf. Isaiah 1:10).
    ii. Not being honest *with others* hinders my prayer-life.
        a) The dishonesty of praying to be seen by men.
        b) "When you pray, you are not to be as the hypocrites; for they love to stand and pray in the synagogues and on the street corners so that they may be seen by men. Truly I say to you, they have their reward in full" (Matthew 6:5, NASB).
        c) The phoniness of refusing to admit and confess our faults to one another.
        d) "Therefore, confess your sins to one another, and pray for one another, so that you may be healed" (James 5:16a, NASB).
    iii. Not being honest with God hinders my prayer-life (cf. Psalm 10:1; 22:1; 22:2; 42:6 and the honesty of Hannah, Moses, David, and Job, etc.).

4. **Roadblock 4: Asking with wrong motives hinders prayer**
  a. The principle: I must evaluate my motives to be effective in prayer.
  b. The Biblical proof
    i. Pleasure-seeking hinders my prayer-life.

"You ask and do not receive, because you ask with wrong motives, so that you may spend it on your pleasures" (James 4:3, NASB).

    ii. Not wanting God's will hinders my prayer-life.

        a) "And this is the confidence which we have before Him, that if we ask anything *according to His will*, He hears us. And if we know that He hears us in whatever we ask, we know that we have the requests which we have asked of Him" (1 John 5:14-15, NASB).

        b) Jesus said "If you ask anything in My name..." (John 14:7ff); meaning, anything consistent with His will.

    iii. The love of money hinders my prayer-life.

        a) A House of Prayer vs. Den of Thieves (cf. Matthew 21:12-17; Luke 19:45-47).

        b) "For the love of money is a root of all sorts of evil...But flee from these things, you man of God, and pursue righteousness, godliness, faith, love, perseverance and gentleness" (1 Timothy 6:10-11, NASB).

    iv. Selective praying hinders my prayer-life.

        a) "...I urge that entreaties and prayers, petitions and thanksgivings, be made on behalf of all men..." (1 Timothy 2:1, NASB).

        b) "Moreover, as for me, far be it from me that I should sin against the LORD by ceasing to pray for you..." (1 Samuel 12:23, NASB).

        c) "But I say to you, love your enemies, and pray for those who persecute you so that you may be sons of your Father who is in heaven..." (Matthew 5:44-45, NASB).

5. Roadblock 5: Mistreating people hinders prayer

    a. The principle: I must not think I can hurt people and still be effective in prayer.

    b. The Biblical proof

        i. Mistreating the needy hinders my prayer-life.

            a) "So when you spread out your hands in prayer, I will hide My eyes from you. Yes, even though you multiply prayers, I will not listen. Your hands are full of bloodshed. Wash yourselves, make yourselves clean; remove the evil of your deeds from My sight. Cease to do evil, learn to do good; seek justice; reprove the ruthless; defend the orphan, plead for the Widow" (Isaiah 1:15-17).

            b) "Pure and undefiled religion in the sight of our God and Father is this: to visit orphans and widows in their distress, and to keep oneself unstained by the world" (James 1:27, NASB).

        ii. Mistreating workers hinders your prayer-life.

            a) "Behold, the pay of the laborers who mowed your fields, and which has been withheld by you, cries out against you; and the outcry of those who did the harvesting has reached the ears of the Lord of Sabbath" (James 5:4, NASB).

        b) This matter of mistreating workers also applies to paying what we owe (e.g., Romans 13:8).

   iii. Mistreating the flock of God hinders your prayer-life.

        a) Speaks of the spiritual shepherds who were abusing the flock by not taking proper care of them (Ezekiel 34; cf. 1 Peter 5).

6. Roadblock 6: Mistreating my spouse hinders prayer

   a. The principle: I must honor my spouse in order to be effective in prayer.

   b. The Biblical proof

     i. "This is another thing you do: you cover the altar of the Lord with tears, with weeping and with groaning, because He no longer regards the offering or accepts it with favor from your hand. Yet you say, 'For what reason?' Because the Lord has been a witness between you and the wife of your youth, against whom you have dealt treacherously, though she is your companion and your wife by covenant..." (Malachi 2:13-14ff, NASB).

     ii. "You husbands, in the same way, live with your wives in an understanding way, as with someone weaker, since she is a woman; and show her honor as a fellow heir of the grace of life, so that your prayers may not be hindered" (1 Peter 3:7, NASB).

7. Roadblock 7: Anger and bitterness hinder prayer

   a. The principle: I must deal with my anger and bitterness in order to be effective in prayer.

   b. The Biblical proof

     i. Anger hinders my prayer-life.

        a) "...I want men in every place to pray, lifting up holy hands, without wrath and dissention." (1 Timothy 2:8, NASB; cf. Colossians 3:5; Ephesians 4:26)

     ii. Lack of forgiveness hinders my prayer-life.

        a) "Whenever you stand praying, forgive, if you have anything against anyone, so that you Father who is in heaven will also forgive you your transgressions" (Mark 11:25, NASB).

        b) "And forgive us our debts, as we also have forgiven our debtors" (Matthew 6:12, NASB).

        c) "Be kind to one another, tender-hearted, forgiving each other just as God in Christ also has forgiven you" (Ephesians 4:32, NASB).

     iii. Lack of thanksgiving hinders my prayer-life.

        a) "Be anxious for nothing, but in everything by prayer and supplication with thanksgiving let your requests be made known to God" (Philippians 4:6, NASB).

        b) "Devote yourselves to prayer, keeping alert in it with an attitude of thanksgiving..." (Colossians 4:2, NASB).

8. **Roadblock 8: Laziness hinders prayer**
   a. The principle: I must be diligent to be effective in prayer.
   b. The Biblical proof
      i. Lack of devotion hinders my prayer-life.
         a) Colossians 4:2, speaks of being devoted (Greek = to strongly continue) to the practice prayer.
         b) "...as I *constantly* remember you in my prayers night and day..." (2 Timothy 1:3, NASB).
      ii. Not persevering hinders my prayer-life.
         a) "Now He was telling them a parable to show that all times they ought to pray and not to lose heart..." (Luke 18:1, NASB).
         b) "And I say to you, ask (literally, keep on asking)...seek (literally, keep on seeking)...knock (literally keep on knocking), and it shall be opened to you" (Luke 11:9-10).
         c) "Pray without ceasing" (1 Thessalonians 5:17, NASB).
         d) Jesus spent the whole night in prayer to God ...rising up even before daybreak to do it (Luke 6:12; cf. Mark 1:35).
         e) Elijah who "...prayed earnestly, "....and then..."...prayed again..." (James 5:17-18, NASB).
         f) Hannah cried out to the Lord in what is described as "multiplied prayers" (1 Samuel 1).
      iii. Vain repetition hinders my prayer-life.
         a) "And when you are praying, do not use meaningless repetition, as the Gentiles do, for they suppose that they will be heard for their many words" (Matthew 6:7, NASB).
         b) Note: The point here is not repetition but empty, meaningless repetition.

9. **Roadblock 9: Doubt hinders prayer**
   a. The principle: I must pray with confidence in order to be effective in prayer
   b. The Biblical proof
      i. "But he must ask in faith without any doubting, for the one who doubts is like the surf of the sea, driven and tossed by the wind. For that man ought not to expect that he will receive anything from the Lord, being a double-minded man, unstable in all his ways" (James 1:6, NASB).
      ii. "And all things you ask in prayer, believing, you will receive" (Matthew 21:22, NASB).
      iii. "Therefore I say to you, whoever says to this mountain, 'Be taken up and cast into the sea', and does not doubt in his heart, but believes that what he says is going to happen, it shall be granted him. Therefore I say to you, all things for which you pray and ask, believe that you have received them, and they shall be granted you" (Mark 11:23-24, NASB).

10. Roadblock 10: Lack of physical rest hinders prayer

    a. The principle: I must be rested if I am going to be effective in prayer.

    b. The Biblical proof

        i. *Keep alert* in prayer (Colossians 4:2).

        ii. "When He rose from prayer, He came to His disciples and found them sleeping from sorrow, and said to them, "Why are you sleeping? Get up and pray that you may not enter into temptation" (Luke 22:45-46, NASB).

        iii. ANYTIME of the day is a good time to pray.

            a) Jesus rose up to pray "a great while before day" (Mark 1:35, NASB).

            b) "In the morning, O Lord, Thou wilt hear my voice. In the morning I will order my prayer to Thee and eagerly watch" (Psalm 5:3, NASB).

            c) "May my prayer be counted as incense before Thee; the lifting up of my hands as the evening offering" (Psalm 141:2, NASB).

            d) "O Lord, I remember Thy name in the night" (Psalm 119:55, NASB).

            e) "At midnight I will rise to give thanks to Thee" (Psalm 119:62, NASB).

            f) "Seven times a day I will praise Thee" (Psalm 119:164, NASB).

11. Roadblock 11: Discouragement hinders prayer

    a. The principle: I must not let my weakness in prayer keep me from being effective in prayer.

    b. The Biblical proof

        i. Jesus wanted His disciples to pray and not lose heart (Luke 18).

        ii. "'For I know the plans that I have for you,'" declares the LORD, 'plans for welfare and not for calamity to give you a future and a hope. Then you will call upon Me and come and pray to Me, and I will listen to you. And you will seek Me and find Me when you search for Me with all your heart. And I will be found by you...'" (Jeremiah 29:11-14, NASB).

        iii. "Call to Me, and I will answer you, and I will tell you great and mighty things, which you do not know" (Jeremiah 33:3, NASB).

12. Concluding Challenge

    a. "Even those I will bring to My holy mountain, and make them joyful in My house of prayer...for My house will be called a house of prayer for all the peoples" (Isaiah 56:7, NASB).

"Lord, may our lives...our homes...and our churches be Houses of Prayer for all peoples. Give us the strength to remove the hindrances...and restore to us the joy of talking to You as Our Heavenly Father."

The Value of Accountability

One of the key aspects for making this class as effective as possible is for each of us to have a strong accountability relationship throughout our many weeks together. We take to heart the words of Solomon:

> *"Two are better than one, because they have a good return for their work: If one falls down, his friend can help him up. But pity the man who falls and has no one to help him up!" (Ecclesiastes 4:9-10, NIV)*

Jesus especially poured His life into His 12 men. Of those, he developed an even more personal relationship with three of them—Peter, Andrew, and John. Jesus understood the importance of developing close personal relationships.

> *"Wounds from a friend can be trusted, but any enemy multiplies kisses"*
> *(Proverbs 27:6, NIV).*

ACCOUNTABILITY: THE MISSING LINK

This class is about developing leadership. However, a key attribute of a strong leader is to have strong relationships. One of the best tools for doing this is having someone hold us accountable for how we are doing. If you are truly serious about making a change in your life regarding relationships, there is probably no more important tool than regular open and honest accountability.

> *"…not looking to your own interests but each of you to the interests of the others"*
> *(Philippians 2:4, NIV).*

> *"As iron sharpens iron, so one man sharpens another" (Proverbs 27:17, NASB).*

We all have a tendency to engage in self-deception. We all have blind spots. It is for this reason we are not able to hold ourselves accountable. We need another person to challenge us and ask the hard questions. We need someone to be committed to tell us the truth, even when the truth is hard. As said in 1 Corinthians 13, "love rejoices in the truth."

> *"One of the greatest reasons men get into trouble is that they don't answer to anyone for their lifestyles" (Patrick Morley, Author "Man in the Mirror").*

Accountability requires having an open and honest relationship with at least one other person with whom you regularly and honestly share your struggles and needs.

Given the above definition, is there anyone to whom you are currently accountable?

_____

What have you gained from that relationship?

_____

What are some goals of having an accountability relationship? How would you define its purpose?

_____

Men especially have trouble developing close relationships with each other. Many of us can say we have men we enjoy friendships with and care about, but often we rarely share with them the deeper struggles. We are afraid to open up because we fear vulnerability and rejection. We need another person to challenge us the way Jesus would if He was our accountability partner. Obviously, other than our spouse, the accountability partner should be someone of the same sex.

List three questions you would rather _not_ have a person ask you on a regular basis:

1. _____
2. _____
3. _____

If these were addressed, how would your life improve?

_____

_____

Accountability means giving someone the right and responsibility to ask the hard questions.

> _"But I tell you that everyone will have to give account on the day of judgment for every empty word they have spoken"_ (Matthew 12:36, NIV).

> _"So then each of us will give an account of himself to God"_ (Romans 14:12, NASB).

If we are ultimately accountable to God, how can a solid accountability relationship with others help now?

_____

_____

THE CHALLENGE OF TRANSPARENCY (THE ACCOUNTABILITY ICEBERG)

We know our "deeper" self, and we would rather others not know us at that level. There is a safer, "surface" area in our lives we are okay with others seeing and judging. However, like the iceberg, there is more often that which isn't seen than is seen. Accountability requires letting someone see what is below the surface. There is tremendous risk whenever we open ourselves up.

What are some reasons people don't want to be in an accountability relationship?

_____

_____

The following statements are reasons given for why men have trouble forming accountability relationships. Which do you think might create hesitancy in you?

1. Men are self-reliant:

   _____

2. Men are tough and don't feel:

   _____

3. Men don't touch physically or emotionally:

   _____

4. Men don't need relationships:

   _____

5. Men use people and love things:

   _____

6. Men are too competitive:

   _____

7. Men are too macho:

   _____

We need to get to know another person and learn to trust before we can really share. When we finally share with a partner how we really feel about things and what our real needs are in life, we have reached a level where accountability can be effective and lead to real growth.

What are some characteristics you believe an accountability partner should possess?

_____

_____

Ultimately, anyone who has the makings of an accountability partner must love Jesus Christ and love us.

AREAS WHERE WE ALL NEED ACCOUNTABILITY

> *"So, if you think you are standing firm, be careful that you don't fall!"*
> *(1 Corinthians 10:12, NIV)*

Name another person (of the same sex) you can discuss the following areas of your life:

1. Relationship with God: _____
2. Relationship with spouse: _____
3. Relationship with kids: _____
4. Use of money and time: _____
5. Moral and ethical Issues: _____
6. Areas of personal struggle: _____
7. Consistency in Scripture and prayer: _____

Do you meet regularly with any of the above listed people and if so how often?

_____
_____

It is impossible to be accountable if our lives are not open to someone else for review. Regularity in meeting shows our true level of commitment. It is easier to start an accountability relationship than to maintain it over an extended period.

We may find we need more than one person to hold us accountable. The person who is best for family matters may not be the best person for financial or business matters. We should open ourselves in all areas of our lives. Those areas where we aren't accountable are areas where we are most likely to go astray.

Accountability is a special relationship and is different from other types of relationships. There are unique aspects to accountability that differ from counseling and even fellowship. Even though they are inter-connected, each has a value of their own.

ACCOUNTABILITY VS. COUNSEL

> *"Brothers, if someone is caught in a sin, you who live by the spirit should restore*
> *that person gently. But watch yourselves, or you also may be tempted. Carry*
> *each other's burdens, and in this way you will fulfill the law of Christ"*
> *(Galatians 6:1-2, NIV).*

What is involved in seeking counsel, and how might it differ from seeking accountability?

_____
_____

Scripture is full of instructions on the benefits of giving godly counsel to others. However, accountability is giving another person the right and responsibility to ask us the hard questions on a regular basis, even when we aren't seeking their counsel.

ACCOUNTABILITY VS. FELLOWSHIP

What is fellowship and how does it differ from accountability?

_____

While there is a sense of fellowship in an accountability relationship, that isn't the primary purpose. We can have fellowship with people we barely know. However, accountability requires a deeper personal knowledge of each other.

What are some questions you would ask a person you were holding accountable that you wouldn't ask someone who you were getting together with just for fellowship?

_____

_____

What are some of the reasons a proposed accountability relationship can often simply become fellowship?

_____

_____

WHY WE AVOID BEING ACCOUNTABLE

What do you perceive are the three biggest obstacles you face in getting a solid regular accountability relationship going?

1. _____

2. _____

3. _____

Some final thoughts on accountability:
1. This is a person-to-person, face-to-face activity.
2. We should not form an accountability relationship with a person of the opposite sex (though your spouse certainly can hold you accountable).
3. The accountability relationships should be built on small, intimate groups of no more than five.
4. Meeting regularly is important.
5. Without a sincere desire to grow in Christ, an accountability relationship will not work.
6. The accountability relationship begins by sharing general information about yourself, including:
   a. How you became a Christian.
   b. How you met your spouse.
   c. Your home life growing up.
   d. Your greatest success in life.

e. Your biggest disappointment in life.

f. A person you greatly admire, and why.

7. What is shared is held in absolute and strict confidence.

8. An accountability meeting is to foster a mutually beneficial relationship in which all honestly participate.

LIVING THE ACCOUNTABLE LIFE

1. A definition of spiritual health: Growing closer through fellowship; stronger through doctrine; more passionate through worship; broader through service; larger through evangelism; deeper through discipleship; and more effective through prayer.

2. What does "growing closer through fellowship" really mean?

   a. Fellowship = Greek: *koinonia/koinos* = Meeting one another's needs (based on what we have in common).

   b. Key words: Connection, accountability

THE THREE ARENAS OF ACCOUNTABILITY

1. **Arena 1: Accountability to myself**

   a. "No man is fit to command another who cannot command himself."

   b. "…discipline yourself for the purpose of godliness…" (1 Timothy 4:7, NASB)

   c. "Watch your life and doctrine closely. Persevere in them…" (1 Timothy 4:16, NIV)

   d. "But a man must examine himself…" (1 Corinthians 11:28, NASB)

   e. "But each one must examine his own work…" (Galatians 6:4, NASB)

   f. "Let us examine and probe our ways…" (Lamentations 3:40, NASB)

      i. (probe = Hebrew: *chaqar* = examine, search, investigate, ponder, taste)

   g. "But thanks be to God, who always leads us in His triumph in Christ, and manifests through us the sweet aroma of the knowledge of Him in every place" (2 Corinthians 2:14, NASB).

   h. "When people are right with God, they are apt to be hard on themselves and not on other people. But when they are not right with God, they are easy on themselves and hard on others." (John Newton)

2. **Arena 2: Accountability to others**

   a. "Iron sharpens iron, so one man sharpens another" (Provers 27:17, NASB).

   b. "…the members may have the same care for one another" (2 Corinthians 12:25, NASB). I need you. You need me. We need each other.

   c. "Two are better than one because they have a good return for their labor. For if either of them falls, the one will lift up his companion. But woe to the one who falls when there is not another to lift him up. Furthermore, if two lie down together they keep warm, but how can one be warm alone? And if one can overpower him who is alone, two can resist him…" (Ecclesiastes 4:9-12, NASB).

   d. The three facets of accountability to others

      i. Facet #1: Defensive accountability

1. "Before things get worse, I want to share my particular struggles with you."
2. "Therefore, confess your sins to one another, and pray for one another, so that you may be healed" (James 5:16, NASB).

ii. Facet #2: Consistent accountability
1. "I need to meet with you regularly."
2. "...and let us consider how to stimulate one another to love and good deeds, not forsaking our own assembling together, as is the habit of some, but encouraging one another; and all the more, as you see the day drawing near" (Hebrews 10:24-25, NASB).
3. Stimulate = Greek: *paroxusmos* = provoke, stimulate, prod
4. "...and all the more, as you see the day (of Christ's return) drawing near" (Hebrews 10:25, NASB).

iii. Facet #3: Offensive accountability
1. "I am struggling right now. I need help immediately."
2. "But encourage one another day after day, as long as it is still called 'Today,' lest anyone of you be hardened by the deceitfulness of sin" (Hebrews 3:13, NASB).

iv. The Spiritual Rescue Workers Creed
1. "We urge you, brethren, admonish the unruly, encourage the fainthearted, help the weak, be patient with everyone" (1 Thessalonians 5:14, NASB).
2. The Commandments for caring for people:
   a. Thou shalt continually admonish the unruly.
   b. Thou shalt continually encourage the fainthearted.
   c. Thou shalt continually help the weak.
   d. Thou shalt continually be patient with everyone.

3. **Arena 3: Accountability to God**
   a. "My greatest thought is my accountability to God" (Daniel Webster).
   b. "A cord of three strands is not quickly torn apart" (Ecclesiastes 4:12, NASB).
   c. I need to be accountable to you. You need to be accountable to me. We need to be accountable to each other. We both need to be accountable to God.
   d. "Examine me, O Lord, and try me; Test my mind and my heart" (Psalm 26:2, NASB).
   e. "Search me, O God, and know my heart; Try me and know my anxious thoughts; And see if there be any hurtful way in me, And lead me in the everlasting way" (Psalm 139:23-24, NASB).
   f. "Now if any man builds upon the foundation with gold, silver, precious stones, wood, hay, straw, each man's work will become evident; for the day will show it, because it is to be revealed with fire; and the fire itself will test the quality of each man's work" (1 Corinthians 3:12-13, NASB).
   g. If you and I were standing before Him today, what would we say? What do we think He would say?

h. "You were running well; who hindered you from obeying the truth?" (Galatians 5:7, NASB)
i. The Reasons for Relapse
    i. Reason #1: Relapse happens when we get in a hurry.
    ii. Reason #2: Relapse happens when we ignore the whole process.
    iii. Reason #3: Relapse happens when we let pride get in the way.
    iv. Reason #4: Relapse happens when we revert back to self-help and willpower.
    v. Reason #5: Relapse happens when we forget how much of a problem the old pattern really was.

THE CHALLENGE

"And He gave some as apostles, and some as prophets, and some as evangelists, and some as pastors and teachers, for the equipping of the saints for the work of service, to the building up of the body of Christ; until we all attain to the unity of the faith, and of the knowledge of the Son of God, to a mature man, to the measure of the stature which belongs to the fullness of Christ. As a result, we are no longer to be children, tossed here and there by waves and carried about by every wind of doctrine, by the trickery of men, by craftiness in deceitful scheming; but speaking the truth in love, we are to grow up in all aspects into Him who is the head, even Christ, from whom the whole body, being fitted and held together by what every joint supplies, according to the proper working of each individual part, causes the growth of the body for the building up of itself in love" (Ephesians 4:11-16, NASB).

Leadership Principles

One of the favorite topics for business books over the last 30 or so years has been suggesting that a set of principles could be set out that define what makes a successful leader. Over the years, we have collected statements from several sources. Some are insightful and others are indicative of twisted viewpoints. In order not to unduly influence you we have not mentioned the source of the quotes.

Read through the list of statements below, checking off at least five you strongly agree with. Then make a check mark next to at least three you disagree with.

		Agree	Disagree
1.	Leaders cannot be autonomous. They are an inseparable part of the groups to which they belong.		
2.	To succeed in getting things done through others is the highest type of leadership.		
3.	Leadership action that is not based on careful listening is apt to be the wrong action.		
4.	Either lead, follow, or get out of the way.		
5.	A servant-leader does not have a secret agenda.		
6.	A leader is the one who climbs the tallest tree, surveys the entire situation, and yells, "Wrong jungle!"		
7.	Great leaders inspire people to go places they would never go on their own, and to attempt things they never thought they had in them.		
8.	A key function of leadership is coping with change.		
9.	The gift of leading is found in people who have a clear, significant vision and are able to communicate it in such a way that they influence others to pursue that vision.		
10.	Leadership and management are two distinctive and complimentary systems and actions.		
11.	The Christian leader is the servant of the servants of God.		
12.	Spiritual leadership as ministry is not giving orders, but nurturing the people of God.		
13.	A leader is one who has the ability to get others to do what they do not want to do and like it.		
14.	The bigness of a leader is determined by the cause he lives for, and the price he is willing to pay for its achievement.		
15.	Leaders have to remember that God's choice does not always follow conventional wisdom.		
16.	The best test of whether one is a qualified leader is to find out whether anyone is following.		
17.	Leaders must keep their associates and subordinates fully informed.		
18.	Effective leaders monitor their progress.		
19.	A good leader is able to transmit his core values and vision.		
20.	Delegation of authority must always follow delegation of responsibility.		
21.	Management of people begins with management of self.		

		Agree	Disagree
22.	There is risk involved in every decision a leader makes.		
23.	A leader communicates standards to followers.		
24.	Leadership is the ability to move and influence people.		
25.	Effective leaders are always on the lookout for good people.		
26.	Good leaders staff their weakness.		
27.	A leader is a developer of people.		
28.	Flexibility is the most repeated objective used to describe good leaders.		
29.	Giftedness is not a status symbol, but rather a tool for service.		
30.	Leadership requires clear theological perspective.		
31.	In leadership, if people don't hear and follow peacefully, a gun can make them do so.		
32.	Great leaders must possess that knowledge of what makes people tick and what motivates them.		
33.	Spend as much time with "possibility people" as you spend with "problem people."		
34.	A leader must express his love and appreciation for the people close to him.		
35.	Leadership is a blending of natural and spiritual qualities.		
36.	A leader must be able to envision the end result of the policies or methods he advocates.		
37.	A man who is impatient with weakness will be defective in his leadership.		
38.	The successful leader is a man who has learned that no failure need be final.		
39.	When God calls an individual and gives him a job to do, He will supernaturally provide the capabilities needed for that specific job.		
40.	The gift of leading is found in people who have a clear, significant vision, and are able to communicate it in such a way that they influence others to pursue that vision.		
41.	Christian leaders are Godly people (they have character, who know where they are going, have vision, and have followers (influence)).		
42.	When godliness and vision are combined in the same person, that individual is able to exert a great influence over people.		
43.	Strong servant leaders are the kinds of people who lead with sustained excellence.		
44.	Finishing well is an important measure of success in leadership.		
45.	Leadership is seeing the consequences of our action further in the future than those around us can.		
46.	The leader, whenever he accomplishes his work, should be able to say "I could not have done it alone."		
47.	Always analyze the past in preparing for the future.		
48.	Confusion and bickering at the top filters down to the bottom.		
49.	Leadership requires an awareness of contemporary surroundings.		
50.	Resistance to change is universal.		
51.	One of the great sins of Christian leadership is to think one is irreplaceable in an organization.		

		Agree	Disagree
52.	A life isn't significant except for its impact on other's lives.		
53.	The price of greatness is responsibility.		
54.	A leader who produces other leaders multiplies his influence.		
55.	True success comes when every generation continues to develop the next generation.		
56.	We can lead others only as far along the road as we ourselves have traveled.		
57.	Effective leaders first touch people's hearts before they ask them for a hand.		
58.	The people's capacity to achieve is determined by their leader's ability to empower.		
59.	Leaders need to be able to reconcile opposing viewpoints without giving offense or compromising principles.		
60.	As leaders, we should minimize stress whenever possible.		
61.	Followers tend to see the pain involved with change. Leaders provide the vision which helps them look above the pain to the potential.		
62.	Leadership is more a matter of quality than of seniority.		
63.	The true test of a person's leadership is the health of the organization when the organizer is gone.		
64.	Leaders think big.		
65.	Leaders think in terms of other people.		
66.	Leaders think continually.		
67.	Leaders think bottom line.		
68.	Leaders think in terms of intangibles.		
69.	Leaders think quickly.		
70.	A secure and honest leader is not afraid to share the weaknesses and failures that God has helped him to overcome, to help his people and encourage them along the way.		
71.	No change will make everyone happy.		
72.	A leader must realize that God is not merely concerned with 'what we do'; He is greatly concerned with 'why' we do things.		
73.	Good leadership simplifies.		
74.	Thin-skinned, easily swayed, insecure persons won't lead well or last long.		
75.	A guide points the way, but a leader leads the way for others to follow him in whatever he is doing and wherever he is going.		
76.	The quality of a leader is reflected in his people and in what they produce.		
77.	Good leadership ensures that people reach their maximum potential and go beyond the personal limitations of the leadership itself.		

[Optional assignment] Write down three of your favorite leadership principles that don't appear on this list and briefly explain why you selected them.

1. _____
   _____

2. _____
   _____

3. _____
   _____

A Guide to Daily Devotions

"See, I have set before you today life and prosperity, and death and adversity" (Deuteronomy 30:15, NASB).

"So teach us to number our days, that we may present to You a heart of wisdom" (Psalm 90:12, NASB).

Today is really the first day of the rest of your life. It is a day when you can choose the road to life and prosperity, or the road to death and adversity. In other words, life really is the total of the choices you make every day. As one man rightly expressed, "Yesterday is a canceled check. Tomorrow is a promissory note. Today is the only cash you have, so spend it wisely." It's almost as if, Biblically-speaking, today is a verb in which, as strange as it may seem, you need to have as my daily prayer: "Lord, help me to 'today' well. I may not have 'yesterday-ed' well. I may not 'tomorrow' well. But I can choose to 'today' well."

We encourage you to follow this simple guideline for having a G.R.E.A.T. day.

PRINCIPLES FOR HAVING A G.R.E.A.T. DAY

1. **GREET the day with PRAISE**
    a. "This is the day the Lord has made; let us rejoice and be glad in it" (Psalm 118:24, NASB).
    b. "rejoice" = Hebrew: gil = shout out with joy.
    c. "be glad" = Hebrew: samach = cheer.
    d. "Today, I choose to resign as General Manager of the Universe. Lord, God Almighty, this is going to be a great day!"

Alphabetical Worship: "Thank you. Lord that you are A_____ B_____ C_____"

    e. The Daily Joy Stealers
        i. Joy-stealer #1: "I don't have enough time to do all that I need to do today."
        ii. Joy-stealer #2: "I am still carrying over frustrations and hurts from yesterday" (cf. Romans 12:18; 14:19).
        iii. Joy-stealer #3: "This is going to be a horrible day" (cf. Deuteronomy 30:15; Psalm 95:7; Nehemiah 1:11; Genesis 24:12; Exodus 32:29).

2. **REPORT to the day with PURPOSE**
    a. "For David, after he had served the purpose of God in his own generation, fell asleep, and was laid among his fathers..." (Acts 13:36, NASB).
    b. Rehearsing my daily purpose
        i. "I am a Child of God."
             "Today, I will not lose focus on who I am." (cf. John 1:12-13; 2 Corinthians 5:17; Colossians 3:1-5)
        ii. "I am a Soldier of the Cross."

> "Today, I will not let myself get distracted from my duty to my Commander." (cf. 2 Timothy 2:3-4)

    iii. "I am a Servant of God."

> "Today, I will obey my Master at all costs." (cf. Deuteronomy 11:26-28; Joshua 24:15)

    iv. "I am an Ambassador of Jesus Christ."

> "Today, I will represent My King in everything I say and do." (cf. 2 Corinthians 5:20; Ephesians 6:18-20)

3. ENGAGE the day with a PLAN (cf. James 4:13-15)

a. "The plans of the heart belong to man, But the answer of the tongue is from the LORD. All the ways of a man are clean in his own sight, but the LORD weighs the motives. Commit your works to the LORD, and your plans will be established" (Proverbs 16:1-3, NASB).

b. My daily priority plan:

    i. The things I <u>must</u> do.

    ii. The things I <u>should</u> do.

    iii. The things I would <u>like</u> to do.

c. "For He is our God, and we are the people of His pasture, and the sheep of His hand. Today, if you would hear His voice..." (Psalm 95:7, NASB).

4. ANALYZE the day with PERSPECTIVE

a. "They were all struck with astonishment and began glorifying God; and they were filled with fear, saying, 'We have seen remarkable things today'" (Luke 5:26, NASB).

b. Questions for the end of the day

    i. Question #1: What remarkable thing did God do today? (Deuteronomy 5:24)

    ii. Question #2: In what ways was today successful?

    iii. Question #3: In what areas would God say I did poorly today? (Hebrews 3:15; 2 Samuel 3:39; 1 Samuel 14:38)

    iv. Question #4: What would He have me do better tomorrow? (Matthew 6:34; 2 Chronicles 20:16-17)

5. TERMINATE the day with PRAYER

a. "At the time of the offering of the evening sacrifice, Elijah the prophet came near and said, 'O LORD, the God of Abraham, Isaac and Israel, today let it be known that You are God in Israel and that I am Your servant and that I have done all these things at Your word'" (1 Kings 18:36, NASB; cf. Nehemiah 1:11).

6. **The Challenge: Carpe Diem = Seize the Day**
    a. "Rejoice while you are alive; enjoy the day; live life to the fullest; make the most of what you have. It is later than you think." (Horace, the Roman Poet, writing around 50 B.C.)
    b. "Conduct yourselves with wisdom toward outsiders, making the most of the opportunity" (Colossians 4:5, NASB).
    c. "But encourage one another day after day, as long as it is still called 'Today,' so that none of you be hardened by the deceitfulness of sin" (Hebrews 3:13, NASB).
    d. "The fear of the Lord leads to life, So that one may sleep satisfied, untouched by evil" (Proverbs 19:23, NASB).
    e. "When you lie down, you will not be afraid; When you lie down, your sleep will be sweet" (Proverbs 3:24, NASB).
    f. "Blessed is the LORD who has not left you without a redeemer today…" (Ruth 4:14, NASB).

(For further study, read "The Value of Accountability," in Appendix C. You may also order the book, "Have a G.R.E.A.T. Day: Living Our Lives One Blessed Day at a Time," by Dr. James M. Cecy, available at www.jaron.org and www.amazon.com.)

The Bible on Trial: Evidence for Its Reliability

INTRODUCTION
1. The Prosecutors: Those who question the reliability of the Bible.
2. The Defenders: Those who can rightly defend the reliability of the Bible.

> *"…always being ready to make a defense (Greek: apologia = a legal defense) to everyone who asks you to give an account for the hope that is in you, but with gentleness and respect…" (1 Peter 3:15, NASB).*

> *"I believe the Bible is the best gift God has ever given to men. All the good from the Savior of the world is communicated through this book" (Abraham Lincoln).*

THEOLOGICAL PRE-SUPPOSITIONS
1. God spoke…Genesis 1:3 – "And God said, "Let there be light and there was light."
2. God spoke through men…2 Peter 1:21 – "…men moved by the Holy Spirit spoke from God."
3. God spoke through men that which is reliable.

> *"All Scripture is inspired by God and beneficial for teaching…"*
> *(2 Timothy 3:16, NASB)*

> *"For the word of God is living and active, and sharper than any two-edged sword, even penetrating as far as the division of the soul and spirit, of both joints and marrow, and able to judge the thoughts and intentions of the heart" (Hebrews 4:12, NASB).*

OPENING STATEMENT

> *"I believe the Bible is the inspired Word of God and is the direct revelation of God to man."*

PRESENTATION OF THE EVIDENCE

Defense Exhibit #1: The Internal Evidence

> *"The best evidence of the Bible being the Word of God is found between its covers" (Charles Hodge).*

Defense Statement #1: The human writers of the Scriptures claim them to be God's Word.
1. The Bible states 2,600 times "The Word of the Lord came unto me," or, "Thus saith the Lord."

Internal Witness #1: The Apostle Paul

1. 2 Timothy 3:16 – "All Scripture is <u>inspired</u> by God..." (Greek: theopneustos = God-breathed)

Internal Witness #2: The Apostle Peter

1. 2 Peter 1:20-21 – "But know this first of all, that no prophecy of scripture is a matter of one's own interpretation, for no prophecy was ever made by an act of human will, <u>but men moved by the Holy Spirit spoke from God.</u>"

Internal Witness #3: The Apostle Paul

1. 1 Thessalonians 2:13 – "And for this reason we also constantly thank God that when you received from us the word of God's message, <u>you accepted it not as the word of men, but for what it really is, the word of God,</u> which also performs its work in you who believe."

Internal Witness #4: The Apostle Peter

1. 2 Peter 3:15-16 – "...just as also our beloved brother Paul, according to the wisdom given him, wrote to you, as also in all his letters, speaking in them of these things, in which some things are hard to understand, which the untaught and unstable distort, <u>as they do also the rest of Scriptures...</u>"

Defense Statement #2: Christ Himself claimed the Scriptures to be God's Word.

1. cf. Matthew 5:17-18; 6:29; 10:15; 21:13-16; 22:28-33, 36-40.
2. John 17:17 – "Thy Word is truth!"

Defense Exhibit #2: The External Evidence

External Witness #1: The Bible's Unique Archaeological and Historical Accuracy

"It may be stated categorically that no archaeological discovery has ever contradicted a Biblical reference" (Nelson Glueck, Rivers in the Desert, p. 31).

1. The Nuzi Tablets, the Ras Shamra Tablets, ancient City of Ur, Sodom and Gomorrah, the Cylinder of Cyrus: King of Medo-Persia.

External Witness #2: The Bible's Unique Scientific Accuracy

1. Although the Bible is not primarily a science book, when it speaks scientifically, it speaks accurately.
2. For example:
   a. Genesis 1:1 – "In the beginning (time) God (force) created (action) the heavens (space) and the earth (matter)...."
   b. The earth is suspended in space (Job 26:7), is round (Job 26:10), and spins on an axis (cf. Job 38:12-14); e.g. Leviathan is real (Job 41:18-21).

External Witness #3: The Bible's Unique Prophetic Accuracy

1. Psalms 22: Written about the suffering Messiah 600 years before Christ was born, and hundreds of years before crucifixion was even invented.
2. Numbers 24:17, Genesis 49:10 and Micah 5:2: All predict that the Messiah would come from the line of Jacob, the line of Judah and the family of David. Jesus did (cf. Matthew 1:1-17; Luke 1:31-33).
3. Isaiah 7:14: Written 700 years before the fact, foretells of the Messiah who would be born of a virgin.
4. Micah 5:2: Predicts that the Messiah would born in Bethlehem.
5. Zechariah 11:12 -13: Foretold that the Messiah would be betrayed for exactly 30 pieces of silver and that the one who betrayed the Messiah would buy a plot of land with the money.
6. Isaiah 53:9-12: Tells us that He would be hung between two thieves and that his body would be laid in a rich man's tomb.
7. Psalms 22:18; Zechariah 12:10; Psalms 34:20; and Exodus 12:46, 16:8-11 and 68:18: Foretell about:
   a. Spear thrust in His side.
   b. Garments divided in four.
   c. Executioners gambling for his robe.
   d. Legs not broken, though this was a common practice in crucifixion.
   e. Raised from dead.
   f. Ascending into Heaven.

External Witness #4: The Bible's Unique Harmony

1. 66 books • 3 languages • 1600 years • 40 authors • 3 continents • One world view • One assessment of human nature • One Lord • One faith • One central theme

External Witness #5: The Bible's Unique Character

> *"It's not such a book as man would write if he could or could write if he would" (Lewis Sperry Chafer).*

External Witness #6: The Bible's Unique Preservation in History

1. Dead Sea Scrolls, some 5,000 Greek manuscripts plus thousands of relevant documents.

> *"My Word abides forever."*

> *"If we would destroy the Christian religion, we must first of all destroy man's belief in the Bible" (Voltaire).*

External Witness #7: The Bible's Unique Influence on People and Nations

1. Regarding the Bible's influence on civilization…
2. Regarding the Bible's influence on government…
3. Regarding the Bible's influence on law…

4. Regarding the Bible's influence on literary thought…
5. Regarding the Bible's influence on lives…

External Witness #8: The Bible's Unique Influence On Us

> *"Other books were given for our information; the Bible was given for our transformation."*

MY SUMMATION AND CLOSING ARGUMENT

> *res ipsa loquitur = "The thing speaks for itself."*

1. God spoke…
2. God spoke through men…
3. God spoke through men that which is profitable and reliable!
4. God has preserved the Bible.
5. God has called men to translate it into our own language.
6. God has provided born-again believers with an Indwelling Holy Spirit who enables us to read the Bible with comprehension (cf. 1 Corinthians 1-2).

> *"The Bible is either true or false; it is either the Word of God or the work of man, one or the other. If the Bible is the work of man, then it is not the Word of God; and if the Bible is just the work of man, it is the greatest imposter this world has ever known. From its first page to its last, the Bible claims to be the revealed will of God; if it can be convicted of being a lie, it not only must come down from its high place to the level of man-made books, but it will sink lower than that. if it can be convicted of being an imposter, it never can survive the odium which that conviction will place upon it. But, if it is true, then there is no other book to be mentioned in comparison with it. If it is true, then no guesses of any man can be substituted for the Word of God" (William Jennings Bryan as quoted by C.E. Colton in "Questions Christians Ask").*

Safeguarding My Personal Purity

LINE OF DEFENSE #1: GUARDING MY MIND

> *"Watch over your heart with all diligence, for from it flow the springs of life"* (Proverbs 4:23, NIV).

1. **Protect It**
   a. The definition: Protecting my mind from anything that <u>distorts</u> my understanding of God's design for my sexuality.

   > *"For from within, out of the hearts of people, come the evil thoughts, acts of sexual immorality…acts of adultery…wickedness…indecent behavior…"* (Mark 7:21-22, NIV).

   b. The discussion: List the garbage that is polluting your life (Make a mental or even written list).

2. **Provision It**
   a. The definition: Feeding my mind with what God says about immorality.

   > *"How can a young man keep his way pure? By keeping it according to Your word. With all my heart I have sought You; Do not let me wander for Your commandments. I have treasured Your word in my heart, So that I may not sin against you"* (Psalms 119:9-11, NIV).

   b. The discussion: Write out two key verses concerning how God feels about immorality.

3. **Purify It**
   a. The definition: Purifying my mind by <u>meditating</u> on what God says about Himself and His creation.

   > *"And do not be conformed to this world, but be transformed by the renewing of your mind…"* (Romans 12:2, NIV).

   > *"…whatever is true, whatever is honorable, whatever is right, whatever is pure, whatever is lovely…think about these things…and the God of peace will be with you"* (Philippians 4:8-9, NIV).

   b. The discussion: List some of the attributes of God and how this truth might affect my sexuality? For example: God is all-knowing and therefore he understands my struggles.

4. **Prepare It**
    a. The definition: Visualizing in my mind the <u>devastating results</u> of immorality.
    b. The discussion: If I were caught in the act of sexual immorality, I could expect the following impact in my life (Be specific. Use names of wife, children, friends, etc. Write them down).

LINE OF DEFENSE #2: GUARDING MY BODY

1. **Present It**
    a. The two-part definition:
        i. Part One: Presenting myself to the One who has the <u>heavenly title deed</u> to my body—God (1 Corinthians 6:12-20; Romans 6:11-14).

        "…Present your bodies as a living and holy sacrifice, acceptable to God, which is your spiritual service of worship" (Romans 12:1).

        ii. Part Two: Presenting myself to the one who has the <u>earthly rights</u> to my body—my spouse (1 Corinthians 7:3-4).
    b. The discussion: Prayerfully complete the following:

    I, _____present the heavenly title deed of my body to my God and the earthly rights to my body to my spouse.

2. **Promise It**
    a. The Definition: Making a covenant agreement with God concerning every part of my body.

    "I have made a covenant with my eyes…" (Job 31:1, NIV).

    b. The discussion: Prayerfully complete the following:

    I, _____, make a covenant agreement with God concerning:
    My eyes not to look at _____,

    my ears not to listen to _____,

    my mouth not to speak about _____,

    my hands not to touch _____ ,

    my feet not to run toward _____,

    my mind not to dwell on _____,

    my knees not to neglect praying for_____.

3. **Protect It**
   a. The definition: Protecting my body from falling into immorality by <u>running from</u> <u>evil</u>.
      i. The example of Joseph in Genesis 39.
      ii. 2 Timothy 2:22: "Flee youthful lusts and pursue righteousness…"
      iii. Proverbs 5:8: "…don't go near the door of her house."
      iv. Proverbs 7:25: "Don't let your heart turn to her ways or stray to her paths."
      v. I Thessalonians 5:22" "Avoid every kind of evil…"
   b. The discussion: What morally dangerous situations exist in your environment and how can you avoid them: at home, at work, in the community, at church, while traveling? List them and then write down ways you can avoid them.

LINE OF DEFENSE #3: GUARDING MY COMPANIONS

"Even so the body is not made up of one part but of many…"
(1 Corinthians 12:14, NIV).

"And let us consider how we may spur one another toward love and good deeds…" (Hebrews 10:24, NIV).

"As iron sharpens iron, so one person sharpens another…"
(Proverbs 27:17, NIV).

1. **Pray for Them**

2. **Protect Them**

3. **Regarding Accountability**

"…glorify God in your body" (1 Corinthians 6:20, NIV).

The Taste Test for Godly Speech

"Do not let any unwholesome talk come out of your mouths, but only what is helpful for building others up according to their needs, that it may benefit those who listen" (Ephesians 4:29, NIV).

Before you enter a conversation, ask yourself the following questions:

1. **Question #1: Is what I am about to say good for edification?**
   a. Is what I am about to say intended to build up or destroy?
   b. Is it intended to lash out and hurt or to restore?
   c. Is it good for their emotional and spiritual progress?
   d. Am I about to attack the person or the problem?
   e. Does what I am about to say bring hope for resolution?
   f. Will these words feed or starve the soul? (Proverbs 10:21)
   g. Am I about to use "loaded" words? (Galatians 5:15)
   h. Am I just "digging up the dirt?" (Proverbs 16:27)

2. **Question #2: Is what I am about to say according to the need of the moment?**
   a. Is what I am about to say fitting for the occasion? Is it timely?
   b. Does it really need to be said?
   c. Should this be said at another time?
   d. Is there a better way to say it? (Proverbs 12:18; Matthew 12:36-37)

3. **Question #3: Will what I am about to say give grace to those who hear?**
   a. Does the way I'm communicating "minister grace" to others?
   b. Does what I am saying benefit those who listen?
   c. Are my words a well-packaged grace-gift?

Questions for the Man Who Would Serve as an Elder

The following is a word of encouragement and a brief study by Mike Wilhelm, who has served as a church leader and elder in a number of churches. From that perspective, he writes from "one elder to another."

FROM ONE ELDER TO ANOTHER

Let's pretend for the moment you have been asked by the Nominating Committee at Men in Action Bible Church to consider a position in church leadership. In addition to the unanimous consent of the Nominating Committee, your name was also reviewed by the Elder Board.

Any role in church leadership is a serious obligation and should never be entered into lightly. While the Nominating Committee and the Elder Board may believe the Lord has led them to select you, the most important analysis has yet to be done and can only be done by you. You must examine yourself to determine if you are ready to accept a position in leadership. You need to take some time and look to the scriptural requirements and obligations of a leader and measure yourself against them. You need to pray over all these things as you seek the Lord's direction for your life. You should also seek the counsel of others, especially your wife. It is important to have her support before you take this important and significant step.

Those that serve in leadership must be those God has called and gifted to those positions. If God is calling you, it is also important you heed His call. At the same time, you need to realize church is not the only time commitment you have, and you do not want to take on something that will be the final straw under which you crash to the ground. This is ultimately a decision to be made between you and God. Whether you accept or decline your decision should be well thought out and prayed through.

Please begin by looking at the following sections of Scripture (1 Timothy 3:1-13, Titus 1:5-9), which sets forth the requirements of those in leadership. While these provisions deal specifically with elders and deacons, they can serve as a general standard for those who enter into any leadership role. You should determine how you fare against God's checklist for leadership. Don't expect to get an A+ in every category. In fact, if you did, you would be fooling yourself. However, you shouldn't fail in any category, and every category should provide you with challenges for growth and improvement.

Titus 1:5-9 defines the following characteristics of a person in leadership in the church. He must be:

1. Blameless: You should be striving in all things to live a life of moral purity.
2. The husband of but one wife: This is the subject of the greatest debate of all the listed characteristics. At a minimum this means the leader is a one-woman man. In no way can a flirt or a womanizer be a leader in Christ's church. The leader must be devoted to his wife.
3. Children must be under control: If you have major problems at home you are not free to be in leadership in the church. The home is your primary responsibility.

4. Not overbearing: This means thinking too highly of yourself and not enough of others. Your opinion is not the only opinion that counts. You must be balanced in your approach to others.

5. Not quick tempered: You must have the ability to be patient with people in all circumstances.

6. Not given to drunkenness: This means you are temperate in all aspects of your life, not just alcohol.

7. Not violent: Your temper should never turn physical or abusive.

8. Not pursuing dishonest gain: You should never use your position in the church to seek material or other types of advantages. You should show the utmost fidelity in all that you do.

9. Hospitable: You should be open, friendly, and giving to others, especially strangers. Do you long to make visitors at the church feel truly welcome?

10. Loves what is good: You should be excited when the truth triumphs and grieve when wrong prevails. Can you be truly joyful for the good that happens to others, as if it had just happened to you?

11. Self-controlled: Better yet, this means Christ-controlled and speaks of control of passions and desires in a way that is pleasing to Christ.

12. Upright: You should stand for what is right without wavering.

13. Holy: You should live your life with a real concern for God's reputation. While you certainly cannot avoid being "in" the world, you must not be "of" the world.

14. Disciplined: You should have a focus and consistency in the way you do God's work.

15. Hold firmly to the message: You should stick by God's word against the philosophies of the current age.

16. Encourage others through sound doctrine: You must be an encourager but not an ear-tickler. You will give people a hope and joy found in the truth of God.

17. Refute those that oppose sound doctrine: You should always be ready to give an account of the faith that is yours and do it with sound doctrine. You must be capable of actually refuting the naysayers.

Notice how little this list has to do with the functionality of leadership. Primarily it focuses on character. More than anything, God wants people of solid character leading.

Additionally, there are things that are expected of leaders. As you examine your willingness to take a leadership role ask yourself the following questions:

1. Why do I want to be (or at least am willing to be) in leadership (cf. 1 Peter 5:1-4; 1 Timothy 3:1)?

1. Am I willing to be accountable to God for the spiritual welfare of this body (cf. Acts 20:28-31; Hebrews 13:17)?

2. Am I willing to be an example to those in the body (cf. Acts 6:3; Philippians 4:9; Hebrews 13:7; 1 Corinthians 4:6; 1 Peter 5:1-4)?

3. What am I willing to sacrifice for the body (cf. Matthew 10:38-39; Luke 22:26; John 13:1-17; Acts 20:24; 1 Pet 5:1-4; Mark 10:43-45)?

4. Am I willing to hold those in the body accountable to scriptural standards (cf. Matthew 18:15- 17; Galatians 6:1; 1 Thessalonians 5:13-14; Colossians 13:16; Hebrews 10:24-25; Hebrews 13:17; 1 Thessalonians 2:3-12; 2 Timothy 4:1-4)?

5. Do I love the body and do I evidence that in my interaction with its members (cf. Luke 10:27; John 13:1-17; John 15:12-17; Ephesians 4:29; 1 Corinthians 13; Philippians 2:3-4)?

6. Am I willing to give of my time and resources to care for the body and build the church (cf. John 3:17; Acts 20:28; Hebrews 10:25; 2 Corinthians 9:6; Luke 6:38; Acts 2:44-45; James 5:14)?

7. Am I willing to commit to a consistent prayer life, especially for the needs of the body (cf. 1 Thessalonians 5:17; John 17:9; John 17:20-21; 2 Corinthians 13:7; Ephesians 3:17-19; Ephesians 6:8; Col 1:9-11; 1 Thessalonians 3:10; 2 Thessalonians 1:11-12; James 5:14)?

8. Am I willing to be a student of the Word and grow in my knowledge of it on a regular basis (cf. Luke 11:28; 2 Peter 3:18; 1 Timothy 4:13; 2 Timothy 3:15-17)?

9. Do I get a real joy out of my service for God (cf. James 1:2-4; John 1:4; Romans 14:17; Philippians 1:4; 1 Peter 4:13)?

10. Am I prepared to be submissive to Christ's leading for His church (cf. Matthew 10:38-39; Luke 6:46; Luke 22:26; John 2:5; Ephesians 1:22-23; Ephesians 4:15-16; John 15:5; Ephesians 5:23)?

11. Am I willing to live my life to glorify God in all I do and say (cf. 1 Corinthians 10:31; Romans 15:6-7; John 8:50; John 15:8; Ephesians 1:12-14; Philippians 1:11; 1 Timothy 1:17; 1 Peter 4:11; Revelation 1:6; Revelation 4:11)?

While all the above questions would be fair to ask any Christian, they are crucial to ask those in leadership. There is no higher calling for your life than the calling to lead Christ's church.

Go back through the above lists and circle at least five items where you feel you have the most work to do.

My Physical Body: Blood Pressure, Diet and Exercise Tracking

1. The following pages have tracking logs for you to use. Make additional copies as required.
2. Keep track of when you go to sleep and when you wake up each day.
3. Track the amount of time you spend exercising.
4. "B/P" stands for blood pressure, if and when you take it.
5. Record any food you eat, including the amount, number of calories, and amount of fat the food item contains.
6. You may also be able to find an app you can use to track all of these items, as well as to help identify and follow an exercise routine.

Date:		Sleep:		Awake:	
Weight:		Exercise:		B/P:	
Time	**Food item**		**Amount**	**Calories**	**Fat**
	Total:				

Men in Action Game

Instructions:

Put on your nametag. Fill in all the items below. Each entry must have a different man's name in it. You may only use your name once. The first one to fill in ten entries wins.

	Item	Name
1.	Has, or once had, an airplane pilot's license:	
2.	Played on a college/university sports team:	
3.	Owns a motorcycle:	
4.	Has never played Checkers:	
5.	Can do 50 push-ups (Be ready to prove it!):	
6.	Has never caught a fish:	
7.	Knows the Prophet Isaiah's second son's name:	
8.	Can name the United States presidents, in order, since 1950 (Be ready to prove it!):	
9.	Owns a boat:	
10.	Has never shot a rifle or a gun:	
11.	Plays an instrument besides piano, guitar, or drums:	
12.	Has been in a country outside the United States:	
13.	Has never driven over 100 miles per hour in a car:	
14.	Is current in, or completed, their MIA assignments:	
15.	Can name the New Testament books, in order (Be ready to prove it!):	
16.	Can name the Old Testament books, in order (Be ready to prove it!):	

Solomon's Fatherly Financial Principles

*"Honor the Lord from your wealth and from the first of all your produce
so your barns will be filled with plenty and your vats will overflow with new wine."*
(Proverbs 3:9-10, NASB)

1. **The History of King Solomon's Wealth and Wisdom**
   a. Solomon's request and God's answer (1 Kings 3:6-13)
      i. Solomon was the wisest man in the world (1 Kings 4:29-31; 4:34; 10:24).
      ii. Solomon became the richest man in the world (1 Kings 10:23).
   b. Solomon was also a wise father (cf. Proverbs 1:8-9; Matthew 6:19-21; Luke 16:11).

2. **Solomon's Fatherly Financial Principles: General Financial Principles**
   a. Principle #1: Everything we have belongs to God (cf. 1 Chronicles 29:11; Psalm 50:12; Deuteronomy 10:14; Haggai 2:8; Leviticus 25:23; Psalm 50:10-11; Job 41:11b; 1 Corinthians 4:2).
   b. Principle #2: God gives to us as He pleases (cf. Proverbs 22:21; 10:22; Deuteronomy 8:18; 1 Chronicles 29:12; Ecclesiastes 5:19).
   c. Principle #3: There is great danger in focusing on money (cf. Proverbs 11:28; 23:4; 22:1; Psalm 39:6; 1 Timothy 6:6-12; Hebrews 13:5; Ecclesiastes 5:13).
   d. Principle #4: Earthly riches are temporary (cf. Job 27:19; Proverbs 27:24; 23:5; Psalm 39:6; James 5:2-3).
   e. Principle #5: You can't worship God and money at the same time (cf. Proverbs 3:9; 13:7; Psalm 52:7; Exodus 20:23; Luke 16:13-15).
   f. Principle #6: More money will not bring you happiness (cf. Ecclesiastes 10:19; 5:10; Job 36:19; Revelation. 3:17; 1 Timothy 6:17-19).
   g. Principle #7: Be content with what God gives you (cf. Proverbs 30:8; Philippians 4:11-13; Hebrews 13:5).
   h. Principle #8: Riches are a reward for following Godly counsel (cf. Proverbs 1:7; 3:16; 8:18, 21; 22:4; 28:20; Ecclesiastes 7:12; Matthew 6:28-33; Isaiah 55:1-2; Jeremiah 9:23-24).

3. **Solomon's Fatherly Financial Principles: Regarding Earning Money**
   a. Observation #1: The foolish avoid work; the wise seek it (cf. Proverbs 12:27; 16:26; 21:25; 26:15; Ecclesiastes. 9:10; Proverbs 31:13, 15, 18, 27).
   b. Observation #2: The foolish crave much but earn little; the wise crave little and earn much (cf. Proverbs 13:4; 20:4).
   c. Observation #3: The foolish would rather sleep; the wise would rather work (cf. Proverbs 6:9-11; 19:15; 20:13; 26:14; Ecclesiastes 11:6; 5:12).
   d. Observation #4: The foolish are full of excuses; the wise get the job done (cf. Proverbs 22:13; 26:13).
   e. Observation #5: The foolish are dishonest workers; the wise strive for integrity (cf. Proverbs 11:18; 13:11; 28:6; Titus 2:9-10; Genesis 29-31).

f. Observation #6: The foolish chase after worthless pursuits; the wise engage in successful endeavors (cf. Proverbs 12:11; 21:25; 23:4; 28:19).

g. Observation #7: Foolish workers attract worthless friends; the wise attract the godly (cf. Proverbs 18:9; 22:29; 2 Corinthians 6:14-17).

h. Observation #8: The foolish think they are wise; the wise learn from the mistakes of the foolish (cf. Proverbs 6:6; 24:30-32; 26:12, 16).

i. Observation #9: The foolish and the wise reap their just reward (cf. Proverbs 10:4; 12:11; 12:14; 12:27b; 13:4; 22:29; 28:20; 31:31).

4. **Solomon's Fatherly Financial Principles: Regarding Spending Money**

a. Spending Advice#1: Deal with your coveting and greed daily (cf. Proverbs 11:6; 13:7; 22:15; Exodus 20:17; Colossians 3:5; Ephesians 5:3).
    i. Learn to be content with what you have (cf. 1 Timothy 6:8; Philippians 4:11-13).
    ii. Learn to distinguish between needs, wants and desires (cf. Philippians 4:19; Matthew 6:11).
    iii. Learn to simplify your life (2 Timothy 2:4).

b. Spending Advice #2: Don't borrow to finance your foolish desires (cf. Proverbs 5:10; 22:7; Deuteronomy 28; Nehemiah 5:2-4).

c. Spending Advice #3: Pay your debts immediately (cf. Proverbs 3:27; 22:1; Psalm 37:21; Romans 13:7-8; Luke 20:25).

d. Spending Advice #4: Make a spending plan and stick with it (cf. Proverbs 21:5; 27:23-27).

e. Spending Advice #5: Get help from the right people (cf. Proverbs 11:14; 12:15; 13:20; 14:15; 15:22; 19:20-21; 27:12; Eccl. 4:13).

5. **Solomon's Fatherly Financial Principles: Regarding Saving Money**

a. Saving Principle #1: Everyone should have a savings plan (cf. Proverbs 16:1; 21:5, 20; 24:27; Luke 14:28-30).

b. Saving Principle #2: Save consistently in the abundant times in preparation for the lean times (cf. Proverbs 6:6-11; 30:24-25).

c. Saving Principle #3: Save to provide for your family in an uncertain future (cf. 1 Timothy 5:8; 2 Kings 20:1; Proverbs 13:22; 19:14; 20:20-21).

d. Saving Principle #4: Teach your children to save (cf. Ecclesiastes 7:11; Proverbs 22:6).

e. Saving Principle #5: Beware of risky investments (cf. Proverbs 12:11; 28:19; Ecclesiastes 5:13-15).

f. Saving Principle #6: Diversify your investments in case of troubled times (cf. Ecclesiastes 11:2).

g. Saving Principle #7: Pray for wisdom and understanding regarding your savings and investments (cf. Proverbs 24:4; 28:11; Deuteronomy 28:12; 15:8).

6. **Solomon's Fatherly Financial Principles: Regarding Lending Money**
    a. Lending Principle #1: Lend freely, but lend wisely (cf. Psalm 37:25-26; Proverbs 14:20).
    b. Lending Principle #2: Lending money to the right people results in blessing for you and your family (cf. Psalm 37:21, 26; 112:5).
    c. Lending Principle #3: Don't charge interest on what you lend to others (cf. Psalm 15:1-2, 5; Exodus 22:25; Ezekiel 18:13; Proverbs 22:16; 28:8; Luke 6:34-35).
    d. Lending Principle #4: Beware of entering into co-signing for loans for others (cf. Proverbs 11:15; 17:18; 20:16; 22:26-27; 6:1-5).
    e. Lending Principle #5: Lending money can be an expression of worship (cf. Proverbs 19:17; Ecclesiastes 5:10-20; Psalm 52:7; Mark 8:36).

7. **Solomon's Fatherly Financial Principles: Regarding Giving**
    a. Giving Principle #1: The God who created us in His image loves to give (cf. Psalm 84:11; 37:4; Proverbs 2:6; 3:34; 8:20-21; Ecclesiastes 5:19).
    b. Giving Principle #2: God gives to us so we will give to others (cf. Psalm 112:9; 146:7; Proverbs 3:9-10; 22:2, 9; 29:7, 13; 31:20; James 2:5; Luke 12:33; 1 John 3:17; 1 Timothy 6:17-19).
    c. Giving Principle #3: Our giving is to be a form of worship (cf. Proverbs 3:10; 14:31; 19:17; Matthew 10:8).
    d. Giving Principle #4: Our giving is to be generous (cf. Proverbs 22:9; James 1:5; Mark 12:41-44; 2 Samuel 24:24; 2 Corinthians 8:1-5; Leviticus 27:30; 1 Timothy 6:17-18).
    e. Giving Principle #5: Our giving is to be gracious (cf. Proverbs 14:31; 19:17; Exodus 25:2; 2 Corinthians 9:7).
    f. Giving Principle #6: Giving is to be our first financial priority (cf. Proverbs 3:9-10; Exodus 23:19a; 2 Corinthians 9:15).
    g. Giving Principle #7: Faithful giving results in incredible blessings (cf. Proverbs 3:9-10; 11:24-25; 13:21; 14:21; 19:17; 22:9; 28:27; Psalm 41:1-3; Luke 6:38; 2 Corinthians 9:6; Philippians 4:17; Malachi 3:8-12).
    h. Giving Principle #8: Holding back our giving has serious consequences (cf. Proverbs 11:24b; 21:13; 28:27; Ecclesiastes 5:13; Luke 16:10-11; 2 Corinthians 9:6).
    i. Giving Principle #9: The habit of Biblical giving is a learned behavior (cf. 1 Chronicles 29; Proverbs 22:6).

8. **The Challenge**
    a. Money is a TOOL God uses to mold us into His image.
    b. Money is a TEST of our faithfulness.
    c. Money is a TESTIMONY to the world.

NOTES

APPENDIX D
My Life Focus

You will develop your "My Life Focus" statement in stages. Over the next few weeks, you will complete certain tasks that form the framework of what eventually will become your personal life focus. When you are done, you will have a wealth of material from which to focus attention on the things that really matter in your life.

Do not rush through the tasks. Give thoughtful and substantive answers to every response. Open yourself up to yourself. Seek the Holy Spirit's infallible insight into who you really are. This is more of a process to experience than an assignment to complete. What you are about to undertake has the potential to be one of the most important exercises you have ever completed. It can help transform you and enable you to take daily steps to become the man God wants you to be. Bathe this process in prayer. Meditate on your answers and let the Holy Spirit open your eyes to a better and clearer understanding of yourself and His plan for you. For a complete overview of "My Life Focus" see Session 4. As you develop your "My Life Focus" we encourage you to share your journey with your accountability partner.

To ensure you are progressing in the development of your "My Life Focus," follow the schedule below.

	Tasks	Complete by:
1.	Goals, Tasks 1-3	Session 5
2.	Tasks 4-5	Session 6
3.	Tasks 6-7	Session 7
4.	Tasks 8-10	Session 8
5.	Tasks 11-14	Session 9
6.	Finalize, submit	Session 10

GOALS

What are some specific goals you want to set for each of the following areas of your life?

1. **My relationship with Christ**

   _____

   _____

2. **My marriage**

   _____

   _____

3. **My children/grandchildren**

   _____

   _____

4. **My extended family**

   _____

   _____

5. **My work**

   _____

   _____

6. **My church**

   _____

   _____

7. **The lost**

   _____

   _____

8. **Other**

   _____

   _____

TASK #1: TIMELINE OF GOD'S FAITHFULNESS

> *"For I am confident of this very thing, that He who began a good work in you will perfect it until the day of Christ Jesus" (Philippians 1:6, NASB).*

There are many life-impacting events that have occurred in your life. Below, or on a piece of paper, create a timeline, beginning with the year of your birth. Using this timeline, chart out where, when, and how you have most seen the Lord's power and guidance in your life, even in the difficult times. Be specific with dates, events, and other details.

My Spiritual Journey

||--||------
Birth

-- -------

-- --

---||
Today

Building a Life Focus requires you to not only assess the past and the present, but to look to the future. Instead of imagining a future you worry may be coming your way, envision a future you really want. As a man once said, "Figure out what you would like your obituary to say and then backwards map from there to the present and make your plans accordingly to achieve that goal." Each week we have you taking another step.

TASK #2: MY DESIRES AND DREAMS

"Delight yourself in the Lord; and He will give you the desires of your heart"
(Psalms 37:4, NASB).

"A plan in the heart of a man is like deep water, but a man of understanding draws it out" (Proverbs 20:5, NASB).

What do I want to accomplish before I die?

_____

_____

What do I want people to say about me after I am gone (wife, kids, others)?

_____

_____

Who do I most want my life to impact?

_____

_____

TASK #3: MY MOST SEEMINGLY IMPOSSIBLE DREAMS

When you dream about what your life could mean, what are those goals that just seem out of reach? What are those things you desire to do that seem impossible and are doomed to failure, if God does not make them happen? God has His part, and you have your part in the process. There is nothing wrong with dreaming and reaching for that which seems beyond your reach. We are more likely to limit ourselves than God is likely to limit us.

"…with man this is impossible, but with God all things are possible"
(Matthew 19:26, NIV).

"I can do all things through Him who strengthens me" (Philippians 4:13, NASB).

Name three things you would like to accomplish in the next few years:

1. _____
2. _____
3. _____

How would God be honored by you accomplishing these things?

_____

_____

What specific things do you need to do to move yourself towards those goals?

_____

_____

What is holding you back, and what do you need to do to overcome those obstacles?

_____

_____

Life is full of accomplishments and setbacks. Each of them teaches lessons that informs who we are becoming. There is tremendous value in assessing those times of victory and failure and the impact they have had on our lives. This is especially true in our relationships.

TASK #4: MY VICTORIES

List the things you have accomplished in your life you are most proud of. Consider those things you could not have done without God's power working within your weakness.

1. _____
2. _____
3. _____
4. _____
5. _____

TASK #5: MY FAILURES

"And He has said to me, 'My grace is sufficient for you, for power is perfected in weakness.' Most gladly, therefore, I will rather boast about my weaknesses, that the power of Christ may dwell in me" (2 Corinthians 12:9, NASB).

It has been rightly said that sometimes failures are the back door of success, if we learn from them. In fact, we often learn things from failures that an unending series of successes will never teach us. Failure often prepares us for greater success down the road.

List some failures that have impacted your life. For each one, identify why the failure occurred, and what God taught you from that failure.

1. _____

   Why did it occur?

   _____
   _____

   What did God teach you?

   _____
   _____

2. _____

   Why did it occur?

   _____
   _____

   What did God teach you?

   _____
   _____

3. _____

   Why did it occur?

   _____
   _____

   What did God teach you?

   _____
   _____

Life is full of opportunities to do the right thing and build positive relationships. So often, we fail to take charge of our lives, merely reacting to things that come our way. This reactive approach often makes us ineffective in service for God and in carrying out the goals He has for our lives. Many are the times God provides us with opportunities and we simply let them pass. This is the very definition of leading an ineffective life.

TASK #6: THE OPPORTUNITIES

"The mind of man plans his way, but the Lord directs his steps"
(Proverbs 16:9, NASB).

"Conduct yourselves with wisdom toward outsiders, making the most of the opportunity" (Colossians 4:5, NASB).

"...praying at the same time for us as well, that God may open up to us a door..."
(Colossians 4:3, NASB)

What opportunities are available to you at this time in your life? What do you believe God is calling you to do as it relates to your goals, dreams and objectives?

1. **My spouse**
   _____
   _____

2. **My children**
   _____
   _____

3. **My extended family**
   _____
   _____

4. **My work**
   _____
   _____

5. **My church**
   _____
   _____

6. **My neighborhood**
   _____
   _____

7. **My community**
   _____
   _____

8. **Other**
   _____
   _____

TASK #7: THOSE I NEED TO CONSULT WITH

> *"Without consultation, plans are frustrated, but with many counselors they succeed"* (Proverbs 15:22, NASB).

> *"Prepare plans by consultation..."* (Proverbs 20:18, NASB)

One specific opportunity we often miss is seeking counsel from godly people. God did not create any of us to be islands, operating independently from others. Building an effective "My Life Focus" statement requires we get input and advice from others we trust and respect. These are the people willing to give us counsel, point out areas we've missed, and share opportunities we might never have considered. They might even assist you in the next action step.

Who are those you need to consult with concerning your Life Focus?

1. _____
2. _____
3. _____

It is important that when we talk to others about our Life Focus, that we deal in specifics about fulfilling our dreams and goals. Today might be the first step in that process for you.

Who do you need to consult with concerning those specific relationships, goals and objectives?

I will contact _____ about_____

I will contact _____ about_____

I will contact _____ about_____

I will contact _____ about_____

Part of who you are is influenced by the training, education, and experiences you have had. God has used these to equip you in ways you might not even realize at this point. As you consider your past training and experience, ask yourself what *additional* training you might need to prepare you for what God has called you to do.

TASK #8: MY GENERAL EDUCATION/TRAINING
> *"I am a Jew, born in Tarsus of Cilicia, but brought up in this city, educated under Gamaliel..."* (From the testimony of Paul in Acts 22:3, NASB)

Educational background

1. **High School graduate: Yes___ No ___**
   a. If no, have you completed a high school equivalency? Yes___ No ___

2. **College:**   None ___   Some ___   A.A. ___   4 Year Degree ___
   Masters ___   Doctorate ___

3. **Other educational experiences and certificates:**

   _____

   _____

4. **How has this education/training equipped you to do what God is calling you to do?**

   _____

   _____

5. **What additional education or training might you benefit from?**

   _____

   _____

TASK #9: MY MINISTRY-RELATED EDUCATION

"I am a Jew, born in Tarsus of Cilicia, but brought up in this city, educated under Gamaliel, strictly according to the law of our fathers, being zealous for God just as you all are today" (Acts 22:3, NASB).

Do you have any official training in Bible or ministry? If you do list it. If not, how have you obtained the Bible knowledge you do have?

_____

_____

TASK #10: MY MINISTRY EXPERIENCE

Even if you have not attended formal seminary or Bible college, you may have had years of training in Sunday School classes, listening to sermons and studies, attending Bible studies, reading books and articles, taking seminars and attending conferences. All of these make up your own resume of God's personal training program, designed by the Holy Spirit just for you.

What types of ministry experiences have you had? Include all types of activities and services with which you have been involved, including courses, conferences, books, etc.

_____

_____

What ministries are you currently involved with?

_____

_____

What type of future ministry work interests you? What have you already learned that best prepares you for that work? What more do you need to do?

_____

_____

Finish your Spiritual Gifts Survey in next week's lesson first (Session 9), and then consider how your gifting fits into the goals and objectives we are establishing for ourselves. Finding a fit for our gifting in the activities we undertake and the goals we set for ourselves is a way to find true contentment and fulfillment in our spiritual journey.

However, it does not end with our spiritual gifts. We also have natural talents and skills we can use to achieve our goals. If we are musical, we honor the Lord with our music. If we are athletic, we are to be the best athlete we can be for the Lord. If we can cook, we cook to honor our Creator. Our talents and skills need to be central to our Life Focus. How do the things we enjoy doing fit into our life purpose? How do we make them have eternal value?

Finally, we all have limitations. Some of these can be overcome, others are simply the way things are. It is important to learn the difference. No matter how much we may try, the Olympics are probably not within our reach. We need to accept the limitations we have. There are things we will never be able to do. We need to focus on the things we can do. At the same time, conquering limitations when they stand in our way can be one of the most fulfilling things we do in life.

TASK #11: MY SPIRITUAL GIFTS

> _"...the whole body, being fitted and held together by what every joint supplies, according to the proper working of each individual part, causes the growth of the body for the building up of itself in love" (Ephesians 4:16, NASB)._

> _"As each one has received a special gift, employ it in serving one another as good stewards of the manifold grace of God" (1 Peter 4:10, NASB)._

God has given you gifts to assist you in carrying out the purpose He has uniquely laid out before you. For additional insights into the use and importance of spiritual gifts, read Romans 12, and 1 Corinthians 12.

List your top three spiritual gifts. Write down how you are _currently_ using them. Then, list some _opportunities_ you see where your gifts can be used.

Spiritual Gift #1: _____

1. **How are you currently using it?**

   _____

   _____

2. **What are your opportunities in the future?**

_____

_____

Spiritual Gift #2: _____

1. **How are you currently using it?**

_____

_____

2. **What are your opportunities in the future?**

_____

_____

Spiritual Gift #3: _____

1. **How are you currently using it?**

_____

_____

2. **What are your opportunities in the future?**

_____

_____

TASK #12: MY TALENTS AND SKILLS

The Apostle Paul was skilled as a tentmaker and he used it to enhance and support his ministry. David was musical and used it to serve King Saul. Jacob was skilled at animal husbandry and used that skill to increase his flocks over Laban's.

Aside from spiritual gifts, what talents has God given you, and how can you use them to serve Him?

_____

_____

TASK #13: MY HOBBIES AND INTERESTS

List your hobbies and interests. How can God use these in serving Him (be specific)?

_____

_____

TASK #14: MY LIMITATIONS

"There is a way which seems right to a man, but its end is the way of death" _(Proverb 16:25, NASB)._

"The lot is cast into the lap, but its every decision is from the Lord"
(Proverbs 16:33, NASB).

"Many are the plans in a man's heart, but the counsel of the Lord, it will stand"
(Proverbs 19:21, NASB).

We all have limitations (physical, emotional, spiritual, financial, social, educational, etc.). Some we can do something about; others are immovable and immutable. Some limitations may be there to close off certain options God does not want us to pursue. Other times God will use our limitations to cause us to put our full faith and trust in Him as He takes us to places where might never have gone.

What are some limitations you face (list at least three)?

1. _____
2. _____
3. _____

How do those limitations affect the goals you have for yourself?

_____
_____

Which of those can be overcome, and which do you feel God is calling you to overcome?

_____
_____

Are there any goals you feel God is calling you to pursue, despite your limitations?

_____
_____

RELATIONSHP WITH CHRIST

1. **History:**

_____
_____
_____

2. **Current status:**

_____
_____
_____

3. **Future goals:**

_____
_____
_____

a. Steps to accomplish future goals:

_____

_____

b. Timeline for taking steps:

_____

_____

c. What I hope my goals accomplish:

_____

_____

d. What may happen if I do not pursue these goals:

_____

_____

RELATIONSHIP WITH MY WIFE

(If not currently married, project your answers for what you desire for your future marriage.)

1. History:

_____

_____

_____

2. Current status:

_____

_____

_____

3. Future goals:

_____

_____

_____

a. Steps to accomplish future goals:

_____

_____

b. Timeline for taking steps:

_____

_____

c. What I hope my goals accomplish:

_____

_____

d. What may happen if I do not pursue these goals:

_____

_____

RELATIONSHIP WITH MY CHILDREN/GRANDCHILDREN

(If you do not currently have children, project your desires for your children/grandchildren.)

1. **History:**

_____

_____

_____

2. **Current status:**

_____

_____

_____

3. **Future goals:**

_____

_____

_____

    a. Steps to accomplish future goals:

_____

_____

    b. Timeline for taking steps:

_____

_____

    c. What I hope my goals accomplish:

_____

_____

    d. What may happen if I do not pursue these goals:

_____

_____

RELATIONSHIP WITH MY EXTENDED FAMILY

1. **History:**

     _____
     _____
     _____

2. **Current status:**

     _____
     _____
     _____

3. **Future goals:**

     _____
     _____
     _____

     a. Steps to accomplish future goals:

          _____
          _____

     b. Timeline for taking steps:

          _____
          _____

     c. What I hope my goals accomplish:

          _____
          _____

     d. What may happen if I do not pursue these goals:

          _____
          _____

RELATIONSHIPS IN MY WORK-LIFE

1. **History:**

     _____
     _____
     _____

2. **Current status:**

     _____
     _____
     _____

3. **Future goals:**

_____
_____
_____

    a. Steps to accomplish future goals:

           _____
           _____

    b. Timeline for taking steps:

           _____
           _____

    c. What I hope my goals accomplish:

           _____
           _____

    d. What may happen if I do not pursue these goals:

           _____
           _____

RELATIONSHIPS WITH MY CHURCH FAMILY

1. **History:**

_____
_____
_____

2. **Current status:**

_____
_____
_____

3. **Future goals:**

_____
_____
_____

    a. Steps to accomplish future goals:

           _____
           _____

    b. Timeline for taking steps:

           _____
           _____

c. What I hope my goals accomplish:

_____

_____

d. What may happen if I do not pursue these goals:

_____

_____

RELATIONSHIP WITH THE LOST

1. History:

_____

_____

_____

2. Current status:

_____

_____

_____

3. Future goals:

_____

_____

_____

a. Steps to accomplish future goals:

_____

_____

b. Timeline for taking steps:

_____

_____

c. What I hope my goals accomplish:

_____

_____

d. What may happen if I do not pursue these goals:

_____

_____

OTHER AREAS AND GOALS NOT IDENTIFIED ABOVE

1. **History:**

   _____
   _____
   _____

2. **Current status:**

   _____
   _____
   _____

3. **Future goals:**

   _____
   _____
   _____

   a. Steps to accomplish future goals:

      _____
      _____

   b. Timeline for taking steps:

      _____
      _____

   c. What I hope my goals accomplish:

      _____
      _____

   d. What may happen if I do not pursue these goals:

      _____
      _____

TIMELINE OF MY SPIRITUAL JOURNEY DURING MEN IN ACTION (list major milestones)

MIA start date ||--

--**|| Today**

How am I different since starting Men in Action?

_____

_____

I commit to carry out this Life Purpose and pursue these goals with diligence.

_____   _____
Signature   Date

Date last reviewed and updated: _____

[Once you have completed your My Life Focus document, make a copy and turn it in. If you have typed the document, then print and/or email the finished document.]

About the Authors

James Michael Cecy was born in Toronto, Canada, and moved to California when he was 11 years old. He entered the U.S. Navy in 1969 and served on the aircraft carrier, USS Kitty Hawk, during the Vietnam War. On November 17, 1971, the day he was discharged from active naval duty, God stirred his heart and Jim trusted in Jesus Christ alone for his salvation. He quickly became an avid student of the Bible.

Jim was called to pastoral ministry in 1975, serving churches in California for over 40 years. He has served as the Senior Pastor-Teacher at Campus Bible Church of Fresno (formerly Campus Baptist Church) since 1995. He is known for his commitment to Scripture, his enthusiastic expositional teaching, and his passion to equip God's people locally and globally.

Pastor Jim has a Bachelor of Arts degree in Speech-Communication from San Jose State University (1975). He earned his Master of Divinity degree in Bible Exposition from Talbot Theological Seminary (1978). In 1992 Jim received his Doctor of Ministry degree from Western Seminary (San Jose Campus).

Dr. Cecy is the founder and president of JARON Ministries International, a training ministry that equips pastors, missionaries, chaplains, and Christian leaders around the world. It is based in Fresno, California. In addition to his domestic ministry in North America, Jim has traveled extensively in numerous countries. His training seminars have reached hundreds of thousands of people on five continents. Jim has produced a variety of written, audio and video materials on a wide variety of subjects, which are available in a number of languages through JARON Ministries International (www.jaron.org) and his personal website (www.puritywar.com). His weekly expository sermons and messages are also available at www.campusbiblechurch.com.

Jim and his wife, Karon, were married in 1973. They raised three daughters and, since 1987, have cared for 23 foster children. Two, even as adults, remain a part of the family. Jim and Karon are abundantly blessed with an increasing number of grandchildren. Jim and Karon enjoy short trips in their 21-foot travel trailer.

Michael Lynn Wilhelm was born in Delano, California in 1955, which remained his hometown until he was 25 years it old. It was there, at the age of 17, he accepted Jesus Christ as his Lord and Savior. He has never doubted the value of that decision or its impact on his life.

In 1978 Mike graduated first in his class, earning a bachelor's degree in Business Administration from California State University, Bakersfield. He then attended UCLA School of Law, graduating in 1981. That same year he passed the California Bar Examination and began his legal career in Fresno. He has practiced law in three firms in California's Central Valley. He recently left the partnership of the Walter, Wilhelm Law Group and now serves at the law firm of Wanger, Jones and Helsey. His primary emphasis is in business law. He is an AV-rated attorney, the highest national rating a lawyer can receive, speaking of his integrity and the quality of his legal work. He also received numerous awards for his work in the local schools in Fresno County.

Michael has also been gifted by God with an uncanny ability to retain facts, often surprising people with his ability to discuss baseball, including the precise details of every world series since 1903. If only he could find his car keys!

Mike has served in a number of local churches, mainly as a Bible teacher and local church leader. Over the years, he has developed a number of Bible studies on a variety of subjects and is sought after as a teacher. Michael came to Campus Bible Church in 2010 and served on the elder board for four years. Presently, he serves as legal advisor to Campus Bible Church

Michael first attended Men in Action in 2007. Seeing the value of this program for training and equipping men, he soon joined Pastor Jim Cecy in leading the course and was instrumental in helping teach the class, developing a number of additional materials.

Mike was married in 1982 to Marilyn Ockel and has three grown daughters and one grandchild. When he is not practicing law, he enjoys exercising, traveling to the Central Coast and studying in the wee hours of the morning. His commitment to the pursuit of Biblical truth and the training of godly leadership makes him imminently qualified and sought out for his wisdom and counsel for church leaders. Mike's plan is to retire and become, in his words, "a bum of eclectic tastes."

About JARON Ministries International

JARON stands for *Jesus' Ambassadors Reaching Out to Nations*.

JARON exists to:

- Build a team of Ambassadors of Jesus Christ (pastors, missionaries, chaplains and Christian leaders) who will teach, disciple, and encourage Christian leaders in the United States and abroad.
- Serve as a ministry of instruction and motivation to local churches and Christian organizations through pulpit supply, classroom instruction, conferences, seminars, retreats, short-term ministries, and special services.
- Produce and provide Biblically sound and currently relevant written, audio and video training materials.
- Provide Biblical, Christ-centered counseling to those in need.

JARON is a registered non-profit organization (501c3) in the State of California.

For further information about materials or seminars, please contact:
JARON Ministries International, Inc.,
4710 N. Maple Avenue, Fresno, CA. 93726
559-227-7997   www.jaron.org

MEN IN ACTION
Equipping Men to Lead in the Home, the Church, and the Community

God is calling men to be Men of God, Mighty Men of Valor, and Men in Action. He desires they be Servant-Leaders:

- Who expect to have great impact for generations to follow.
- Who are well-equipped to do battle with anything that stifles their effectiveness.
- Who admit they need help from God and others.
- Who know how to lead themselves.
- Who understand that God-given leadership comes in many shapes and sizes.
- Who never stop improving as leaders who are accountable before God.
- Who understanding the challenging times in which they live and serve.
- Who know how to properly care for themselves and others.
- Who know how to prioritize and set boundaries.
- Who are committed to a life of personal purity and holiness.
- Who understand the value of spiritual gifts and talents.
- Who know how to love their wives, train their children, and prepare a generation.
- Who stay healthy physically, mentally, emotionally, and spiritually.
- Who pursue a life of wisdom and knowledge.
- Who desire to fulfill the purpose of God in every area of their lives.
- Who witness the lasting fruit of the indwelling Holy Spirit in their lives.
- Who know the importance of godly leadership in Christ's Church.
- Who have learned how to wisely solve problems, especially with the help of others.
- Who have identified their life focus and are pursuing God's will.
- Who are Men of the Word and Men of Prayer.
- Who P.U.S.H.—i.e., who "Pray Until Something Happens!"

This well-tested, twelve-week intense study is designed for groups of accountable men who strive to build their lives, their homes, and their local churches on solid biblical principles. Besides being a course of group study, there are a number of outside assignments that will reinforce what was learned in class. The appendices also contain a number of alternative sessions, study helps, and worksheets. An extensive teacher's guide is also available at *www.jaron.org.*

James Cecy is the founder and president of JARON Ministries International, as well as the Senior Pastor of Campus Bible Church, a multi-site church in Fresno, California. Jim and his wife, Karon, have been married since 1973 and live in Fresno, where their main hobbies are reading, studying, and spending time with their adult children and growing number of grandchildren.

Michael Wilhelm is an attorney in Fresno, California. He has served in church leadership and as a Bible teacher for many years. He and his wife, Marilyn, have been married since 1982. They have three children and one grandchild. Mike's main hobbies are exercising, traveling, and studying. He is also a baseball trivia expert.

JARON
MINISTRIES
INTERNATIONAL

4710 N. Maple Avenue
Fresno, CA 93726
www.jaron.org

Revised: August 2021

Made in United States
North Haven, CT
13 May 2022

19152502R00196